The
Devil's Chariots

The Devil's Chariots

The Birth and Secret Battles of the First Tanks

JOHN GLANFIELD

'The Devil's Chariots' – headline above a despatch from the Western Front correspondent of the *Düsseldorfer Generalanzeiger* reporting the first appearance of the tanks, 15 September 1916, and their effect on German troops.

SUTTON PUBLISHING

First published in 2001 by
Sutton Publishing Limited · Phoenix Mill
Thrupp · Stroud · Gloucestershire · GL5 2BU

British Library Cataloguing in Publication Data
A catalogue record for this book is available from the British Library

ISBN 0 7509 2706 2

Typeset in 10.5/15 pt Photina
Typesetting and origination by
Sutton Publishing Limited.
Printed in Great Britain by
J.H. Haynes & Co. Ltd, Sparkford.

This book is dedicated to the brave men who took the first tanks into battle, and to the determined pioneers who fought to forge them the new weapon.

'All his armour wherein he trusted'
St Luke xi 22

CONTENTS

LIST OF ILLUSTRATIONS

ACKNOWLEDGEMENTS

Of the many who helped so willingly with research, guidance and timely encouragement in the preparation of this account, special thanks must first go to David Fletcher, librarian at the Bovington Tank Museum and fount of knowledge of all things armoured on tracks and wheels. David has given generously of his time and researches for the past six years and has contributed more than he may realise to the emergence of this book. Other custodians to whom the author's grateful thanks are due for their unfailing efficiency and patience are William Spencer and Paul Johnson and their many colleagues at the Public Record Office in Kew; Keith Moore, senior librarian at the Institution of Mechanical Engineers; Patricia Methven, the director of archive services, and Kate O'Brien and Marie Taylor at the priceless Liddell Hart Centre for Military Archives, King's College, London; Colin Starkey, Meredith Wells and Alan Giddings at the National Maritime Museum; the staff in the old British Library and their colleagues at the Newspaper Library in Colindale; Colin Harris of the Department of Special Collections and Western Manuscripts at the Bodleian Library; Mrs Vallis at Nuffield College Library, Oxford; Alan Kucia, late of the Churchill Archives Centre at Churchill College, Cambridge; senior archivist Jonathan Smith and his colleagues at Trinity College Library, Cambridge; John Breslin in the House of Lords library; Angela Wooton of the Imperial War Museum's Printed Books and Documents Department and the indefatigable John Delaney in the museum's Photographic Department; Prof David Jeremy at the Centre for Business History, Manchester University; Alan Crookham in the Modern Records Centre at Warwick University; archivist Robert Sharp and photo researcher Martin Stephens at the Science Museum; Tim Robinson at the Royal United Services Institute for Defence Studies; the library and photo archive staff of the RAF Museum, Hendon; Miss Wraight of the MoD Admiralty Library; Josephine Grant at the London Transport Museum and the staff at the London Metropolitan Archive for much help in tracing members of the 'motor bus elite'; Elizabeth Dracoulis, Research Centre manager at the Australian War Memorial, Canberra; Susan Applegate of the Boston Public Library, Massachusetts; Bill Woods and Claire Leblanc at the National

Archives of Canada in Ottawa for unearthing service records; Tom Tytor in the National Library of Canada, Ottawa; Jennie O'Keefe at the Greenwich Local History Library; Ian Johnston at Cricklewood Library for information on the Dollis Hill establishment; Christine Bayliss of the London Borough of Hammersmith and Fulham Archives Centre; David Hufford of Huntingdon Library and Susan Thomas at the County Record Office in Huntingdon; Georgina Hammond at Gravesend Central Library; the staff at Tyne & Wear Archives, Newcastle upon Tyne; Adrian Wilkinson at Lincolnshire Archives; Alison Lindsay at the National Archives of Scotland in Edinburgh; Edmund Wyatt in the Mitchell Library of the Glasgow City Archive; Richard Jones and the staff at the Archives and Business records centre, University of Glasgow; Margaret McGarry and the splendid Motherwell Heritage Centre; archivist Peter Miller and the researchers at the National Motor Museum, Beaulieu; Margaret Sanders at Worcester City Library; Dawn Winter of the Sandwell Community History Service in Smethwick and Yvonne Richards of West Bromwich library concerning Patent Shaft; Colin Savage, director of the Staffordshire Record Office, Stafford, and the helpful staff at the adjoining Wm Salt Library.

The author was privileged to have met the late Bryan Wilson, son of Maj Walter Wilson, for a long interview at his Winchester home. John and David Stern, sons of Sir Albert Stern, have willingly made available Sir Albert's private papers and, with their sister Mrs Patience Marriott, gave wholehearted support. Paul Tritton has provided information on his distinguished relation Sir William. For personal papers and photographs of Col Dumble of the Landships Committee, special thanks go to Gill de Auer in Toronto, Sally Archibald in Scotland and the editor of the *Toronto Star* for bringing us together. Likewise to Fiona Harris for her kindness in tracing photos and papers relating to Maj Tom Tulloch, and to Geoffrey Jarvis for introducing us. Ray Hooley in Lincoln typically and unhesitatingly offered for study his large archive of material on Foster's of Lincoln and the early tanks. Others who must be warmly thanked for providing information or special permissions are Lord Addison for clearance to copy the Addison papers in the Bodleian Library, Idris Bowen, the dogged Jack Chamberlain, Wilfred Duncombe, Richard Farman, Stuart Gibbard, author of the masterly *The Story of the Wellington Foundry, Lincoln*, Michael Lane who wrote the equally impressive *Roadless – the Story of Roadless Traction*, Charles Lothingland, Dorothy Reid, Ricardo Consulting Engineers Ltd and Margaret Dean for information on Sir Harry Ricardo, John Reynolds whose *Engines and Enterprise – the Life and Work of Sir Harry Ricardo* is the definitive account, Bill Souster, His Grace the Duke of Westminster and his ever helpful archivist Eileen Simpson, and Anne Williamson and the Henry Williamson Literary Estate.

The author's good friend Ven Dodge, retired sales director of Col Johnson's Roadless Traction Ltd, generously provided material on the Colonel's tank and later developments. He also prepared for publication many of the illustrations in this book, numbers of which entailed challenging restoration. Jonathan Falconer, Sarah Moore and Georgina Pates of Sutton Publishing have ensured a smooth passage through their friendly and professional attentions, for which grateful thanks. Though many have contributed, responsibility for any errors and misinterpretations is rightly mine alone. Last, but most importantly of all, my thanks go to my dear wife Caroline for encouragement and forbearance, freely given by her and in equal measure.

List of Abbreviations

AEF	American Expeditionary Force	ICA	Inspecting Captain of Aircraft
ASC	Army Service Corps		(Royal Naval Air Service)
BEF	British Expeditionary Force	MCD	Munitions Contracts Dept
CGS	Chief of the General Staff		(Ministry of Munitions)
	(GHQ France)	MCWF	Metropolitan Carriage, Wagon
CID	Committee of Imperial Defence		& Finance Co.
CIGS	Chief of the Imperial General	MG	machine gun
	Staff (War Office)	MGC	Machine Gun Corps
CRE	Commandant Royal Engineers	MGO	Master General of Ordnance
D of A	Director of Artillery	MMGS	Motor Machine Gun
DAA	Deputy Assistant Adjutant		Service
DAD	Director of Air Department	MoM	Ministry of munitions
	(Royal Naval Air Service)	MWD	Mechanical Warfare Dept
DCGS	Deputy Chief of the General		(Ministry of Munitions)
	Staff (GHQ France)	MWEE	Mechanical Warfare
DFW	Director of Fortifications &		Experimental Establishment
	Works	MWS	Mechanical Warfare
DMC	Director, Military Cooperation		Supply (Ministry of Munitions)
DMRS	Director, Munitions	MWSD	Mechanical Warfare Supply
	Requirements & Statistics		Dept (Ministry of Munitions)
	(Ministry of Munitions)	NBL	North British Locomotive Co.
DNC	Director of Naval Construction	O&A	Overseas & Allies Dept
DSD	Director of Staff Duties (War		(Ministry of Munitions)
	Office)	QF	quick firing
DTDE	Department of Tank Design &	QMG	Quarter Master General
	Experiment (War Office)	RNAS	Royal Naval Air Service
GC	gun carrier	RUSI	Royal United Service
GHQ	General Headquarters (of the		Institution
	BEF, France)	SAA	small arms ammunition
GSO	General Staff Officer	TSD	Tank Supply Dept (Ministry of
HE	high explosive		Munitions)
IAE	Institution of Automobile	WD	War Dept
	Engineers	WO	War Office

INTRODUCTION

Hundreds of tanks covered a Dorset heath in the first years of peace after 1918. Machines salvaged from the final assaults in France lay beside others on little more than delivery mileage from the railhead at Wool. The Armistice had transformed them overnight from assets to war junk. Production cancellations had gone out to nearly 4,000 tank builders and component suppliers. The Slough Trading Company bought the machines for scrap in 1920. When the breakers hammered out the rivets and torched them, twenty-six were spared.

An engineer officer with a sense of history had earlier searched the graveyard for experimental and representative types. Those he found he marked for reprieve. The machines were hauled to a broken-fenced acre of scrub near the tank training schools at Bovington camp where they lay ignored for years in mounting thickets of bramble. Much of the compound became a lagoon after heavy rain, the weapon's old enemy. A high sun on the closed-up hulls could still sweat the familiar miasma of warm oil, stale petroleum and hot armour. Most of them stayed forgotten for two decades until the heath was combed again in another hunt for scrap to be melted down for another world war.

A few of those first tanks have survived to mark the bravery and suffering of all crews, and the high engineering achievement and labours of a different and unremembered army. The terrifying new weapon brought the first advance in firepower with mobility across the battlefield since cavalry first carried rifles. Because the machine gun and the tank transformed the conduct of land warfare at that time, their combat histories are well known. Less familiar are the events surrounding the tank's astonishing birth – the sometimes bizarre experimental work, the endless battles to overcome military prejudice and to get them built, and the men behind it all.

Here is the pioneers' story. The heroism of the fighting men is not overlooked, but this is an account of other very different conflicts which were fought out in great secrecy by – and sometimes between – the visionaries and builders, and the High Command at home and in France. Controversy surrounded the tanks from their earliest beginnings until the Armistice and beyond. The lives of tens of thousands of Allied and German soldiers depended on the outcome, yet if the Army had had its way in 1915 no tanks would have rolled out of British factories to become the first to enter battle.

Some personalities and events have become obscured by time, myth or misconception. A number have never received the recognition they deserve, while others later claimed more than the facts rightly allow. The author hopes that those involved in this supreme and ultimately triumphant endeavour will now be seen in a truer light, whatever that reveals.

The machines will speak for themselves.

One

THE TRACKLESS WASTE

Before going on further with these trials it would be well to discuss the object of introducing this form of tractor into the service. What is it for? Is it to take the place of horses altogether . . . and if so, is it because horses are getting scarce or because it is thought mechanical draught is better?[1]

Brig Gen Stanley von Donop, Director of Artillery, on the proposed
introduction of tracked gun tractors, December 1911

Before the onset of winter in 1914 the series of running battles across Belgium and northern France had seized into deadlock. The Allied and German armies had reached the sea in October after a leapfrogging north-westerly drive as each tried to outflank the other. Now locked in a static and bloody clinch, they were digging in. Their growing trench lines and defence works would tie Switzerland to the North Sea along a 300-mile front. In the ensuing siege war Germany's *Maschinengewehr '08* Maxims dominated the battlefield. The machine gun became the supreme defensive weapon.

The shock of early and severe British losses for negligible gain brought many suggestions for breaking the stalemate. They came from the public as well as serving officers, reflecting a deep national anxiety to find some new weapon to overcome wire defences, smash trenches and neutralise the Maxims. A few ideas held promise – most were bizarre. Lord Hankey, Secretary to the Committee of Imperial Defence, wryly observed, 'For the most part it is found that the "bright ideas" of the outside inventor are not new and that the new ideas are not bright.'[2]

To overcome the very serious problem of barbed wire, Sir Charles Parsons the shipbuilder and father of steam turbines proposed a fleet of small unarmoured cars fitted with front-mounted wire-cutting mowers powered by compressed air. They would operate on the principle of the farmer's reaping machine, with a crew of two or three men. The cars were to be driven at night across no-man's-land to nose into the enemy's wire entanglements. As their slowly revolving iron sails swept the wire against a high-speed cutter bar, the vehicles were intended to mow a lane through for the following infantry. Other considerations apart, the cutters would have seized the instant they bit on an iron picket. The idea was not followed up.

A wire-crushing solution was preferred by Mr Harcourt of Portarlington, near Dublin, who submitted a design comprising twin 20ft rollers inside a heavy timber frame. The 8ft diameter leading drum would be clad in sheet iron and ribbed with steel strakes to provide a cutting face when in contact with hard ground. The heavier trail roller was 11ft in diameter. Motive power would comprise an engine 'or horses' positioned inside the frame between the widely spaced rollers. This, too, was quickly rejected.

Col Louis Jackson, Assistant Director of Fortifications and Works at the War Office, said that he processed ten or twelve suggestions for trench-destroying machines that first winter. One comprised a 'vessel' 150ft long with an armoured hull like an inverted keel and bunks for the crew. The Inventions Department of the Ministry of Munitions (MoM) received 20,000 suggestions for new weapons and warlike stores in the year following its creation in August 1915; it dealt with fifty ideas for portable bullet-proof infantry screens in its first fortnight. Lt C.A. Smith of the Royal Marines produced his own, a heavy armoured shield on a pair of artillery wheels. It was deployed to protect raiding parties – Smith among them until he was returned home wounded.

In similar vein Ernest Milligan, a Medical Officer of Health in Derbyshire, submitted drawings for 'The Barrow Shield', an armoured wheelbarrow mounting a machine gun protected by a steel screen. It carried a stock of bombs for a three-man crew and could also be used to rush up weapons and supplies under fire. Though never built, the idea was reflected in the sidecars of fighting motorcycle combinations.

A versatile 'Rapid Travelling Armour Clad Field Fortification' was proposed by Evelyn Mills of London. His long narrow motorised fort would carry a battery of 3-pdr guns and 200 riflemen and incorporate a giant plough at each end for charging breastworks. Alternatively, two or more machines could operate in line astern, driving right up to an enemy position before coupling nose to tail to form an elongated boxcar from the front of which its garrison could spill, the armour cladding at each end being hinged for the purpose. Another possibility entailed multiple units being driven in line into water obstacles to form a strong box-section 'bridge'. Designs were submitted in October 1914 and were still under consideration by the War Office the following April.

'Lemon's Wheel and Rotating Machine' produced disconcerting trials results. In October 1915 the Trench Warfare Department at the MoM conducted experiments with a motorised rig which was designed to rotate a heavy wheel at up to 100mph before releasing it at a hostile trench along a short launching board. The spinning missile carrying a powerful explosive charge would hurtle into the enemy wire, through which Mr Lemon expected it to flay a path for the following infantry, before it exploded above the trench. The experimental wheel duly tore through the wire before hitting the dummy trench parapet and taking off to land in a second trench 50yd beyond. Unfortunately the wire entanglement immediately sprang back, and as there was no means of controlling the detonation of the explosive, the project got no further.

William Stewart of the Atlantic Coast Line Railroad Company wrote from Petersburg, Virginia, advising Lord Kitchener to substitute snuff for shrapnel in artillery shells. He said he initially thought such action would be beneath an Englishman but German atrocities now justified 'almost any retaliation'. The War Office passed his letter to the Director General of Munitions with the implication that the idea was not to be sneezed at.

More seriously, War Office experiments on 6 November 1915 tested the ability of powerful water jets to destroy trenches and incapacitate their occupants. The trials took place in Scotland at the Kinlochleven works of the British Aluminium Company. Water at 400lb per sq in at the delivery nozzle was pumped through steel pipes and directed on to lines of German-style trench works up to 150yd away. The force of the jets lifted parapet sandbags 12ft into the air and flung them 30ft. The blast of mud and stones would have killed or disabled the defenders and jammed their light weapons. However, the operation required some 3,000 horsepower of generating capacity plus heavy turbo pumps, thousands of feet of steel piping (which would have been vulnerable to shellfire) and a large water supply. Kinlochleven was no whimsical stunt. A detailed trials report was on the Prime Minister's desk and in the hands of the Committee of Imperial Defence within three days, but hydraulic artillery was judged impracticable and the scheme was dropped.[3]

*   *   *

By December 1914 British killed and wounded had reached 90,000, exceeding in number the strength of the seven divisions of the British Expeditionary Force. The highly professional Regular Army effectively ceased to exist at the close of its victorious defensive stand with the French at First Ypres in mid-November.

The origins of the deadlock in Belgium and northern France lay in the wreckage of the strategic plans of the French and German general staffs. Their preparations had relied on maintaining a war of rapid manoeuvre supported by the rail system. There was no expectation of or provision for protracted siege warfare, for which their armies and the BEF were untrained and, in varying degrees, ill-equipped. Germany's Schlieffen Plan and the French counter, Plan XVII, hinged on mobility and speed of attack. When the two armies fought themselves to a standstill, both sides dug in and the Germans threw up hasty defences with whatever came to hand. Their troops stripped farms of wire, fence posts, sheet iron – anything to slow rushes of men and deflect them towards the Maxims. Thickening belts of barbed wire soon followed. The machine gun came into its own.

The few British machine guns were dispersed, two per battalion. More often than not they were under command of a subaltern who was sometimes the only officer in the unit with any knowledge of how to use them. The Germans had ensured that every Jaeger battalion and infantry regiment included a specialist machine-gun company of six guns. These groups were free to deploy to greatest tactical advantage. One such company could match the firepower of an entire infantry battalion.

Over the next three years every Allied offensive was either beaten back to its start lines by the Maxims or cost a terrible price in blood for the ground gained. For most of that period the British and French staffs remained confident that artillery could shred wire defences and smash machine guns if enough fire was put down. The assumption was tragically false, but the reality was obscured in the BEF by a prolonged shell shortage of all calibres which became acute as early as the end of October 1914. Ammunition for 18-pdr field guns was then down to an average of seven rounds per gun per day. Most of it was shrapnel for open warfare rather than the high explosive needed to destroy trenches and heavily roofed bunkers and weapons pits. Munitions production was geared to the modest pre-war policing requirements of the Empire. Too often the guns of the BEF had little or no ammunition even to return fire. By April 1915 Britain was producing 2,500 high-explosive shells each week. French output was 50,000 per day.[4] Four months later British output had improved fractionally to eight rounds per gun/day, while the Army was calling for seventeen rounds.

The hiatus in high-explosives supply had been foreshadowed by an incident during the last weekend of peace. Maj Gen Sir Stanley von Donop, Master General of Ordnance, was responsible for supply of the Army's gun ammunition. On that August Saturday, Prime Minister Asquith had refused von Donop's request to buy cordite. Permission was finally given the following Monday by Lord Haldane, the War Minister. Von Donop then discovered to his horror that Winston Churchill had just bought up all available stocks of cordite propellant for the Navy – on the Saturday.[5]

It became chillingly clear to some divisional commanders that massed artillery alone could not prepare lanes for an infantry advance. The guns were incapable of shredding enemy wire and knocking out sufficient Maxims in the initial phase. If an advance was gained despite this, the gunners could not bring up their ordnance quickly enough across shell-torn ground to get back into range and give fire support before the enemy counter-attacked the newly taken positions. It was well understood on both sides of the Channel that Army Council policy was to avoid the production of new weapons and equipment unless previously requested by the Force Commander, Field Marshal Sir John French. Although French implicitly acknowledged the need for a new device when, at the end of December 1914, he approved the development of an experimental armed trench-crossing machine which laid its own bridge, the project was not taken seriously in France or London. GHQ continued to blame the shell shortage rather than the limitations of artillery.

The War Office did not commit itself to devising a mechanical solution to the stalemate until the summer of 1915, and then only after discovering that others had taken the initiative. The year closed with the resignation of Sir John French and his replacement by the commander of 1st Army Corps, Gen Sir Douglas Haig. There came a dawning realisation among some in the Army High Command that if there was to be any chance of a breakout in 1916, the infantry were going to need the support of some kind of cross-country armoured fighting vehicle. But no such machine existed in the British or any other army.

*   *   *

Against this background of rising casualties, mounting public concern and military inertia, a handful of men began the battle to design and build the world's first tanks. But what was the state of chain traction in 1914? Was the British Army involved in its development? Had it already adopted the system? And what of the other combatant armies?

Many of the answers lie in the activities of a small War Office transport research group. Its experiments in the decade before the First World War included the appraisal and development of tracklaying machines. These early trials and the personalities involved would influence the speed, direction and control of the wartime researches which finally produced the tank.

A Military Transport Committee (MTC) had been formed by the War Office in 1900 during the South African War. It coincided with growing interest in the wider possibilities of the internal combustion engine and a surge of popular enthusiasm for the automobile as it entered the new century. Lord Roberts, the Commander-in-Chief, was heavily reliant on the Road Transport Corps of the Royal Engineers to steam-haul his heavy howitzers, field guns and supply trains across the veldt. They had been joined by Lt Col Rookes Evelyn Bell Crompton, a veteran pioneer of overland steam traction. Crompton was a truly remarkable product of his age and a gifted entrepreneur who would later be in at the tank's birth. As a Rifle Corps subaltern in India years before, Crompton's ideas for long-distance steam haulage in place of bullocks had interested the Viceroy, Lord Mayo. With his support Crompton inaugurated a steam road-train service in 1872. It so impressed Lord Roberts that when they met again twenty-eight years later in South Africa he appointed Crompton his Controller of Mechanical Transport. Roberts pressed the War Office hard to expand the Road Transport Corps and sent Crompton back to London in September 1900 to add urgency to his appeal.

The MTC was created in November to consider reports on steam transport in the South African War and to evaluate the respective merits of steam and motorised vehicles of all kinds for the Army. Its six members included Crompton and representatives from Ordnance, Quartermaster's, Engineers and Service Corps departments. Crompton also joined an experimental sub-committee with Maj Henry Holden, Superintendent of the Royal Gun Factory at Woolwich Arsenal, an artilleryman, engineer and motor enthusiast whose inventiveness was recognised by War Office awards totalling

£14,800 by the time he retired in 1912. The two worked together developing
new military vehicles until Crompton left the committee in 1905. Holden
stayed on, by then a lieutenant-colonel, and subsequently became President of
the MTC. The two men later powerfully influenced the initial course of tank
design, but from diametrically opposed viewpoints.

One has to remember just how new and unfamiliar the technology was.
The War Office prohibited petrol engines for motor transport, fearing the fire
hazard in fuel storage and movement. The first lorries purchased by the MTC
in 1903 were paraffin (kerosene) oil fuelled, and the petrol embargo
continued for several more years. When the committee started work,
knowledge of chain traction amounted to little more than a handful of
learned papers and, in Britain, some sixteen patents. In the USA three patents
were granted between 1886 and 1890. A few crude tracked machines had
been built in England over the years, attracting negligible interest. The earliest
patent for endless chain tracks issued by the London Patent Office is no. 277
dated 1691. Another dated 1770 was secured by Richard Lovell Edgeworth
who registered a portable railway comprising short lengths of wooden track
fitted to wheeled vehicles, apparently forming an endless chain. Nothing more
was heard of it.

More ambitiously, John Heathcote, MP for Tiverton, patented a 30-ton
tracked steam ploughing engine in 1832. It was first demonstrated at Red
Moss Bog near Horwich, Lancashire in 1835, and Heathcote claimed it could
plough 10 acres of marshland in 12 hours. A steam engine with a cable
winding drum was mounted on a platform with a pair of 8ft wheels ahead
and astern. The whole rather improbable assembly was encircled by a canvas
belt fitted with wooden slats, and it worked for a time. The machine was
abandoned in a Scottish marsh two years later but it was a true tracklayer
and, literally, broke new ground in steam ploughing systems.

Numerous ideas were floated throughout the 1800s for spreading load on
soft ground. Most were for attachments fitted directly to wheels, generally as
flat, hinged paddles set at a tangent to the wheel which rolled over each in
turn as it was presented to the road. James Boydell successfully fitted several
Burrell steam traction engines with footed wheels on this principle in the mid-
1800s, an observer remarking that it was a pretty sight to watch the action
of the shoes, not being heel-and-toe, but sudden and flat, the whole surface of
the shoe reaching the ground and again leaving it simultaneously. Boydell's
'Steam Horse' road locomotive easily hauled four or five wagons totalling

50 tons, but the problem with the first machines was the need to put a horse in shafts at the front for steering. A horse unfamiliar with the machinery often refused to start precisely when the machine moved off, resulting in the surprised beast being push-started while it dug in its heels until it ended up in a sitting position. Later types replaced 'horse power' with a steersman positioned in front of the boiler at a ship's wheel. Several of Boydell's road locomotives went out to the Crimean War for haulage work.

None of these concept machines progressed much further. The MTC concluded in 1902 that steam power for transport was generally superior to horse haulage. Chain traction and the internal combustion engine were not even mentioned, but they soon saw a need for a wheeled motor tractor which would avoid the steamer's reliance on frequent stops for refuelling and water. The War Office accordingly announced a competition with a £1,000 prize for any tractor which could haul 25 tons 40 miles non-stop. The contest was postponed until 1904 for lack of entrants. In the event only one machine completed the course – a conventional-looking traction engine powered by a 70bhp oil engine submitted by Richard Hornsby & Sons of Grantham, Lincolnshire. As it trundled on another 18 miles before the permitted weight of fuel ran out, the company won a further £180. However, the MTC was not an executive department. It had no engineering resources and operated on a shoestring budget. It relied heavily on the goodwill and sales expectations of commercial vehicle builders whose efforts were almost exclusively concerned with civil markets.

Hornsby's Managing Director David Roberts, a superb design engineer, had been working on a chaintrack system which he patented in July 1904. Construction of a prototype followed. His No. 1 tracked machine was shown informally to MTC members the following summer. It was officially demonstrated at Grantham on 13 February 1906 and sparked a long-running gun haulage debate on the respective merits of crawlers *vs* horse teams. Roberts had mounted his system on an 1896 Hornsby steam tractor converted to a single-cylinder 20bhp paraffin engine. The 16-ton testbed was seriously underpowered and, rather disconcertingly, its steel frame flexed so much while climbing a marsh bank that the engine bearings went out of alignment and stalled the machine. A laborious process with jacks and planks followed to level the frame before restarting. The crawler then easily crossed trenches up to 4ft wide and hauled a 10-ton load over soft sand, neither task being achieved by a competing wheeled 70bhp steam tractor which only attempted three of the ten obstacles on a very testing course, despite its greater power. The committee was impressed.

> . . . this tractor demonstrated to the Committee its peculiar powers to move over ground that would bring any tractor fitted with ordinary wheels to a standstill. . . . The Committee are of opinion that this vehicle, rough as it is, and unsuitable though its engine may be, is in its power of traversing ground difficult and even impossible to other engines, a marked advance upon anything that has heretofore been manufactured. . . . It would appear to approximate to the ideal tractor for military purposes that we are looking for.[6]

The essence of the crawler system is its large bearing surface or footprint as compared with that of a wheel, and its consequently greater ability to spread load over soft ground. Roberts curved the lower section of his track to the equivalent of a wheel 37ft in diameter. If the tracks still sink then proportionally more of the curve comes into ground contact, further distributing load and reducing ground pressure. The big-wheel profile also reduces ground contact on firm surfaces which saves power and track wear, especially from 'scrub' when turning.

The demonstration machine was too light and underpowered, so for reasons of economy Roberts was asked in August 1906 to convert the old wheeled prizewinning Hornsby, which the MTC had purchased for £2,500 following the endurance competition. It was given an improved version of Roberts' tracks before trials began at Aldershot in July 1907. The soldiers immediately christened the 70bhp No. 2 machine the 'caterpillar'. Roberts also wanted to produce a tractor/trailer combination, all on chaintracks, which could carry rather than haul guns over badly broken ground. The MTC referred him to the Royal Artillery to whom he demonstrated the first trailer that November.

Further trials followed in 1908. The 20-ton crawler and trailer took part in the Royal Review at Aldershot that May to the profound astonishment of all present, including King Edward VII and the Prince of Wales, to whom Roberts was presented. A dummy gun was mounted on the trailer at the suggestion of Maj Donohue, an influential member of the MTC. The unsilenced and shatteringly noisy smoking beast topped by a white-faced Army Service Corps driver clawed its way across the Rushmoor arena, its heavily shod track plates spraying clods of turf rearwards.

The thing was an instant sensation. It was almost beyond the imagination of the public and attracted wide interest at home and abroad. 'A motor car that can walk over swamps' was a typical caption. The *Morning Leader* observed prophetically: 'Here is the germ of the land fighting unit when men will fight behind iron walls.' That summer London's Empire Theatre gave bioscope screenings of a Hornsby film clip which climaxed with a horse and cart traversing a reed swamp. The horse sank to its withers, whereupon, to the stupefaction of the audience, the caterpillar hove in sight and effortlessly cruised over to haul out tackle and beast. A special showing was arranged for senior British officers and the military attachés of all the embassies and legations in London. The MTC reported that 'Messrs Hornsby have now overcome the difficulties [and have] developed the chain track system commercially. The Committee are of the opinion that a light tractor built on a chain track would prove very valuable for the haulage of heavy artillery or howitzers.'[7] Ominously, the Royal Artillery representatives were silent.

Lt Col Crompton had kept in touch with Holden and the committee, having resigned in 1905 to co-found and become secretary of the International Electrotechnical Commission. He now produced an improved steam-driven gun tractor in an attempt to overcome the weight problems of an earlier design which he had submitted to the committee. Light steel castings and forgings replaced much traditional cast iron, and the driving wheels were exceptionally large to spread load. The tractor underwent trials at Aldershot where it was outperformed by the Hornsby caterpillar. This experience undoubtedly influenced Crompton's later thinking on motive power, and possibly traction, for armoured fighting vehicles.

The Army took delivery of three more Hornsby tracklayers in 1909. All were four-cylinder 50hp oil-engined machines, Nos 35083–5. The War Office was getting rid of its steamers. Most of the heavy lorries and traction engines were sold out of the Service that year, to be replaced with internal combustion-engined vehicles.

In July the committee instructed Hornsby's to purpose-build a light tractor for gun haulage. The No. 3 machine on further improved tracks was duly handed over on 5 May 1910. Hornsby 35082 cost £1,200 plus £50 worth of spares. The 8-ton machine was driven uneventfully the 140 miles from Grantham to Aldershot. Cold starts for its 70bhp six-cylinder vertical oil engine were assisted by a petrol feed for the first 10 minutes, at which point the vaporiser had been sufficiently heated by exhaust gases to allow a switch to paraffin. A less appealing alternative allowed for starts on paraffin providing a fitted blow torch was first played on the vaporiser for 30 minutes.

Trials began at once in the Long Valley at Aldershot with a 60-pdr gun and ammunition in tow. Holden attended with fellow artillerymen on the committee. The gun was hauled up 5ft banks with gradients of 1 in 3, and speed and cross-country competitions were staged against a horsed gun. The committee concluded that the tractor's work began where that of horses became impossible, but in short-distance haulage the machine's top speed of 7.5mph was outpaced by a trotting horse team.

During the trials Donohue raised with David Roberts 'the desirability of designing a combined Tractor and Gun as one unit carried on one set of Chain Tracks, and fitted with bullet proof shields so as to make a complete fighting machine'.[8] Roberts recalled this prophetic portrait of the tank some years later. It was the kind of authoritative 'steer' which a contractor might have been expected to grasp eagerly. Roberts ignored it. This was his fifth year of unrewarding caterpillar work for the military. Hornsby's were paid for the trials machines from MTC experimental funds but this barely offset their development costs.

The No. 3 tractor went on to an artillery practice camp at Trawsfynydd in the mountains of North Wales where its haulage work was again matched against horses. It proved to be very slow and seriously underpowered. The Battery Commander had other objections, complaining that the tractor was 'impossible in a column with other troops, its noise and smell are abominable and very few horses will pass it. The wooden blocks forming its feet are nearly worn away, and it is unable to carry sufficient fuel for itself for any time, and its machinery appears to be unreliable. The team of eight horses in my opinion is far superior under every condition.'[9] The MTC pointed out that mechanical transport should never be sandwiched between horse-drawn vehicles in a column as it would go slower uphill and faster downhill. The Hornsby's loud noise was conceded – it was still unsilenced – but it had fuel capacity for 100 miles.

Matters came to a head in 1911. The No. 3 machine was converted to petrol, boosting power from 72 to 105bhp and doubling average speeds. The MTC reached precisely the same conclusion as the year before – that the crawler came into its own when the horse gave up. It proposed a competition between a horsed gun and one drawn by the tractor, the two guns to travel independently for a distance of 30 miles and then be brought into action in a difficult place. Time taken by both was to be noted. At this, Brig Gen Stanley von Donop, the newly appointed Director of Artillery, halted further trials and convened a conference to review the whole question of tracklayers and horse haulage. He questioned the purpose and value of the machines:

> Before going on further with these trials it would be well to discuss the object of introducing this form of tractor into the service? What is it for? Is it to take the place of horses altogether . . . and if so, is it because horses are getting scarce or because it is thought mechanical draught is better? . . . the present seems to be the time to settle whether we are to aim at replacing the draught horses of heavy and siege artillery entirely by tractors, or whether we merely wish to have additional means at our disposal for helping the guns over long distances and difficult ground.[10]

The negative reaction of the new Artillery Chief came after five years of slow but productive development by Roberts and the committee. At the conference the MTC pointed out that their objective was to provide a means of draught superior to horses. The experimental work had already produced a flow of advances on the original test machine and an evolutionary process was well under way. Holden reminded the General of the greater distances and rate of travel achievable by machine, the economy in men and avoidance of forage and water, the reduction in road length occupied, and the ability to work in terrain impossible for horses. He considered that if the research continued, they could produce a fully effective tractor. It was an authoritative endorsement of chain traction. Holden was now President of the committee, but it remained an advisory group with few influential supporters. Von Donop reluctantly approved Holden's request for another comparative trial between machine and horses – on condition that they managed without horses. The Director of Artillery deemed that horse haulage speeds and performance were already established and their presence would add nothing to the findings. The question of work with a horsed unit would be decided after the trials.

War Office interest in chain traction had been fading for at least a year. The MTC had sought approval in 1910 to purchase an American Holt crawler for evaluation alongside the Hornsby. Permission was refused despite confirmation that the MTC held adequate funds. It was forced to rely on the Military Attaché in Washington for whatever technical information he could glean. His despatches on the Holt were contradictory and almost valueless in the absence of a test machine. The War Office abandoned all chaintrack development a year later. Holden retired in 1912.

Hornsby's saw the decision coming. The company had been investing in crawler traction since 1904 with no sign of volume orders from any quarter, civil or military. The venture was no longer sustainable despite numerous initiatives including a 4-ton Rochet-Schneider motor car which Roberts fitted with light chaintracks in October 1906. It recorded 15mph in tests by the Army and was the subject of a short movie commissioned by Hornsby's which is reputedly the first 'commercial' on film. In 1908 a tracked Mercedes car was produced for high speeds in the Egyptian desert. Members of the MTC attended its beach trials at Skegness where it achieved 20mph. Hornsby's formed Tractor Transport Ltd to market their caterpillars and a subsidiary offered the machines for contract haulage in Africa and South America, with little success.

The carcass of a truly historic Hornsby chain tractor was discovered in British Columbia in 1974. It was in poor shape and the 80hp compound steam engine and boiler, by Wm Foster of Lincoln, were missing. The 25-ton machine was built in 1909 to the order of The Northern Light, Power & Coal Co. Ltd of London. It needed a prime mover in the Alaskan Yukon Territory for hauling a 100-ton wagon train of coal the 40 miles over summer swamps and frozen tundra to the railhead at Dawson City. As the company was sitting on coal, the vehicle had to be a steamer. The unique machine was shipped out in March 1910 and was worked in the Yukon for fifteen years. It was probably Roberts' only caterpillar tractor sale outside the Army.

Hornsby's now withdrew from the field to concentrate on its profitable oil-engine business. David Roberts had been the first to produce a practical chaintrack machine powered by an internal combustion engine. For him and his company it was a bitter disappointment that the military and civil markets were not ready to share his vision and exploit the achievement. The company's research lead in track technology was already slipping away when lack of business forced Hornsby's to pull out of the crawler market. Three years later the loss of its expertise cost the nation vital time in evolving the tank. As a final irony, the company was heavily engaged with Admiralty contracts throughout the war and had no spare capacity for tank construction beyond the supply of 225hp Ricardo engines. In 1911–12 Hornsby's sold most of its foreign patents on Roberts' system to the Holt

Manufacturing Co. of Stockton, California, for £4,000. The caterpillar name was registered as Holt's trademark in October 1911 and the company later became The Caterpillar Tractor Co.

*   *   *

The overwhelming dependence of all armies on the horse in the last year of peace is well illustrated by the annual British Army exercise in September 1913. Five infantry and two cavalry divisions totalling over 45,000 men manoeuvred across central England. They were supported by over 17,000 horses, 2,220 horse-drawn vehicles and a trifling 192 motor vehicles of all kinds, including staff cars. There were no tracked machines. Motor transport was a growing feature of troop movement and supply in the French and German armies. The American War Department was no further ahead than its European counterparts. Prior to 1912 it had purchased only twenty-eight motor trucks, though it knew that US manufacturers were supplying the French and Russian governments with as many as 125 lorries on a single order. A Holt tracklayer had been evaluated without enthusiasm by the Field Artillery Board in 1912. The following year Benjamin Holt tried to interest the military in a full demonstration of his machines. He got no reply. Repeated approaches were rebuffed until finally in May 1915 a machine underwent trials at the Rock Island Arsenal, Illinois, on condition that Holt's bore all costs. By then Britain and her allies were placing substantial orders with the company.

The German War Department was also dismissive of tracklayers, informing Holt's importer and agent Dr Leo Steiner after a demonstration near Magdeburg in 1913 that the machine was of no importance for military purposes. The German Army had first used motor transport on an organised basis in 1908 when four light lorries were employed in support of a cavalry brigade. Steiner, a Hungarian engineer and farmer, had no more success at first with the Austro-Hungarian War Department which arranged a secret field trial in October 1912. This pitted his Holt against several European tractors in hauling heavy howitzers over sand and marsh. At the third such trial in Austria in May 1914 a Porsche tractor hauled a gun 500ft into a semi-swamp before sinking, while the Holt managed the full 750ft crossing. On reaching the far bank its driver raced the engine before throwing in the clutch and hauling the gun clear. Steiner recalled that he heard a crash like a gun shot and saw the Holt rear up and almost somersault. The next moment it returned to horizontal, lifted the gun wheels out of the ground and hauled it away. The troops cheered and members of the military committee waved their hats.[11]

It is not clear whether Steiner's competition was wheeled or tracked, but the Austrians were sufficiently impressed to negotiate a local assembly agreement with Holt's. When the war prevented shipments of components from the US the venture collapsed. Capt Davidson from the MTC had attended Austrian War Department subvention lorry trials three years earlier in 1911, noting that they operated thirty Daimler 100hp four-wheel-drive tractors for howitzer haulage.

The French chose a similar approach, deciding early in 1913 on a phased replacement of artillery horses by four-wheel-drive tractors. They began with their heavy 8.6in gun teams. Britain's *Commercial Motor* acidly observed: 'It is not to be expected that our own War Office will be the first to prove the practicability of such a scheme.'[12]

Hornsby's caterpillar No. 1 was sold off by the War Office in 1913. All four crawlers delivered in 1910 were still on Army Service Corps inventory in 1919. The equally historic Hornsby No. 3 survived both world wars and is now preserved in running order at the Tank Museum, Bovington. It was trundled out in June 1914 for the Royal Military and Naval Tournament at Olympia. In those last days of peace it was an amusing novelty, nothing more.

That month the gunshots that killed Archduke Franz Ferdinand and his consort in Sarajevo reverberated through the chancelleries of Europe and triggered the mobilisation of armies. Germany invaded Belgium on 4 August, prompting a swift ultimatum from London. When it expired that night at 11 p.m. Berlin time, Britain found herself at war.

Col Holden was recalled and almost immediately appointed Assistant Director of Mechanical Transport Supply. He found that motor vehicle purchases for the Army in 1913 totalled only 254 of all types. There were no crawlers. He began a search for tracked gun tractors, and with Hornsby's out of the running he turned to America. Some Holt engineers who had serviced Steiner's Austrian trials were invited to demonstrate their machine in England that October. It was the first Holt to reach Britain, arriving at Woolwich Arsenal on the 26th. The Army had two in service by January 1915. Ten more were ordered in March and by June seventy-five were awaited. By the

Armistice the War Office had bought 1,651 US-built Holts, most of them the 15-ton 75bhp semi-track type. More than 400 were built under licence by Ruston, Proctor & Company, agricultural engineers of Lincoln. (They merged with Hornsby's in September 1918 to form Ruston & Hornsby Ltd.) Though the cross-country performance of Holt's early machines was poor by later standards, the company's tracked workhorses were outstanding machines for their day and made haulage history.

The belief persists in America that the first tanks were no more than armoured Holts, and the company appears to have been happy at the time to see the US press repeatedly make this claim. However, the tanks were entirely British in design and construction and Holt's very properly sought neither recognition nor reward after the war. The story broke three days after the first tank action in 1916 when Murray M. Baker, Vice-President of the Holt Manufacturing Company, told reporters in Washington that the British government had bought 1,000 Holt crawlers and intended to armour some of them for employment other than gun haulage. Possibly as a result of genuine ignorance on Baker's part, the myth took off. Benjamin Holt was acclaimed a national hero for inventing the tank and was ranked alongside Christopher Columbus, while his company received nationwide recognition and an avalanche of orders.[13]

* * *

To its credit the War Office ran pre-war competitions between motor lorry manufacturers to stimulate improved design and performance. It introduced subsidy schemes to encourage production of commercial vehicles adaptable to military requirements, so creating a transport pool for requisition in time of war. The MTC had worked conscientiously within its remit as an advisory body, though it was starved of the personnel, facilities and money to do the job adequately. It never secured its own workshops and engineers, and was pleading in 1912 for funds to set up an experimental station. The committee relied on *ad hoc* arrangements with unit commanders for all its field trials and experiments, which could be disrupted at any time. The Hornsby No. 3 completed only one day of its trials with horsed guns in July 1911 before the Brigade of Artillery limbered up and left Aldershot for exercises in Okehampton. The MTC team was only told on the morning of the Brigade's departure.

In the higher reaches of the British and most other armies in 1914 the prevailing mindset was deeply suspicious of innovation, technical or otherwise. Cavalrymen predominated. Only ten years earlier the Army Council had agonised over a proposal to designate the rifle as the cavalry's primary weapon in place of the sword and lance. The opinion of Lord Francis Grenfell commanding IV Army Corps was typical: 'It would be a fatal mistake to permit the Cavalry to regard the rifle as their principal weapon. All spirit and élan would go with this new departure, and if engaged in a European war such an organisation might be fatal.'[14] Lt Gen Sir John French (commander-in-chief of the British Expeditionary Force in 1914) agreed. Senior commanders had spent the formative years of their careers, and much of their later service, in an era before the automobile, powered flight and the quick-firing gun. The new century opened with a bewilderment of advances in military sciences from aviation to wireless telegraphy. They were viewed by many with a mixture of distrust and incomprehension. Here would be the tank's first and longest battle; not in any shooting war but in men's minds.

Two

EARLY TRIALS – AND VERDICTS

I am fully aware that the Navy have the most of the credit for the tanks. It will not I hope be forgotten that some soldiers at least had a vision of possibilities.[1]

Maj Gen Sir George Scott-Moncrieff, 4 November 1918

The author of the November 1915 report on the Kinlochleven 'water-gun' trials was Lt Col Ernest Dunlop Swinton, Royal Engineers. It was a desperate idea which the CID quietly dropped. Swinton, aged forty-seven, was a perceptive observer and writer on the military scene. He had been pressing the case for a tracked fighting machine for over a year and for much of that time his difficulty lay in finding anyone at GHQ or the War Office who would take him seriously.

The events that led Swinton to his own conclusions about how to overcome machine guns and wire began during the South African War fifteen years before. He had commanded the 1st Railway Pioneer Regiment, a locally raised body of irregulars whose task was to keep open Lord Roberts' rail lifeline to his force in the Transvaal. Swinton's unit fought off many trackside skirmishes by Boer raiders. These encounters, for which he received the DSO, left him with an abiding respect for the devastating potential of the machine gun, which was still an unreliable novelty.

After three years as Chief Instructor in Fortification at the Royal Military Academy, Woolwich, Swinton took charge of the historical section of the Committee of Imperial Defence in 1910. ('"Oh boy that <u>was</u> dry" I said to a soldier friend, "you make history, I write it, and no one reads it".')[2] He became immersed in preparing the Official History of the Russo-Japanese War which was marked by fearful carnage in the face of concentrated machine-gun fire. His fears reawakened, Swinton co-produced in 1911 *A Handbook on Machine Gun Tactics* with Captain R.V.K. Applin, 14th Kings Hussars. Their thesis was the need to produce specialist machine gunners and to concentrate fire in batteries. The message was prophetic but ignored by the British Army in which it remained customary until 1915 to delegate responsibility and a couple of guns to an untrained regimental junior officer.

In 1911 Germany began secretly to amass a huge reserve of machine guns. Swinton heard of this from Captain T.G. ('Tri-nitro Tom') Tulloch, an explosives expert and former Chief Experimental Officer at the Royal Arsenal, Woolwich. He retired from the post in 1903 aged thirty-five to join the board of the Chilworth Gunpowder Company near Guildford, a subsidiary of Vereinigte Rheinisch-Westphalische Pulverfabriken, a German explosives firm. His appointment gave him direct and exceptional access to the German munitions industry. Tulloch's nickname arose from his many visits to Germany during which he noted the military adoption of TNT, a new propellant superior to Lyddite. For six years before the outbreak of war in 1914 he repeatedly but unsuccessfully urged the British military and naval authorities to follow suit, handing them detailed information on German TNT production methods. His persistence earned him the tag from Adm Sir Gordon Moore, Director of Naval Ordnance. Moore was to become tank production supremo in the coming war.

Tulloch learned of Germany's covert stockpiling of machine guns during a visit to Berlin in November 1911. He had been asked by Albert Vickers, whose company had a 40 per cent interest in Chilworth, to find out why Deutsche Waffen und Munitionsfabriken (DWM) had stopped paying royalties on the Vickers-Maxim machine guns which they had been making under licence from Vickers Sons & Maxim of London since 1901. Tulloch had just secured the rights from DWM to use German methods of block-filling shells with TNT but he found its directors evasive on the subject of royalty payments. With the scent well up, he went on to the company's small-arms ranges at Koenigswusterhausen where over dinner and several bottles with the experimental officer, a Col Jacob, he skilfully trapped the luckless fellow into confirming that the Prussian government had imposed the royalties embargo to conceal the enormous increase in the numbers of machine guns it was then ordering.[3] Alcohol seems to have featured regularly in Tulloch's investigatory technique. In 1904 at a naval explosives factory at Duneberg an over-lunched officer confided to him that a pointed bullet was soon to be introduced throughout Germany's armed services. As the *spitzgeschoss*, it would revolutionise prevailing thinking on small-arms ammunition. Tulloch alerted a surprised Gen Hadden at the War Office, which knew nothing of it, and produced a purloined sample.[4]

On his return this time he alerted Capt Maurice Hankey, Secretary of the CID; Swinton was also present. Tulloch was referred to the War Office where his information was noted with scepticism. He was eventually told that it could not be true because the British Military Attaché in Berlin had no knowledge of it. Undeterred, he sketched out his ideas for a wildly ambitious machine-gun destroyer based on twin coupled Hornsby caterpillars, each set mounting six 12-pdr guns and twelve machine guns, and carrying a hundred men. Tulloch tried to convince Vickers of the need for such a huge attack platform which he wanted armoured and powered with locomotive steam engines. He sounded out other military and civil contacts but there were no takers.[5]

The next stage in Swinton's formative journey came days before the war. He had been Assistant Secretary of the CID under Hankey for a year when, in July 1914, he received a letter from an old mining friend from his South Africa days. Hugh Marriott had been searching for a heavy prime mover and had just attended a demonstration near Antwerp of a 60bhp Holt semi-track tractor. He had seen the big machine climb out of a waterhole, surmount a near-vertical 4ft embankment and draw a six-furrow plough, sunk to its platform, across mud flats. 'Unbelief was pardonable', he said.[6] Its military possibilities as a gun tractor so impressed Marriott that he alerted Swinton, who passed the letter to Hankey and the directors of artillery and transport. This sporadic accumulation of information crystallised in Swinton's mind eleven weeks into the war. In September he was appointed the sole official war correspondent for the British Expeditionary Force. Lord Kitchener, Secretary of State for War, had kept the press out of the operational zone in France but soon came to realise that without authoritative news the papers could only report rumour. Swinton found himself with an open brief; he was free to move and gather information wherever he pleased, from GHQ to field dressing stations. By late September he was likening the battle along the Aisne to semi-siege warfare:

> I gathered . . . from wounded men and officers who had been through the fighting, what was happening to them. . . . It was known that the Germans had many machine guns, and I think it was a revelation to us when we moved forward on the Aisne and on every other occasion to find what a

machine gun was capable of. . . . I was also impressed with the heavy casualties caused to our infantry when they went forward.[7]

Swinton returned briefly to London on 19 October. What he had seen and heard at the front worried him deeply. The rationale of the High Command appeared to be circular. New measures against wire and well-concealed machine-gun positions did not exist. Therefore, these obstacles should be overcome with shellfire. If shellfire was ineffective, intensify it. Therefore, new measures were uncalled for. He was convinced the cycle could only be broken by a tracked fighting vehicle. It was no good designing one 'off the board' – it was needed now. Could a production machine be adapted? He remembered Marriott's Holt.

Next day, the 20th, in Hankey's office at 2 Whitehall Gardens, Swinton described the near deadlock, the growing strength of enemy defences and firepower and the need for a new remedy. The war was only weeks old. News at first hand rather than from staff reports was scarce and Swinton was exceptionally well informed. He urged the conversion of a number of Holt tractors to make them armoured fighting machines. Hankey was well placed to promote the idea and promised to do so. The following day the two met for lunch at the United Services Club where they were joined by Tom Tulloch. Notes were compared. Swinton and Tulloch (fellow cadets at the RM Academy twenty-five years before) were of like mind. The three agreed, in Hankey's words, a kind of pact. If Swinton was summoned by Lord Kitchener, he would make his case to him. Swinton would also tackle the General Staff and technical people in France in the hope of generating demand for the machines. Tulloch would explore the engineering aspects and identify specialist designers and builders. Hankey would sound out ministers and the War Office.

When Prime Minister Herbert Asquith summoned Swinton that afternoon for a private meeting at 10 Downing Street to hear his news of the front, the Colonel kept his ideas for motor machine-gun destroyers to himself. Though he stressed the weakness in British artillery and machine guns and its consequences, he left the 20-minute interview feeling that Asquith had not appreciated the implications and urgency of the situation. Swinton had lost his nerve. He was conscious that he was simply the official war correspondent, the scribe in the sandwich between Army and press, with no authority to raise wider issues with anyone; and Hankey had agreed to tackle the politicians. Nevertheless, it was a lost opportunity. Swinton had the PM's undivided attention and was a consummate communicator. His first-hand knowledge would have reinforced Hankey's more distanced pleading.

Kitchener gave Swinton an appointment for 22 October but was unable to keep it. Swinton had no permission to delay his return to GHQ. Though he left London the next day he later considered it a mistake. On arrival at St Omer he reported his actions in London and explained his ideas to the Engineer-in-Chief, Lt Gen George H. Fowke, who heard him out but was unpersuaded. Probably the only surviving contemporary document which records any of these discussions is a letter from Swinton to Hankey marked 'GHQ 11.11.14':

> Re Caterpillar. I put your idea before Gen. Fowke the Chief Engineer on 22.10. He wrote to the W.O. (D.F.W.) [Director of Fortifications and Works, Maj Gen Sir George Scott-Moncrieff]. Whether it is the result of this or of the original information given by me (from Marriott) before the war, Marriott tells me that several have been ordered. This may be for purely tractive purposes, or for bursting in against positions as suggested by you.[8]

It is curious that Swinton should have credited Hankey with his idea of a fighting Holt. Hankey said later that the solution had evolved jointly and that he did not believe his part in the discussion could justify a claim that the tank idea was his. Swinton denied that he deliberately attributed the idea to Hankey to improve the chances of acceptance of his scheme, pointing out that 'Hankey and I were pals and such Machiavellian cunning was unnecessary'. He added rather lamely that he may have been referring specifically to mention by Hankey of rollers, or else it was a slip.[9] For his part Hankey raised the subject with Kitchener on two occasions, finding the Secretary of State 'not receptive of the idea and very preoccupied'.[10] He recalled:

> Swinton did not have much luck at GHQ. Nor did I at first. Balfour bit at once, but he was not yet a member of the Government. He practically offered to find £2,000 to build a tank. Asquith was most appreciative and promised full support – if I could get WO to play. But that was the rub. MGO [Master General of Ordnance, Maj Gen Sir Stanley von Donop] was too overwhelmed with his own job to take it on. Wolfe Murray [member of Army Council] was not much use and Callwell [Director of Military Operations] had not yet enough grip to push a new idea unless egged on by

GHQ. Lord Kitchener, always a good friend to me, heard me out but said the armoured caterpillars would be shot up by guns. I was stymied.[11]

Hankey's abortive discussions with Kitchener effectively closed the subject as far as the Secretary of State was concerned. Kitchener was submerged beneath an almost unendurable burden of responsibility, not only for the day-to-day conduct of the land war but also for the raising, equipping and training of the vast New Armies which were his own creation. A bad situation was made worse by the absence of the cream of his General Staff whom he had assigned to GHQ in France. To cap it all, Gen Sir Charles Douglas, Chief of the Imperial General Staff, died on 25 October just at the time when Hankey was trying to press the harassed 'K'.

Swinton concluded that those in control at GHQ had failed to appreciate the nature and implications of the German defence. It followed that Kitchener too was dangerously unaware. Hankey spent the whole of Christmas Day 1914 at home drafting an appreciation of the war situation. On 28 December he sent copies to Winston Churchill at the Admiralty and to Kitchener, and a few days later to the newly created War Council which had assumed Supreme Command and to which he was promoted Lieutenant-Colonel and Secretary. His so-called 'Boxing Day memorandum' was an impressive assessment of the current stalemate. It detailed historical precedents for breaking such deadlocks, suggested new weapons and identified strategic options. Reflecting the Swinton/Tulloch proposals he said:

Is it possible by the provision of special material to overcome the present impasse? Can modern science do nothing more? Some of the following devices might possibly be useful:

Numbers of large heavy rollers, themselves bullet proof, propelled from behind by motor engines, geared very low, the driving wheels fitted with caterpillar driving gear to grip the ground, the driver's seat armoured, and with a Maxim gun fitted. The object of this device would be to roll down the barbed wire by sheer weight, to give some cover to men creeping up behind, and to support the advance with machine gun fire.[12]

Hankey later told Swinton:

My description of [the armoured caterpillar] was rather unfortunate and departed from the original machine that you had propounded. At the moment I had got the idea, which I afterwards dropped, that heavy rollers were necessary to work with the Caterpillars in order to break down the barbed wire. I got this idea from a mechanically propelled roller I had seen on the Horse Guards Parade, and I then thought that the addition of a roller might be an improvement.[13]

Hankey had placed the caterpillar concept first in a list of tactical ideas which included bullet-proof shields or armour for those leading the first wave of attacking troops, massed smoke balls to screen assaults, rocket-thrown grapnels with ropes attached to grip enemy wire before winching back the whole tangle, and spring catapults or pumping apparatus to throw oil or petrol into enemy trenches. He proposed the formation of a small expert committee to design such devices, stressing that it should include officers of the Royal Engineers with personal experience of trench warfare. No such organisation or means of coordinating the development of new weapons then existed. He had Swinton in mind for the job:

> Thereafter my policy was to back Swinton, to get him on to the development committee, and eventually into the command. I was also 'selling' Tanks all the time to the small circle of influential people 'in the know' – Asquith and his entourage, Balfour, Lord K. (who remained sceptical) and especially McKenna who, as Chancellor of the Exchequer, held the purse strings.[14]

Hankey's memorandum was timely. No comparable appreciation was to hand from the military or naval staffs. His references to a caterpillar machine and other devices prompted Churchill to write to Asquith at length on 2 January:

> I entirely agree with Colonel Hankey's remarks on the subject of special mechanical devices for taking trenches. It is extraordinary that the Army in the field and the War Office should have allowed nearly three months of trench warfare to progress without addressing their minds to its special problems. . . . The question to be solved is not therefore the long attack over a carefully prepared glacis of former times, but the actual getting across of 100 or 200 yards of open space and wire entanglements. All this was apparent more than two months ago, but no steps have been taken and no preparation made.

It would be quite easy in a short time to fit up a number of steam
tractors with small armoured shelters, in which men and machine guns
could be placed, which would be bullet-proof. Used at night they would not
be affected by artillery fire to any extent. The caterpillar system would
enable trenches to be crossed quite easily, and the weight of the machine
would destroy all wire entanglements. Forty or fifty of these engines
prepared secretly and brought into position at nightfall could advance quite
certainly into the enemy's trenches, smashing away all the obstructions
and sweeping the trenches with their machine gun fire and with grenades
thrown out of the top. They would then make so many *points d'appui* for
the British supporting infantry to rush forward and rally on them. They
can then move forward to attack the second line of trenches. The cost
would be small. If the experiment did not answer, what harm would be
done? An obvious measure of prudence would have been to have started
something like this two months ago. It should certainly be done now.[15]

Churchill went on to criticise the absence of protective shields of all types,
saying that a month earlier he had ordered twenty shields mounted on
wheels for experiment. He also advocated the large-scale use of smoke. All
these devices had been listed in Hankey's memorandum. Churchill expanded
them before echoing Hankey in urging that 'a committee of engineer officers
and other experts ought to be sitting continually at the War Office to
formulate schemes and examine suggestions'. Asquith moved quickly. He later
told Churchill that on 7 or 8 January 'I sent for K. and made him read your
letter, at the same time expressing my strong personal concurrence. He
promised to set the experiments in train without delay, and I know that he did
so. I was myself a very early victim of "Crocodilitis" . . . having caught the
virus originally from Hankey.'[16]

Just before this surge of prime ministerial interest in a mechanical solution
could take effect, however, Swinton at last got the War Office moving. On
4 January 1915 during a brief period of leave he visited Maj Gen Sir George
Scott-Moncrieff, Director of Fortifications and Works (DFW) and Commander
of the Royal Engineers. Scott-Moncrieff was responsible for mechanical devices
for trench warfare, but with the proviso that he could initiate nothing unless
GHQ requested it or gave prior approval. He reminded Swinton that since
neither condition had been met his hands were tied by the Army Council, and
Swinton had no formal authority to raise the matter with him. Swinton made

a stand, putting his case for a mechanical weapon with more conviction and in greater detail than to Hankey ten weeks before. The DFW relented and agreed to set up a committee of experts to investigate the conversion of a Holt Caterpillar or other suitable machine to fighting use. Swinton nominated Tulloch for membership because he was an armaments and motor expert. Scott-Moncrieff invited them both to see him the next day. The two met in Swinton's club before the appointment, where they ran into Col Louis Jackson, Assistant DFW. On hearing of the impending meeting Jackson said the subject fell within his area of responsibility. He enthusiastically supported their ideas and it was agreed that the matter be left with him. As Swinton had to return to France, Tulloch would submit the technical aspects of their case. Scott-Moncrieff minuted von Donop that same day:

> Yesterday two officers back from the seat of war pointed out to me the necessity for some means of holding on to the front trenches of the enemy, which now are difficult to hold after an assault owing to their being enfiladed by machine gun fire. One of them suggested to me an armoured motor car with caterpillar traction, manned by a small crew sufficient to work two machine guns. I spoke to D. of A. [Director of Artillery, General H. Guthrie-Smith] and Colonel Holden about it today, after mentioning the subject to you. The former agreed that the experiment was worth trying, though practical details might be difficult. The latter said there were two of the caterpillar tractors now at Aldershot which he thought might be fitted up with machine guns and armoured. I asked permission to form an informal committee for the purpose.[17]

Von Donop approved. Scott-Moncrieff's minute confirms that he was responding solely to Swinton's initiative. Kitchener's instructions to begin mechanical trench-taking experiments were issued a week later. The committee comprised Scott-Moncrieff and Guthrie-Smith, with Holden as technical adviser. It inspected the Holt semi-tracks at Aldershot on 13 January and decided to put one over a prepared course on the ranges at the Proof Establishment and Gunnery School, Shoeburyness.

Tulloch submitted proposals for a heavily armoured 'caterpillar land cruiser' and a lighter 'land destroyer'. Each version comprised a pair of coupled chassis on Hornsby-type chaintracks, both chassis being independently steam driven. Fleets of these articulated push-me/pull-you sets would, he claimed, overcome barbed-wire defences and trenches. The cruiser was to mount four 2-pdr automatic guns and carry a double skin of 7mm armour to withstand field-gun fire. Two machine guns and an encircling high-tension electrified rail would protect it from close infantry attack. The lightly armoured smaller machine would mount two or three machine guns only. Amphibious versions were suggested. He concluded:

> The quickest way to tackle the problem is to enlist the interest of a thoroughly sound professional automobile engineer and designer, who has at his back the facilities for designing offered by a well equipped drawing office and a factory where the vessels could eventually be built if the design is approved. An Artillery and Explosives expert [i.e. Tulloch], in Committee with the Engineer, should not take long in getting out a general design of the whole at small expense for ultimate approval for the building of a series of vessels. . . . The cost of design and drawings would probably be covered by £200 or so. . . . The suggestion to form a Committee . . . is an essential, as experience shows that every design involving several sciences is bound to be a compromise.[18]

The thrust of Tulloch's submission was directed as much at overcoming prejudice as at proposing solutions. His custom-build approach was at odds with Swinton's scheme for a modified production machine, which Tulloch dismissed as impracticable. Instead, he had dusted off his sketch of 1911 and changed little. Swinton was familiar with Tulloch's ideas but was unaware of his rejection of his own concept. Jackson strongly supported Tulloch:

> . . . it is only a question of time before some such war machine appears, and the nation which first produces it will have a great advantage. . . . It does not seem probable that any use can be made of the Holt caterpillars that we saw recently at Aldershot. There would be difficulty in armouring them as they stand and they could not be armed but would have to pull an armed trailer. I think the sound plan is to let a committee build up from the egg, beginning with the requirements and the possibilities and [then] going on the design.[19]

Scott-Moncrieff was also positive. He thought that to save time they should prepare designs for armouring a Holt tractor and trailer combination in advance of the trials. Holden was pessimistic:

. . . the difficulty of course is in making an engine of warfare of this description which is capable of doing what is required of it without excessive weight and being liable to destruction by the enemy's fire . . . I am afraid Captain Tulloch does not appreciate the mechanical difficulties with which the problem is beset, and also that the time taken in working this out, if an entirely new design of engine is to be produced, will be so great that unless the war is going to last for many years, the war will be over before the engine is ready. It seems to me . . . that the only thing that can be usefully done at the present time is to experiment with such engines as are available viz: the caterpillar type and the traction engine type, fitted with some means of bridging ditches, trenches and other obstacles. . . . The designing and building of new engines specially for this work is quite out of the question in view of the time involved.[20]

Von Donop and Guthrie-Smith agreed with Holden. On 17 February 1914 a 120bhp Holt was duly tested in heavy rain on the mud flats of the Shoeburyness ranges. It hauled a chaintracked trailer representing a 4-ton fighting module laden with the equivalent of two QF guns, ammunition and a crew of six. The course simulated battlefield conditions with a 24ft deep belt of wire fronting two parallel fire trenches 12ft apart and each 2ft wide. Beyond these were open and roofed trenches up to 8ft wide, and finally a sunken entanglement. Guthrie-Smith, Jackson and Holden attended. Swinton and Tulloch were not invited.

There were serious shortcomings in the tractor and the trial. The Holt was poorly prepared. Its engine ran badly and despite the waterlogged ground conditions no track extension plates (grousers) were attached because, in the words of Major Haynes, the superintendent of experiments, 'they take a very long time to fit'. The Holt was also ill-matched to the more testing obstacles. Holden had proposed that the trial machine be fitted with some means of bridging trenches but no action was taken to provide the tackle. The heavy trailer was a deadweight on the drawbar whereas Tulloch's proposal called for both units to be powered. Haynes reported:

The wire entanglement was easily knocked down and the tractor reached the second fire trench without difficulty. The trailer was then in the first fire trench. The tractor stuck in the second fire trench and even when uncoupled a long time was spent in getting out, empty sandbags and odds and ends of timber being put under the track. At a second attempt to cross the same obstacle the tractor failed to extricate itself from the second fire trench. The tracks cut away the soft wet ground until there was no weight on the tracks, and the machine was resting on the driving chain covers. The tractor was eventually helped out by a stem sapper and winding rope, but in doing this the sapper became so bogged that it in its turn had to be pulled out by the caterpillar. The ground was saturated with water, the trenches were half full and heavy rain was falling most of the time.[21]

Realising that the project was about to sink like the Holt, Jackson tried to set it on firmer ground by suggesting to von Donop that perhaps their approach was flawed. He reminded the MGO of his original view that the machine needed more power and a longer track for trench crossing: 'That such a machine could be designed to given conditions seems quite possible. How long it would take to design and build it is a question on which I cannot give an opinion.'[22] Von Donop told Scott-Moncrieff that he had discussed the matter with Guthrie-Smith and Holden. He concluded that the project was unlikely to succeed because of the time required for design and production, the great weights involved, vulnerability to gunfire and difficult battlefield terrain. He added that he was open to persuasion and invited Scott-Moncrieff and Holden to nominate a competent designer.

Scott-Moncrieff to Holden: Can you suggest the name of any person competent to design a land cruiser, not too heavy, that will cross any ordinary country and negotiate the usual fences? I do not myself know of any, but perhaps the President of the Institute of Civil Engineering could advise.[23]

Holden to Scott-Moncrieff: I am afraid I cannot. The only firm in this country who have had any experience in this line are Hornsby's of Grantham.[24]

The leads were not pursued and with this lacklustre closing exchange the investigation ended. Tulloch had freely offered his services and had told Jackson that he could find an eminent automobile engineer, but after his initial submission in January 1915 he and Swinton heard no more. Tulloch later told the Ministry of Munitions that he had forewarned Jackson in January:

... that he should avoid taking the opinion of a certain official, as I felt quite certain that if that official was consulted he would most certainly 'crab' the whole idea and throw difficulties in the way. Unfortunately . . . the official was consulted and he, together with another official, who had really no claim whatever to be considered an expert, joined in condemning the idea, with the result that much time was wasted. The plea put forward by these two people was that quite apart from the feasibility or otherwise of the idea, the preparation of the drawings etc. would certainly take a year, and therefore it did not seem worth while troubling about the matter.[25]

The expert 'official' was Holden, as Tulloch confirmed to Swinton.[26] Holden's standing in military transport development was unassailable. His view proved decisive. Tulloch knew him well because the two had worked together at Woolwich where he was principal experimental officer when Holden was superintendent of the Royal Gun Factory. They continued to meet after Tulloch's retirement through a mutual enthusiasm for motor transport – both were leading lights of the fledgling Institution of Automobile Engineers.

Recriminations and evasions surfaced over the Holt investigation when the tank finally emerged. Scott-Moncrieff remarked that 'Holden missed a great opportunity in declining the idea.'[27] In his memoirs Maj Gen Sir Charles Callwell, Director of Military Operations at the time, blamed the system and conceded that the War Office came badly out of the business: 'The technical branches had not been put in their place before the war, they did not understand their position and did not realise that on broad questions of policy they were subject to the General Staff.'[28] As Master General of Ordnance, von Donop was responsible for all forms of military transport. His past mistrust of tracklayers when he was D of A may have influenced his thinking on the Swinton/Tulloch scheme but he was deeply preoccupied with the crisis over shell supply and relied heavily on Holden's judgement.

Holden remains the enigma. His belief that it would take years to produce a fighting machine probably sprang from his bitter experience of the excruciatingly slow pace and parsimony of peacetime military research. He appears to have overlooked the greater impetus of a war-driven and well-funded development project. Whereas he had vigorously defended the Hornsby system and the crawler principle when challenged by von Donop three and a half years before, his opinion of chain traction had nosedived by the beginning of the war when he spoke to veteran engineer Col Crompton.

The old warrior told Holden of his concern at the complete absence of motorised cross-country gun tractors. Crompton mentioned chaintracks which, he says, Holden dismissed immediately as having no military value because of 'the nutcracker action of the track shoes which had put them out of action when trials were made for heavy artillery at Lydd'.[29] Holden was recalling a tendency for Roberts' system to pick up stones which became trapped between the shoes, sometimes damaging the track. No such fault is mentioned in numerous MTC trials reports, which tended to accentuate the positive, but the susceptibility was noted by others and was not peculiar to Roberts' design. By February 1915, however, Holden was sufficiently confident of chain traction to be buying Holts in quantity.

In his evidence for the Crown at a High Court hearing in 1925 Holden offered a much more upbeat version of his thinking in 1914–15. (The action was brought by Capt Bede Bentley who claimed £300,000 for inventing the tank when, he said, he personally handed the design to the late Lord Kitchener during an alleged three-hour interview at Kitchener's home in October 1914. The claim failed.) Holden said under cross-examination that he had been an exponent of the caterpillar since 1906. At the outbreak of war the MTC had two. Counsel – 'Had either of them been a success?' Holden – 'As a machine one of them undoubtedly was.' Counsel – 'A machine to be used in warfare?' Holden – 'Certainly.'[30] He must have been referring to experimental Hornsbys Nos 2 and 3. Holden added that the experiments 'were so successful that it was decided to build another embodying all the improvements'.[31] This last is unsupported by the many surviving documents but he may have been seeking to suggest, incorrectly, that the MTC Hornsbys formed part of the chain of causation of the tank. He made no mention of 'nutcracker' problems. In the light of Holden's High Court statements it is all the more surprising that he responded so limply to von Donop's request for a specialist engineer. His casual attitude to Hornsby's in 1915 was at odds with his 1925 testimony.

* * *

The War Office was involved at that time with another trench-crossing device – 'Foster's Portable Bridge Machine'. A spin-off from an Admiralty order for gun tractors, its sponsor was the First Lord, Winston Churchill. The origins of the machine lay in the aftermath of the first tactical surprise of the war, the destructive power of German heavy howitzers which demolished the Belgian fortresses of Liège and Namur in late August 1914. The 42cm monsters threw a half-ton shell, reducing in days defences intended to survive for months. Shortly before, Churchill had been amazed to learn from Rear Adm Reginald Bacon, General Manager of Coventry Ordnance Works Ltd, that his company had designed a 15in (38cm) howitzer which could be dismantled for road transportation. It was a remarkable claim for ordnance weighing some 60 tons. The Army's heaviest howitzers comprised a solitary 9.2in and a handful of obsolescent 6in pieces, against nearly 400 enemy guns in this class. Bacon had earlier offered the howitzer to the War Office. He was given to understand, rightly or wrongly, that it was against the policy of the Army Council to employ heavy guns in the field as they would encourage the infantry to hang back and let the ordnance do the work. When the fortresses fell, Churchill ordered twelve of Bacon's heavy guns. This was Admiralty business because the weapons were destined for his Royal Naval Division, then in formation. He assured Bacon that if he could meet his own very tight delivery forecast, the Admiral should himself command them in France.

Bacon approached the Daimler Company for road transport. Daimler happened to be supplying petrol engines for some giant tractors nearing completion for the South American market as a joint venture with Wm Foster & Company, agricultural machinery makers of Lincoln. Daimler referred Bacon to William Tritton, Foster's Managing Director, and it was agreed that the Daimler–Foster 'Agrimotors' should be adapted as the prime movers. An order followed for 97 wheeled tractors at £1,866 each and 291 special wagons. It was, claimed Fosters, the largest single order ever placed for motor tractors.

The machine's acceptance trials at Lincoln on 10 December 1914 included a bridging demonstration. The big tractor of nearly 14 tons hauled two trailer-loads of bridge timbers to a broad ditch which engineers spanned in three minutes before waving the outfit across. Unfortunately, a wagon toppled over the side, collapsing the deck. As the spectators waited, Tritton recalled that Bacon casually remarked to him that it would be of great value if an armed and armoured machine could be constructed which laid its own bridge. He continued to badger Tritton until howitzer tractor No. 44 was modified as a self-bridging testbed. These big machines were driven through traction-engine-type rear wheels 8ft in diameter and 2ft wide. The sleeve-valve engine developed 105bhp and the machine could haul a 35-ton load. (Exactly a year later Fosters would be installing the engine and transmission into the first tank.) OHMS 44 dispensed with the usual pair of smaller front wheels. Instead a sub-frame was fitted as a forward extension to the chassis, increasing overall length to approximately 31ft. Within this frame two road wheels were fitted in tandem. Two 15ft steel bridging girders were slung beneath it, one on either side, hanging just forward of the rear wheels. The girders were secured by an endless chain enabling them to be lowered, raised or dragged.

On reaching a trench the machine was run forward until the second of the front in-line wheels was at its near edge, the leading wheel being on or approaching the further side. The bridge girders were duly lowered to span the trench and the machine was driven across, at least one of the front wheels always remaining in ground contact. The tractor then had to travel sufficiently beyond the trench to drag the girders clear before reversing over them to restore them to their travelling position. The whole operation took three minutes to clear an 8ft trench on firm ground, all the while a crewman sitting over the sub-frame furiously turning a highly geared hand wheel controlling the girder lifting chains.

Bacon proposed to fit every machine with a pair of electric headlights plus a single light on either side, all with a 2ft-diameter glass front on which was painted the ferocious head of a Chinese warrior. At a given signal as forty or fifty thunderous vehicles approached an enemy trench in a night attack, headlights would be switched on to further unnerve the defenders. The machines would then straddle the trench on their bridges, switch to the sidelights and enfilade it in both directions.

The basic idea was sketched out and put to Churchill later that month. By the end of December he had ordered an experimental machine and had instructed Bacon to lay the project before Sir John French at GHQ and Lord Kitchener. Bacon recorded in his memoir, *From 1900 Onwards*, that Kitchener was pleased with the idea and authorised the trials. It was at this point – the beginning of 1915 – that Hankey's Boxing Day memorandum forced the issue of weapons development into the open. Bacon had no difficulty in securing military assistance and he expected to have the trials machine ready by 1 February. Meantime, the official proof of his first howitzer was under way at Shoeburyness where it was firing its 1,400lb shells.

The self-bridging project started to slide when difficulties in adapting OHMS 44 forced Fosters to put back trials readiness to 15 February. Churchill nevertheless gave Coventry Ordnance a production order for thirty bridgers on the 13th. The reason why he did not await the trials outcome is probably explained by Bacon's departure next day for France in command of a half battery of his first two howitzers. Churchill had kept his promise. Bacon was highly regarded by him and the order was very probably a parting salute from Churchill. In any event, much drive departed with Bacon; the bridge machine became nobody's baby.

The Holt trials took place on 17 February. Three days later Churchill cancelled the production order for self-bridgers, instructing Coventry's Mr J.H. Mansell to proceed with the experimental machine only. The project languished without official direction until mid-May when von Donop enquired when the trials machine would be ready. Mansell expected to deliver it the following week, adding privately to von Donop that he could find no official order or correspondence on the project and asking whether the machine should be invoiced to the Admiralty or the War Office.

The trial finally took place on 9 June on dry hard ground over the same course as the Holt had crossed in February. The self-bridger needed at least twice the available distance between the two trench lines in order to retrieve its girders after crossing the first before tackling the second, so it was decided in a mood of unwarranted optimism to put the tractor in top gear at both trenches without deploying the bridging.

After flattening the wire hazard with ease the machine – on full throttle – baulked at the first parapet, and on changing to the lower of its two forward gears it slewed sideways and stuck with one driving wheel in the trench itself. A Holt tractor pulled it free and grousers were fitted to the driving wheels. The trenches were then bypassed. The machine had no difficulty in laying girders over single trenches up to 8ft wide, but it was nose-heavy. Bacon recalled: 'They dug a place 8 feet deep with 4 feet of water and filled with barbed wire . . . Tritton said when we looked at it that we never guaranteed to cross the Channel.'[32]

Holden and Haynes acknowledged the design's ingenuity but their findings were damning: it was underpowered, with inadequate weight distribution and an unacceptable requirement for a clear 25ft run-out after bridging to retrieve girders. The machine was an enemy gunner's gift and would have been blown to bits during the several minutes of shunting entailed in crossing his trenches. It now looks an obvious non-starter but one must never forget the state of the art at the time. Bacon and Tritton shared the general ignorance of battlefield ground conditions. They saw the potential of the new tractors and pressed on with encouragement at the highest level. Their testbed was the first purpose-built machine to be put over trenches since the stalemate had begun eight months before. It was an honourable but inevitable failure. OHMS 44 was rebuilt for howitzer haulage at a cost of £20. Foster's drawing office began work on a bridging machine of juggernaut size before Tritton thought better of it and turned to more promising work.

There are perplexing inconsistencies between Churchill's postwar account of this episode, and the contemporary records and sworn testimony. Churchill claimed in his *The World Crisis* that the tractors were on caterpillars; that the idea of a bridging version originated with him when he was first shown pictures of the tractors in October 1914; and that it was early in November after seeing the design of the self-bridger that he ordered a machine and instructed Bacon to contact French and Kitchener.[33] The records indicate otherwise. Tritton's tractors and the bridger were not tracklayers. It was not until the December trials that Bacon first raised with Tritton the possibility of a bridging machine and then only in the most general terms, as Tritton confirmed in evidence before the Royal Commission on Awards to Inventors in 1919 and in his war history of Fosters.[34] On Churchill's timings Bacon would have sat on his hands for at least six weeks after meeting Churchill before putting the idea to Tritton, even then failing to mention that he already had the design and the First Lord's order in his pocket. He must have delayed even longer before contacting French and Kitchener as instructed.

Churchill concluded with a reference to the machine's failure at the trials, which he considered to be excessively severe and vexatious. One is left with the impression of the author as the mildly aggrieved originator of the machine. Yet Churchill himself pulled the trigger on the project when he cancelled his production order only days after placing it, long before the trials. He deserves the very highest praise for his foresight and drive – without it the tank would never have materialised when it did – but he was careless in suggesting the machine was a tracklayer. Churchill's account served only to thicken the fog of controversy enveloping those who laid claim to inventing the tank.

Three

WINSTON'S CIRCUS

Some more lorries and 3-pdr guns are urgently required.

Armoured lorries cannot work very successfully except on main roads.

The lorries cannot get along the roads very well now they are in such a bad condition.

The armoured cars are useless at present.[1]

Wg Cdr Charles Samson's reports on his fighting motor patrols in northern France and Belgium progressively chart the collapse of the roads
– and of his mobility

The German offensive at Ypres opened on 20 October 1914 against Gen Douglas Haig's battered 1 Corps. The onslaught lasted nearly four weeks before it was beaten off, the BEF suffering over 58,000 casualties. The ensuing siege warfare effectively halted the almost daily firefights of a marauding armoured car force which Churchill at the Admiralty had formed ten weeks earlier. Its activities marked the beginning of a chain of events which led to the emergence of HM Landships – the first tanks. Swinton and Tulloch would discover and become part of the chain, but its first links were forged by Churchill and his airmen.

The Military Wing of the Royal Flying Corps had accompanied the British Expeditionary Force to France in August. Churchill's Naval Air Wing (the Royal Naval Air Service) would soon follow. Before the month was out Belgium's great fortresses had been overrun and her field army of six divisions had fallen back on Antwerp. The continued German sweep pressed the Allied armies into the long retreat to the Marne. If the stand there collapsed, Paris might fall. Churchill won approval for a modest diversionary feint from the sea to threaten the rear of the German flank army. He rushed an ill-equipped brigade of marines to Ostend on 27 August in hopes of relieving pressure on the BEF and encouraging further Belgian sorties from Antwerp. The well-publicised operation misled the German Supreme

Command at a critical moment into believing that a major troop landing had begun. German intelligence assessments turned Churchill's 3,000 marines into 40,000 troops plus possibly twice that number of entirely phantom Russian reinforcements.

The decoy force was supported by the Naval Wing's Eastchurch Squadron, led in gung-ho style by Wg Cdr Charles Rumney Samson, a short, square-rigged and black-bearded buccaneer whose exploits in peace and war read like a 'ripping yarn'. His nine aircraft comprised seven different and mostly veteran types. It was entirely in keeping that the airmen's sole armament was a .45 automatic pistol apiece plus one shared rifle. Each pilot was encircled by two inflated bicycle inner tubes serving as lifebelts for the Channel crossing. Their otherwise unmarked machines flew small Union flags from the wing struts. Over-enthusiastic friendly fire persuaded the squadron to lash 7ft × 5ft flags to the underwings.

The naval force was recalled on 30 August but Samson had no intention of returning home. He signalled a string of spurious reasons for delay ranging from sea fog (actually a slight haze) to the write-off of a Bleriot ('Luckily, Lord Grosvenor smashed his machine on landing'). Samson turned out to be exactly where the First Lord wanted him. Churchill had just accepted Kitchener's request that the Navy should take responsibility for the aerial defence of Great Britain. Churchill feared that forward Zeppelin bases would be created behind the German advance from which to attack dockyards at Portsmouth, Chatham and even London. On 1 September he instructed his Director of Air Department (DAD), Commodore Murray Sueter to assemble the largest possible force of naval aeroplanes and base them in Calais or Dunkirk for daily sweeps to search out and destroy airships on the ground. He growled that it was better to kill the birds while they were still in the nest, rather than await their arrival overhead.

Sueter was a brilliantly resourceful innovator and the father of Royal Navy flying. He would later claim that he also fathered the tank. He had pioneered the Navy's torpedo and submarine development with Adm Bacon before turning to the possibilities of aviation. Sueter supervised the construction of the first RN airships and was appointed Inspecting Captain of Airships in 1910. On the formation of the Admiralty Air Department in 1912 he became its director. It was largely at his urging that the Naval Wing unofficially separated from the RFC to become the Royal Naval Air Service in July 1914.

Enemy cavalry probes and motor patrols were increasingly active, roving freely over the huge area behind the German advance. Samson formed an *ad hoc* road force to support his forward airfields, transport mechanics and equipment, and recover pilots. He used his officers' standard touring cars which had come across with them, ostensibly as squadron transport. They included the vehicles of his brothers Felix and Bill who had joined the squadron in August.

The first road fight took place on 4 September near Cassel while the men were awaiting the return of a scouting aircraft. Samson and eight others crewed an unarmed Rolls-Royce and Felix Samson's Mercedes, which he had fitted with an old Maxim. The Governor of Dunkirk alerted them to approaching enemy cars and the airmen duly shot up the lead vehicle before having to retire with a sheared firing pin in the machine gun. This encounter and Samson's vigorous air activity persuaded the Germans that a significant force was massing ahead of them. They withdrew their 2,000 troops from Lille next morning. The skirmish was a foretaste of the many road fights to follow.

Samson's report of the action requested fifty Royal Marines to accompany the cars; Churchill sent 250. Sueter had proposed to send fifty motor cars armed with Maxims; Churchill told him to double the number. After the Cassel encounter Samson's road strength was fixed at sixty armoured cars and forty support vehicles. Sueter formed the expedition into four Aeroplane Armoured Motor Support Squadrons under Maj Charles Risk, Royal Marines. Subsequent events overtook the force and Samson's strength never approached four squadrons, but the damage and distraction which they caused the enemy was out of all proportion to their number.

The road force was soon in action almost daily. They cast about for local means of protection pending the arrival of the armoured cars. The only available material was 6mm boilerplate which was nominally bullet-proof at ranges over 500yd. It was fitted to Samson's first cars and lorries by Dunkirk shipbuilders Forges et Chantiers de France. All cladding was in flat sheet, angled as far as possible for deflection. Felix Samson's Mercedes was first to be plated, to his own design, and had its first fight on 13 September. Dubbed the 'Iron Duke', the car's protection was more imagined than real but it could manage 55mph on the flat, though well down on its springs. The next conversion was less successful – a 29–30hp Wolseley, the rear axle of which failed under the severe load. These and subsequent boilerplate conversions were little better than wheeled death traps for their occupants, but the cars and crews looked menacing.

On 17 September Forges et Chantiers finished plating a Rolls-Royce and a London General Omnibus Company 'B' Type bus chassis. The 'B' Type was open-topped with slope-sided protection for twelve riflemen crouching at loopholes. Large frontal plates shielded cab and radiator. Another similarly plated 'B' Type followed on the 21st. They were unable to keep up with the armoured cars but proved useful as mobile guardposts.

Churchill visited Dunkirk and was impressed by the growing firepower and effectiveness of the road force. Here was a means of combining with local troops to harass and tie down the enemy and help relieve pressure at the front. It was agreed that Samson should work in support of the Dunkirk garrison, attacking rail and other key installations in the region of Cambrai and Valenciennes. The RNAS armoured cars and lorries became a strike force, though at home, where most of the Sea Lords viewed Sueter's activities with distaste, Churchill let them believe that it was no more than an airfield defence and aircrew recovery unit. This group was not the first to operate armoured cars in the theatre. The Belgian Army produced its first cars in the last week of August, basing them on heavy touring chassis plated in Antwerp. Its officers had earlier fought with considerable verve in their own unprotected Excelsiors and Minervas, but the death of Prince Baudouin de Ligne in one of these brushes underlined the need for crew protection.

While Samson's cars shot up the enemy on the ground, his aircraft were destroying Zeppelins and their sheds in Germany. A price was put on his head. He mobilised country gendarmes, going into action with packs of up to sixty of them at a time when he was not operating with French troops. An intelligence network of boy scouts on bicycles paid one franc per day was formed to report all enemy sightings within 20 miles of Samson's base. By the time his small force returned home the following February the ground and air combats of the unit had won it one Victoria Cross, four DSOs, including Samson's, and a DFC. (Among his earlier exploits he had been the first man to take off from a moving ship (the battleship *Hibernia*), flying a Short pusher amphibian at the 1912 Naval Review off Portland.)

*   *   *

The activities of the RNAS fired the public imagination and offered a short cut into the war for young men fearful that it would all be over by Christmas.

Sidney Ninnim's experience was typical of the resultant stampede. He queued for three days before reaching the recruiting officer's trestle table, only to be turned down as an air rating. On his way out he heard a call for anyone who knew anything about motor transport. As the only man within earshot who did, Ninnim found himself in Dunkirk as a driver/mechanic after twelve days' training.

Some of the wealthier volunteers arrived in France with their own cars. Sub Lt The Earl of Annesley brought an Austro Daimler and was accompanied by Ryan his chauffeur. The car shed so much of its insecurely fitted armour that it had to be stripped and relegated to despatch work. Contrary to Samson's postwar comment that this was a comic affair of soft iron hung about the car by a local garage, it was in fact 9cwt of bullet-proof steel produced to special Admiralty order from Firths of Sheffield and was fitted – poorly – in six days at RN Dockyard, Sheerness.[2] Six weeks later Annesley hitched a lift as observer in a Bristol aircraft on its delivery flight and was killed when it became lost and disappeared over German lines.

Lt Cdr Josiah Wedgwood MP went out in October 1914. After shooting up a patrol of Uhlans near Tournai on his third day, he told Sueter, 'This seems to me a most admirable arm, better far than cavalry for this work.'[3] Lt Cdr Baron de Forest MP – a friend of Churchill's – joined Wedgwood's section before getting command of his own. Hugh Richard Arthur Grosvenor, second Duke of Westminster and reputedly the richest man in the country, joined in November and raised 2 Squadron which he himself equipped with armoured Rolls-Royce cars at a cost of over £30,000, a fortune then. Oliver Locker Lampson MP put in his bid even earlier, writing Churchill on 30 October that he had Sueter's provisional approval to fund and lead a squadron, and requesting permission to man it with Ulstermen. His 15 Squadron drove armoured Lanchesters. Others arriving at the depot that autumn included Lords Torrington, Loughborough, Tollemache and Hardwicke.

The Aeroplane Armoured Motor Support Force was based on the east coast at the Sheerness depot of the RNAS Central Air Office. Responsibility for overseeing the preparation and despatch of the road fleet and its stores fell to the Inspecting Captain of Aircraft, Superintendent Frank Scarlett. All Samson's equipment was shipped from Sheerness, its dockyard additionally providing engineering services. Few men could drive in those days, and Sueter was competing with the Army Service Corps for drivers and trained mechanics. His recruiting relied heavily on the motor industry's workforce, chauffeurs and the comparatively few well-off young owner/driver automobilists. Felix Samson signed up the first batch of drivers, many being skilled testers and mechanics from Sueter's chassis suppliers. The Navy gave qualified men the minimum rank of Petty Officer Mechanic at 10 shillings (50p) per day while serving in France. Army drivers suffered as privates on 6 shillings (30p), bringing resentments which led to exchanges between Kitchener and Churchill.

Rather surprisingly, Murray Sueter ignored Samson's design proposals for armouring the cars. He turned instead to his Admiralty steering committee and adopted the ideas of Lord Wimborne and Mr Macnamara, neither of whom had seen recent action. Their economical open-top approach was certainly dictated by weight considerations and the design was finalised on 11 September. Sixty chassis were scheduled for plating – 18 Rolls-Royce 40/50hp, 21 Wolseley 30hp and 21 Clement-Talbot 25/50hp, all standard assemblies save for dual-rim wheels on the rear axles. The War Office could provide no data on the resistance of armour to penetration by bullets at ranges below 100yd so Sueter set up experiments with steelmakers Wm Beardmore & Co. of Glasgow which continued into 1915. He settled at first for 4mm plate. It was all in flat sheet because no firm in the country at that time could shape thin armour without cracking it. Armour of variable quality was also obtained from other sources.

The three chassis-builders made up templates from which the steel mills produced kits for each firm to fit. Sueter scrounged some Admiralty armour and diverted eight chassis to the Sheerness yard for cladding there (probably all, and certainly three, were Wolseleys).[4] The cars were only plated to door height, the driver alone having the additional protection of a kind of armoured rabbit hutch with a pair of side-hinged doors for forward vision. The rest of the crew remained lethally exposed to fire from trees and windows even if they were lying on the floor. Scarlett recommended replacement of the driver's vision doors by a single top-hinged flap with slit, its upper edge scrolled to deflect bullets from glancing up into the gunner standing behind; the idea was later adopted. Newly built cars were subjected to firing trials where a number failed, .303 rounds penetrating the armour at 150yd. Scarlett's fitters found they could drill it with ease.

Machine guns were scarce and Sueter had to beg round the Fleet for his sixty Maxims; some of Samson's ammunition was date-stamped 1888. Chatham Dockyard made socket mountings for the machine guns and demountable crossheads to enable some cars to be fitted for anti-aircraft work. Sheerness knocked up useful metal carriers for the ammunition belts. These were bolted to the guns to avoid the floor clutter of direct feeding from ammunition boxes, and the risk of jamming from loose rounds which tended to misalign or fall out of long waving belts.

Only two weeks after design approval, the first five Admiralty (Wimborne/Macnamara) armoured cars were landed at Dunkirk with Maj Risk on 26 September – two Rolls-Royces and three Clement-Talbots.[5] Five Wolseleys followed on the 30th with Lt Cdr Wedgwood. Capt Hetherington took over a third section of five Wolseleys on 2 October to complete the fifteen-car fighting strength of Felix Samson's 1 Squadron.[6] On 1 September 28-year-old Flight Commander Tommy Hetherington was appointed RNAS Transport Officer. An officer of the 18th Royal Hussars, he had been on attachment to the RNAS as an airships instructor since July. Hetherington was the epitome of the dashing cavalryman, as well as being an early aviator and a promising motor engineer. He had ridden for the United Kingdom and the Army with great success until an injury caused him to switch to flying. On gaining pilot's certificate No. 105 at Brooklands in July 1911 he had joined the Airship Section of the Air Battalion RE, then in formation – afterwards the RFC. He was happiest at the controls of anything which flew, floated or rolled, and would duly make his mark in the progression towards the first tanks.

On his return to Sheerness, Hetherington sent Scarlett a searingly critical report of Samson's road organisation, communications and operational effectiveness. It is interesting to contrast Samson's swashbuckling approach with Hetherington's regimental orthodoxy. The latter was surprised to find no instructions awaiting him on arrival at Dunkirk with the cars. He phoned Felix Samson at the Morbecque base to be told that Risk and the others had piled into nine armoured cars and disappeared in two separate parties heading for Lille. It transpired that no communication existed between the patrols and base. Samson normally relied on the public telephone system when on the road, sometimes leaving a marine with a motorbike at the nearest exchange to receive and relay messages. He had installed ground/air radio communications in a car at the aerodrome, but the bulky and delicate equipment was impracticable for road operations. The British Consulate at Dunkirk provided his onward link with Sueter in London. Hetherington continued:

The next morning [3 October] I found a wonderful collection of all sorts and classes of cars and what appeared to me complete chaos. I reported to Comm. Samson and was told that the section was to leave immediately for Antwerp and that they were to pick up the gun crews in the town. The only armoured cars belonging to Major Risk's unit which had arrived consisted of half of No. 1 section, with No. 1 Squadron Commander [Lt Felix Samson] in charge, who could not tell me anything about the rest of his squadron. Lt. Samson had to wait until the rest of his squadron turned up, so Lt. Field who was in command of No. 3 section was taken away from his section and sent off with half of No. 1 section, having no time to acquaint himself with anything or to obtain any food. I could get no information of any description to help in seeing how some form of organisation could be arranged – no form of organisation apparently being wanted.

Comm. Samson said I was to form my store depot [for 200–50 packing cases] at St. Pol in spite of there only being room for my stores in the open. I saw Major Risk on his arrival and his account confirmed all the information I had obtained. It was quite impossible for him to keep in any way to the approved organisation as orders were given direct to sections without his knowledge, and owing to sections being split up he had no Officers to take charge. I tried to get some information as to the way in which stores were being supplied, and was informed this is war and a car took what it wanted and if it did not return with it – it had expended it, and that nothing else was necessary. There seems to be a complete lack of organisation of every description, not only in this branch but in every branch of the force operating here. No arrangements are made for rations and I cannot find any definite arrangements about pay. Cars are sent out without any rations at all on journeys of 120 miles. No man has an identity disc.

. . . It is evident that if the present lack of organisation continues in the Armed Motor Aeroplane Support unit it will not exist as a useful force in a month. The men are more or less living on the country, and the cars have no lines of communication for supplies with an organised base. The cars are being driven at excessive speed. . . . [7]

And so it went on. Hetherington added a list of recommendations, the last of which proposed that if Samson required 'more cars for his own use' then he should be given 1 Squadron together with his brother Felix, and the three squadrons still to be equipped should be removed from his command to 'form a proper mobile and self-contained unit'. Scarlett forwarded Hetherington's indictment to Sueter with a note supporting his recommendations, adding that 'for the good name of the AIR SERVICE, Commander Samson should immediately be informed that it is not the proper thing, when conducting operations in a friendly country, to <u>live on</u> that country' (Scarlett's emphasis). Hetherington's report had cellar-to-roof repercussions ranging from the immediate issue of ID tags for the men to the reduction of Samson's own command.

Samson never let secondary considerations get in the way of a good scrap. He was not a great administrator, a handicap which held back his later promotion, but he was a born leader whose superiors assessed him as 'a brilliant pilot and a gallant officer'.[8] The disorganised departure for Antwerp which Hetherington witnessed had followed days of intensive action by the unit. Samson had just provided road guard and fire cover for the withdrawal of French forces from Douai, he and his men having to fight their way out of the town which was surrounded by then, and sustaining heavy casualties in the process. For this action on 1 October he was mentioned in despatches by Brig Gen Paris. Risk and Wedgwood were busily engaged during the evacuation of Lille a day or so later. Those deadly days were lightened by Samson's laconic approach with its echoes of rough shoots at home. Their pursuit of German cavalry patrols was 'Uhlan-hunting', or 'ewe-lamb' hunting as Samson called it.

*　*　*

The general situation could hardly have been worse. The Allied stand on the Marne in September had been followed by French counter-attacks which drove Gen von Bülow's First and Second Armies back to the Aisne where they scraped shallow trenches and stood firm. Ominously, though, their defensive machine-gun fire proved too strong for a frontal breakthrough. The stalemate precipitated a series of moves by each side to envelop the exposed western flank of the other in the so-called 'race to the sea'. The Channel ports of Calais, Boulogne and the entire coast south to Havre had lain open since their evacuation by the British in the earlier retreat. Gen von Moltke could have scooped them up in his advance, isolating the BEF and sealing his sea flank against future attack. He ignored the opportunity and was replaced by Gen Falkenhayn who determined to reach and secure the coast ahead of the Allies. But first he had to reduce Antwerp's fortress from which the Belgian Army was threatening his lines of communication. He began a sustained bombardment of its defences on 28 September.

The threat to the Channel ports persuaded Kitchener to despatch two divisions led by Maj Gen Sir Henry Rawlinson to stiffen Antwerp's defence. Churchill contributed a brigade of marines and two brigades of half-trained reservists which were rushed to the city. Samson was to stand by to proceed to Antwerp with his entire force of armoured vehicles and aircraft. Hetherington watched their departure. Eleven armoured cars and both the soft-plated lorries were to escort a fleet of some fifty-five hastily requisitioned London buses and their volunteer crews plus lorries from Dunkirk to Antwerp to evacuate the marines. They arrived in good order on 4 October. Risk brought up another sixteen buses next day. Churchill and Sueter were already in the city. The First Lord had been sent by the Cabinet to promise support to the King of the Belgians and to persuade him not to withdraw his troops. The defenders held out against punishing fire from 173 heavy guns until the 9th. For the last time Samson took advantage of Antwerp's forward location to get off two aircraft that day for the long flight to bomb Zeppelins in sheds at Cologne and Düsseldorf, with complete success at the latter.

Samson was indignant that his recommendations for armouring the cars had been ignored – the unprotected crews were becoming casualties. Sueter learned of the problem from Lt Arthur Nickerson, Samson's gunnery officer, before the cars caught up with him in Antwerp. He at once ordered Scarlett to cease shipments pending modifications, and called for 1,000sq ft of armour plate to be sent to the Dunkirk yard for *ad hoc* conversion of the existing vehicles. He also instructed Sheerness to make up and despatch sixty bullet-proof Maxim shields. Nickerson was recalled to London to advise on the redesign. Sueter maintained that 'At that time the former war experience [in South Africa] of Captain Nickerson was most valuable as we had so few Officers or men who had ever been under rifle fire before. . . .'[9] Samson's now considerable battle experience was disregarded.

The first of two more Vickers 3-pdr semi-automatics was fitted on a Daimler–Mercedes lorry in the Chantiers yard on 16 October. It was unarmoured save for a lightly plated driver's cab and was in action next day with the Life Guards, getting off sixteen rounds per minute, its jumping gunsight routinely blacking the eye of RM Lt Tom Warner. As the unit was now short of transport, two lorries were acquired that week from a halted Army Service Corps convoy. Samson's men painted 'RNAS' on the sides before making off with them. This freed a 'B' Type for fitting with the remaining 3-pdr. Samson signalled for two more Mercedes lorries and guns.

The coast had been reached soon after Antwerp fell on 10 October but the Channel ports were held safe. Sueter's new road squadrons had barely started training at home when Samson's cars went short of work with the onset of trench warfare. The general expectation was that this was a temporary stalemate, and in the interval Forges et Chantiers got on with modifying the Wimborne/Macnamara hulls. Angled extension panels were fitted to heighten the fighting compartment and drivers were given Scarlett's vision flap. Sueter's gun shields were less necessary because the Maxims on the rebuilt cars were mounted only just above the raised hull and could be operated by one man, thanks to the Sheerness belt-carrier attachment. The shields were accordingly designed for optional removal and disposal over the side. The first five Dunkirk conversions were completed in November, with eight more in hand.[10]

The roads began to disintegrate under prolonged autumn rains, immense traffic and shellfire. For Samson's overladen vehicles, broken leaf-springs were routine. A squadron of twenty-five armoured and support cars was getting through 120 tyres and tubes each week. Studded tyres were fitted and an attempt was made to convert them to semi-solid with a filling of Rubberine compound in place of air, but to little effect. (This was one of several patent fillers, another being Phleumatic Jelly in which Col Crompton had an interest.) Detachable footboards served as dual bridging/mudboards, but cross-country movement on wheels remained unthinkable.

At home the armoured car force had outgrown the Sheerness training facility. It transferred to the cathedral-like Daily Mail Airship Garage at Wormwood Scrubs. (Built by Lord Northcliffe in 1909 as London's first airfield, the site of the shed is now occupied by the Linford Christie Sports Stadium.) Training began there on 8 October, huts for offices and stores sprouting like mushrooms in the corrugated iron cavern. Wg Cdr Frederick Boothby arrived from RN Airships to command the unit. He was another of the Navy's first flyers and a fine test pilot. The force was renamed the Royal Naval Armoured Car Division and its strength was increased to fifteen squadrons. Five of them were equipped as motorcycle machine-gun units with a job lot of 300 Bradford-built Scott machines and 200 sidecars, originally earmarked for the Royal Naval Division. Half the sidecars mounted a Maxim, the others being ammunition limbers. Recruitment was handled from RNAS HQ at the Crystal Palace. Of 4,000 applicants to join the division in September 1914, 400 were accepted. That winter Boothby had 110 officers and 1,474 men under his command, most of them trainees.

*   *   *

Churchill's relations with Kitchener and the War Office deteriorated sharply after the Navy's humiliating reverse on the fall of Antwerp. In the confusion of the withdrawal most of the 1st Naval Brigade had been cut off. The 2,000 reservist sailors had no alternative but to enter neutral Holland, lay down their arms and accept internment. Kitchener resented Churchill's increasing and largely uninvited naval presence on the Western Front, dismissing Samson's force as an 'irregular formation'. Churchill became notorious for his well-intentioned interference in the affairs of other ministries, but a determination to make a significant contribution to final victory in France was his goal of goals. It was an almost uncontrollable urge, his naval responsibilities notwithstanding. Kitchener had asked the Admiralty to provide home air defence and could hardly dispute Churchill's entirely logical decision to fight from French airfields, but for him the rot set in with the appearance in France of itinerant shooting parties of marines, armed to the teeth and racing around in outlandish vehicles. They were soon joined by three armoured Admiralty trains mounting 4.5in guns and the fleet of London buses. Adm Bacon and his naval howitzers were expected in January.

In reality the Navy units were working in close support of the Army, from which they took their orders while remaining subject to the Naval Discipline Act. However, Kitchener became convinced that Churchill was, wittingly or not, undermining his command. The Secretary of State insisted that all naval assets in France be turned over to the Army or shipped out, leaving only an Admiralty air squadron at Dunkirk. Churchill was shaken but defiant. He had no intention of letting Kitchener throw him out of France but concessions were called for.

Henry Rawlinson, now a Corps commander, was glad to be given the additional command of all naval cars, trains and aircraft, leaving only

Samson's reduced air and road force at Dunkirk. Sueter instructed Samson on 12 October to transfer five armoured Talbots, newly arrived that day, to the Queen's Own Oxfordshire Hussars. He was to retain just sufficient officers to service his remaining squadron of fifteen armoured cars and another of eight aeroplanes; the rest of his officers were to return home immediately. He was to place himself at Gen Rawlinson's disposal.[11] Operational control of Samson's force passed from the Admiralty to GHQ on 11 November, by which time his air activities were directed largely in support of the BEF. He was widely respected by the field commanders including Rawlinson, who wrote to Churchill on 14 October:

> . . . a line to express my very sincere thanks for your kindness in allowing me to keep the armoured motors and aeroplanes under Samson. They have all done excellent work. The armoured cars pick up half a dozen prisoners a day and have instilled a holy terror into our opponents. We could do with double the number of them. Samson and his aeroplanes have obtained us the most valuable information . . . Samson himself earns more of my respect and appreciation daily.[12]

Hostility came also from the Admiralty Board. Murray Sueter's activities were disparaged by all but one of the Sea Lords who considered his aerial and automobile sorties to be little better than self-promoting stunts, of no relevance to the maritime tasks and traditions of the Navy. The RNAS was the responsibility of the Fourth Sea Lord, Cdre Cecil Foley Lambert, who gave his low opinion of the armoured car operations in an official paper after Churchill's departure – 'Motor cars have nothing to do with the Naval Service.'[13] He told Boothby they were all 'damned idlers'. The Second Sea Lord, Vice Adm Sir Frederick Tower Hamilton, was incensed to see the White Ensign being flown from jackstaffs on the tails of armoured cars and lorries. Vigorous support came only from the new Third Sea Lord, Rear Adm Frederick Charles Tudor-Tudor, whose appointment that September followed two years as Director of Naval Ordnance & Torpedoes.

For Churchill these were domestic irritations but on 14 November French told him that now that the lines of battle were continuous there was no possibility of using armoured cars. French recommended their immediate return to England for refit together with all the RNAS aircraft. Churchill had cultivated French and the request appears out of character. It may have been sent at Kitchener's insistence. Churchill undertook only to withdraw his remaining aircraft and cars to Dunkirk in order to keep clear of the British Army and its communications. By mid-December he had eight armoured car squadrons under training, two of which were nearing completion. (In January 1915 Sueter would be turning them out at the rate of one a week.) When Churchill tried to persuade French to take more, Kitchener suspected the two were conducting operations behind his back and complained to the Prime Minister. Asquith wrote to Churchill on 18 December: 'I have no objection to your going to Dunkirk to look into naval matters, but after talking to Kitchener who came to see me this morning I am clearly of opinion that you should not go to French's HQ or attempt to see French.'[14] He went on to say that such meetings had produced profound friction between French and Kitchener and their staffs. Churchill reproached Kitchener for going to Asquith, reminding him that he had ensured that the naval units in France were placed under military command. There is no doubting Kitchener's anger. He replied on the 23rd:

I am sorry to see by your letter that you have gone back upon what was agreed between us with regard to the future of the various formations that you have raised at different times for service with the Army. The Navy and the Army have each their definite role to perform, and I think it is a good rule that the Admiralty and the War Office shall confine themselves to the supply of the services required by their respective Departments. Armoured trains, 'bus transport, armoured motor cars are, or can be, provided by the War Office when required. . . .

If these irregular formations are only a means to enable certain officers and gentlemen without military experience and training, to get to the front and take part in the war, then I think it is even more important, if they are to be kept on, that they should form part of the Army, and not claim to be separate entities under the control of the Admiralty; by control I mean what you yourself state, viz;– that they cannot be broken up or used in any other way than as complete Naval units, even though the exigencies of the service may require this to be done.

I know how anxious you are to do all in your power to promote the success of our arms in France, and when I tell you that the morale of the Army in the Field is affected by these irregular Naval additions and therefore its fighting power impaired, as well as that they cause discontent and give trouble to the staff entirely out of proportion to their utility, I think you will agree with me that it is essential that something should be done to regularise the situation.[15]

It was a churlish dismissal of the work of Samson's road force and the still very active armoured trains under Cdr Scott Littlejohns, both units having earned the praise of Kitchener's commanders in France. The volunteer bus fleet remained in demand by the BEF long after Antwerp and was equally undeserving of Kitchener's imputation that because the Army did not provide any of these outfits they could not have been required in the first place. He was careful to confine his objections to Churchill's armoured cars and other 'irregulars', avoiding reference to the RN Division which was shortly to be attached to the BEF. In a pained reply Churchill pointed to the long tradition of naval detachments serving alongside and receiving their orders from the Army. As for the armoured cars:

This is a very good force. It arose out of the practical experiences in connection with the need of establishing flying bases in Northern France while the Army was still near Paris. . . . Altogether there are fifteen squadrons, the majority of the cars being light and mounting Maxims and the others being heavy and mounting 3-pounders. . . . The quality of the officers and men is high. . . . If Sir John French at any time wants these cars abroad, and the War Office apply to the Admiralty for them, they will be placed at the disposal of the Army . . . I can assure you that nothing is further from my thoughts or intentions than ever in any circumstances being lured into attempting to add to the number of naval units serving with the Army.[16]

Churchill proposed that an agreement should be prepared which reflected past precedents and which gave the fullest disciplinary and administrative control of all naval detachments to the Army for as long as they were in the field. Among Kitchener's papers is an undated draft of that period in his own hand and intended for Churchill. It seems unlikely that it was ever sent.

I ought to tell you frankly that your private arrangements with French as regards land forces is [sic] rapidly rendering my position and responsibility as Secretary of State impossible . . . I do not interfere with Jellicoe nor do

I have a private correspondence with him [this sentence struck out]. I am suggesting to the P.M. that you should take the W.O. and let Fisher be 1st Lord then all would work smoothly I hope.[17]

While Churchill continued to dodge these thunderbolts, the Samson brothers and Warner, the squadron's eye-blackened gunlayer, worked throughout the winter to devise means of getting the wheeled unit back into action. Anticipating a return to a war of manoeuvre in the spring of 1915, they built an awesome gunship on a heavily armoured 5-ton Mercedes chassis. On the flatbed behind the cab stood an armoured emplacement for six Vickers .303 machine guns topped by a commander's conning tower. The battery could hose nearly 6,000 rounds per minute over a range of 2,900yd. With that firepower they could have gone into the timber felling business. A rear-facing secondary steersman's position in the back of the vehicle was cable-linked to the driver's steering assembly. If the crew came under heavy attack and there was no time for elegant turning movements, they could reverse out and away on full throttle using this modified French steering system which Samson also fitted to an armoured car. The roads were virtually impassable by the time the truck was completed and it never saw action. It was shipped home in the new year.

Winter brought other problems. The lorry engines in particular would fail to fire up on the starting handle. This necessitated the heating of rags tied around stove pipes; the rags were then rushed in a bucket to wrap round carburettors to aid vaporisation.

Other innovations included the conversion of a lorry-fitted gun mounting to permit vertical anti-aircraft fire. A towed mounting for a 3-pdr gun was also built – a pair of car wheels on a reinforced axle with gun and shield were hauled by a Rolls-Royce fully enclosed in customised armour. It was hoped this combination could tackle the roads better than the lorries. After a successful test firing on 10 December the 3-pdr saw some action before relegation to anti-aircraft duty on Dunkirk aerodrome, its trail sunk deep to secure a 70° elevation in a gunpit ringed with sand-filled petrol tins.

* * *

Samson brought his remaining vehicles and crews back to Wormwood Scrubs after handing over the Dunkirk sector to 1 Naval Air Squadron on

27 February 1915. The following week he took twelve aircraft and a squadron of fifteen armoured cars to Tenedos for the Dardanelles campaign. In those few days in London *en route* from one war front to another, he was booked for speeding.

*   *   *

Kitchener's dispute with Churchill rolled on unabated. Asquith again had to warn Churchill off. On 17 February he wrote to tell Churchill that Kitchener had been to see him 'in a state of some peturbation. He has just received two letters from French in which he announces that you have offered him a brigade of the Naval Division and two squadrons of armoured cars. Kitchener is strongly of opinion that French has no need of either.'[18] Asquith confided to Venetia Stanley (Clementine Churchill's cousin). 'I am rather vexed with Winston who has been tactless enough to offer to Sir John French (behind K's back and without his knowledge) a brigade of his Naval Division and two squadrons of his famous armoured cars which are being hawked about from pillar to post.'[19] He told her that most of Churchill's new armoured cars had been lying practically derelict at Wormwood Scrubs for the past two or three months.

Churchill wrote a conciliatory note to Kitchener proposing the withdrawal of his offer of the Naval battalions and reminding him:

> You have known for months past of the armoured cars and the naval battalions and what was the intention with which they were called into being. It has always rested . . . exclusively with you when and how they shall join the army. So far as the cars are concerned I should be glad if you found it possible to [let me] send over two squadrons. . . . It would be a great pity to have an argument on the turn of a phrase. If [Sir John French's] letters had begun 'I have heard that there are some armoured cars available which the Admiralty have prepared and etc.' instead of talking about 'the offer of the 1st Lord of the Admiralty', this to me wearisome incident would have been avoided.[20]

Some armoured car squadrons went to East Anglia to help meet the threat of invasion. The remainder continued to train. Churchill eventually found work for them all, several ending up in remote theatres where they were out of sight of their critics and free to get on with the war. Wedgwood and his men were stalled and fuming with impatience at the Holkham airship station in Norfolk. In February 1915 Churchill offered the squadron to Gen Botha for service in South West Africa. Awaiting his reply, Wedgwood begged the First Lord to get his squadron to France. 'Please don't leave me in this country now. The squadron will mutiny, which I ignore, but I myself should be seriously incommoded – and I do want to get at them again.'[21]

Wedgwood's 3 Squadron went instead to Gallipoli. Locker Lampson took three squadrons to fight with the armies of the Czar. Their remarkable exploits ranged across Russia into Asia Minor and down through Persia and the Danube delta. Lampson collected so many orders and decorations from grateful governments that he listed one of his recreations in *Who's Who* as 'refusing honours'. Since 1909 he had been, and remained, a director and company secretary of Duff, Morgan & Vermont Ltd, a firm of motor engineers in Norwich. The company later became contractor to the Admiralty for the design and supply of all its armoured cars until the end of the war.[22] The Duke of Westminster's 2 Squadron got to France before moving on to the Middle East. Other RN armoured cars went to East Africa, and six squadrons later fought in Flanders. All would distinguish themselves, but in France the bold improvisations of the RNAS had come up against the limitations of the wheel.

Four

PRELIMINARIES TO A DINNER PARTY

We must crush the trenches in DAD. We must crush them in. It is the only way. We must do it. We will crush them. I am certain it can be done.[1]

> *Winston Churchill to Cdre Murray Sueter, Director of Air Department, Royal Naval Air Service, 18 January 1915*

The demands of the armoured car squadrons generated intense activity at Wormwood Scrubs. Churchill was a regular visitor, constantly urging Sueter to devise new weaponry. In November 1914 Sueter put an observation balloon unit into the airship shed and Boothby moved out, establishing his armoured cars HQ nearby in the imposing (and still extant) Clement-Talbot motor works in Barlby Road. Land adjoining the works became a trials ground for RNAS fighting vehicles. The airship shed was severely damaged by a hydrogen explosion the following July, killing two men of the balloon unit and injuring many more.[2]

The possibilities of chain traction were first seriously raised at Wormwood Scrubs with the arrival in October 1914 of Robert Macfie, a 33-year-old Scots-Canadian aviator, engineer and adventurer who had flown with Hetherington at Brooklands in 1911. Macfie's family had extensive interests in sugar production and processing. He spent the next two years on plantations in the West Indies where he saw Holt tractors in action and he was so struck with their performance that he wrote to alert steam traction engineers Fowler's of Leeds. Macfie's final peacetime assignment was a six-month study of power ploughing in western Canada for a New York group planning to build tractors. It included an appraisal of Holts and other machines. He returned to England in August 1914 intending to enlist as a pilot, but determined first to promote tracklayers to the military. Through his

RFC connections he met senior War Office officials who clearly knew nothing of crawlers and remained blankly unmoved. He turned in October to Lt Harry Delacombe who was working on the balloons with Sueter. Delacombe told the Royal Commission on Awards to Inventors in 1919 that Macfie had urged him to press for the armoured cars to be replaced with fighting tracklayers, dismissing the cars as overmanned, overweight and overreliant on roads.

As Sueter was in Antwerp with Churchill, Delacombe sounded out his fellow officers. They showed little interest in Macfie's ideas but Delacombe never forgot Hetherington's reply: 'If you are going in for a landship on those lines why not go the whole hog and take a thing like the gasometer at the Oval and armour it, put on a couple of wheels like the Earls Court Wheel, put your mechanism inside and put in some decent guns like 12in. naval guns, then you can cross the Rhine.'[3] It struck Delacombe as one of the best ideas of the war. The giant Ferris wheel at the Earls Court pleasure gardens was 100ft in diameter.

Macfie, an RN-trained engineer, was commissioned into the Armoured Car Division as Hetherington's Field Repair Officer. He had taken up flying in Chicago before returning home in 1909 to built his own monoplane in six weeks; a series of dramatic smashes followed. Two years later he built a biplane of advanced design in three weeks, secured pilot's licence No. 45, and was noticed in the aviation press:

Of boundless energy, restless of spirit, occupied perpetually with vast schemes that will revolutionise the industry . . . fuming ever against absurd restrictions that hinder his activity. Withal, sound mechanical and engineering knowledge and an extraordinarily acute perception of the problems of flight. Above all, a mind original in every respect. Unquestionably one of the ablest men in aeronautics.[4]

Having joined the RNAS, Macfie began a chaintrack crusade. Its initial focus was on the benefits of tracked haulage rather than fighting machines. At Sueter's request he produced a report which Boothby forwarded on 7 November 1914 with the comment 'this officer is a thoroughly competent engineer and his report seems worthy of consideration'. Macfie set out the advantages of the caterpillar system for moving heavy guns, claiming that six Holts could haul guns of up to 85 tons over smashed roads. He described techniques for wagon-train haulage over difficult ground, and included a photograph cut from the *Daily Mail* that week showing a Holt at work with the German Army.[5] There was no mention of fighting machines, though he later claimed the report was written with that purpose and that this was self-evident. The paper caused Hetherington to recommend purchase of a Holt for recovery work. Sueter was dismissive, telling him the Army was familiar with such machines.

Hetherington's off-the-cuff reference to an armoured gasometer which had so impressed Delacombe had been made half jokingly. But as its awesome implications sank in, Hetherington became captivated by the idea and he roughed out a design for a 'land battleship' which he put to Sueter in mid-November. Designated 'The Hetherington Proposal', it was to be a strategic super-weapon on three giant wheels and mounting a 12in naval gun weighing 67 tons. The machine would smash its way across country, fording rivers, destroying enemy batteries and dragging up railway lines with ship's anchors as it ploughed into Germany. The idea was timely if nothing else. Churchill was now harrying Sueter, whose drive and engineering skills he respected, to produce a radically new weapon to break the siege war.

Sqn Cdr Wilfred Briggs, who had supervised the armour-plate trials for the cars, and Mr Harris Booth, the RNAS senior technical adviser, calculated the Hetherington machine's engines, fuel, radius of action, speeds, structure, weight of armour, ammunition and stores. They decided on banks of submarine diesel sets to power electric motors geared to the wheels. When all-up weight approached 800 tons Sueter called a halt. Hetherington agreed they should restart on a more rational basis. Design of the 'Revised Hetherington Proposal' continued into the new year. It was still a monster of 300 tons on three 40ft wheels. The hull sported twin 4in guns in each of three standard naval turrets.

*   *   *

On Sunday evening 15 November a strikingly handsome armoured Rolls-Royce pulled into the Talbot works yard; its arrival from Glasgow merited special mention in the daily report from Boothby's office.[6] The Silver Ghost chassis had been part plated to a new design at Beardmore's Dalmuir works where the company's Mr Scott had solved the problem of shaping light steel plate. The engine, driver's and fighting compartments were all armoured. To save weight the open rear body was a shallow wooden tray with lockers, pick-up style. The car was topped by a rotating gun turret, a typically naval touch, with an elegantly dished roof. It mounted a single water-cooled Vickers-Maxim. Refinements included a pair of driver-operated steel doors shielding the radiator, Scarlett's full-width top-hinged visor plate fronting the driver, and a secondary starter in the cab to avoid the need to get out for hand-starts under fire. There were ample side lookouts and revolver ports. Fully laden for action the 4-tonner with its three-man crew could still reach 50mph.

Six more turreted cars had arrived by 10 December, at which point Sueter raised the order from 114 to 120 to equip all eight squadrons then in formation. Around eighty were to be Rolls-Royces, and basically the same hull was built on to three Clement-Talbot chassis and some thirty-six Lanchesters. None went to Samson in France; winter and vile road conditions made an allocation pointless. The first cars were plated in a special 8.5mm nickel chrome alloy developed by Beardmore's. It stopped an ordinary German bullet at 10yd, but if the bullet was removed from the cartridge and reinserted point first, only a 10mm plate would resist the reversed round, as the Germans were discovering.

After the first inadequately armoured Wimborne/Macnamara cars, Sueter had expanded the design team to include Nickerson, Hetherington and Briggs – the latter became the light armour specialist. The turreted Rolls-Royce influenced armoured car design around the world for a generation and was still in service with the British Army in 1936.

At this time Sueter also produced an armoured truck mounting a 3-pdr Hotchkiss on a 5-ton chassis. As most British lorries in this class were steam powered, he chose the Detroit-built Standard's petrol chassis with chain-drive, marketed in Britain as the Seabrook. Thirty-six were ordered.[7] Portholme Coach Works Ltd of Huntingdon, Cambridgeshire, undertook the conversion; it was a struggling firm modestly distinguished by the possibility that it had introduced the first motor hearse to England. Sueter would have been more familiar with its parent company, seaplane makers Portholme Aerodrome Ltd, founded by James Radley who held pilot's certificate No. 12 which he gained in 1910. He broke the world air speed record that year, reaching 75mph. Robert Macfie also knew the place well – he flew a pusher biplane of his own design from Portholme Meadow in May 1910, days after the Earl of Sandwich opened it for aviators.

The armoured open-top hulls in 8mm plate reflected the earlier Admiralty pattern Wolseleys and were built to Hetherington's design. The engine compartment was fully protected, while the driver had the option of no roof or an armoured hood which he could slide sideways for head cover. The semi-automatic 3-pdr behind on the flatbed had a full traverse, providing the driver remembered to slide the hood out of its way and duck his head. Alternatively, a Vickers-Maxim could be mounted at each corner. Full-width ammunition lockers filled the stern.

If the lorry had to withdraw hastily under fire, a full-throttle departure in reverse gear was possible if the driver took his steering instructions via an ingenious arrangement of cables and pointers. A steersman sat at the back of the truck peering rearwards over the ammunition lockers through a slot in a hinged plate. He communicated steering requirements by reference to a quadrant painted on the plating in front of him. A metal pointer could be moved over the quadrant by a hand lever which was cable-connected to a pointer on the driver's dashboard. The driver had to align a white marker on his steering wheel with the moving pointer while accelerating in reverse. Sueter's heavily armed Seabrooks carried a substantial punch, but with a fighting weight of 10 tons the cart-spring suspension was heavily stressed.

The first chassis fitted with a gun was driven down from Huntingdon to Wormwood Scrubs on 15 November, arriving the same evening as the first turreted Rolls.[8] The Seabrook was not armoured and was probably *en route* to Glasgow for trial plating after test firing. The first armoured lorries reached Boothby in mid-December and by 13 January 1915 he had twenty, but trials were revealing serious suspension problems. The order was reduced to thirty. No Seabrooks went out to Samson but three joined the Duke of Westminster's 2 Squadron which crossed to France in March. The Kitchener/Churchill stand-off left the unit stalled at Dunkirk awaiting a formal War Office request for its services. This was not good enough for 'Bend'Or' Westminster who pulled strings and got his cars and Seabrooks into the Neuve-Chapelle action which opened on the 10th. Churchill wrote Kitchener a sardonic letter of apology for the participation of this 'irregular' force, adding that the lorries did very useful work, pumping seventy-five shells into a fortified house despite receiving heavy return fire and casualties. Westminster soon had twelve Seabrooks, telling Churchill:

[We] shell these various fortified houses that are full of Maxims. We go and lie out at night and commence operations at dawn. We have had about eight of these expeditions and manage to get within about 600yd. But now I find that the Germans are strengthening these forts with sandbags and cement etc. and we now want a 6-pdr firing Lyddite, if you have any of these guns to spare we could fix up the mountings and armour out here. Our interviews with the various Military authorities are now most touching, there is generally not a dry eye when we take leave of each other – and they talk with reverence about these 3-pdrs. . . . Now all this fuss and bother that we had to contend with is over, things run smoothly, but I don't mind telling you that I had the devil's own time getting under weigh . . . The Rolls-Royce [*sic*] with the Maxims are being rubbed into them now and they are softening to them all right.[9]

Sueter's output of road-fighting vehicles ended with the Seabrooks, though in September 1915 he formed a mobile anti-Zeppelin brigade for London based on lorry- and trailer-mounted 3-pdr guns. The Portholme work had been supervised by Hetherington who was showing considerable mechanical flair. He was joined by Lt Walter Gordon Wilson RNVR, an outstanding automobile engineer. Wilson, then aged forty, would profoundly influence the direction and ultimate success of tank development. He had served as a midshipman before leaving the Navy in 1894 to gain a mechanical sciences tripos with first-class honours. In 1898 he joined forces with Percy Pilcher, an aero engineer, to form Wilson-Pilcher Ltd. They intended to produce the world's first purpose-built aero engine. A prototype was designed a year later and was about to be constructed when Pilcher died in a gliding accident. Wilson turned to automobile design, creating the Wilson-Pilcher motor car with an advanced epicyclic transmission. The Newcastle armaments firm of Sir W.G. Armstrong, Whitworth & Co. took up Wilson's designs, incorporating them in its own cars. He joined the company in 1904.

Wilson designed and built a 'Military Car' in 1906 at Armstrong's Elswick works. The low-waisted open-top vehicle doubled as a gun tractor or a fighting car mounting a 1-pdr pom-pom beside the driver. Wilson demonstrated its versatility by winching a field gun up and down the steep stone-pitched embankment of the Tyne. This interesting machine attracted little attention and no more were built. Wilson left the company in 1908 to freelance, principally as technical adviser to J. & E. Hall of Dartford where he largely designed the Halford lorry, later widely used in the war. He joined the Armoured Car Division in December 1914.

*   *   *

While Adm Bacon and William Tritton were planning their portable bridging machine that December, Sueter got Messrs Vickers to design a wheeled bullet-proof infantry shield. By the end of the month the company had produced a wooden mock-up of a hand-propelled sheet armour screen on a single central wheel which up to thirty men could push ahead of them. The idea was not new and its great weight made it immovable on soft ground, let alone shell-torn terrain. Sueter now recalled Capt Robert Scott's caterpillar motor sleighs built by the Wolseley Co. for his Antarctic expedition. He had advised Scott on how and where to get the sleighs built. Briggs was instructed to find a similar powered or pushable caterpillar assembly on which to mount the shield.

Lt Lord Tollemache turned up a trade catalogue detailing a small wagon on a full-width chaintrack designed by a perverse genius, Bramah Joseph Diplock of Fulham, West London. Although lacking formal engineering training, Diplock had become interested in heavy traction systems and took out over 100 patents. The first, in 1893, was for a remarkably prescient four-wheel-drive steam traction engine with all-wheel steering and pivoting axles for extreme ground conditions. Tasker's of Andover constructed the machine in 1899. It delivered 50 per cent more hauling power than engines of equivalent weight, encouraging Diplock to produce some highly unorthodox forms of traction. His 'Pedrail' wheel comprised a series of elephant-like feet projecting around the wheel's rim to improve grip and greatly reduce ground pressure. Unfortunately it involved a hideously complex internal assembly of articulated joints, springs, levers and pins almost akin to a scaled-up watch movement. The idea captivated H.G. Wells but few others. Wells wrote the Pedrail into *The Land Ironclads* in 1903, his prophetic and rather chilling story of the emergence of large invincible armoured fighting machines mounted on Diplock's big wheels.

Diplock patented a crawler assembly in 1910 which dramatically reduced the friction and power loss of conventional chaintracks. In a fine piece of lateral thinking he stood the principle of the fixed railway on its head. Instead of rolling laden wheels over a pair of continuous rails, he passed two short laden rails over an endless series of rollers. His chaintrack was an inverted railroad. It retained the rather disconcerting feet of the Pedrail, projecting like upturned soup plates around the track's circumference. The system was ingenious but vastly complicated by a mass of secondary chains, rollers and tensioning springs, promising high wear and constant maintenance. Diplock's chain tractor and trailer were exhibited at London's 1913 Commercial Motor Show at Olympia. He was unsuccessful and permanently short of funds, but went on to produce the horse-drawn 'Colonial' wagons on a single simplified track which had caught Tollemache's eye.

Hetherington inspected the little 1-ton truck on 12 January 1915. Next day Diplock demonstrated it at Wormwood Scrubs, laden with 13cwt of stone. His horse hauled it about in deep mud beside the Talbot works and sank to its hocks while the wagon, despite its weight, rode on top of the morass. Sueter bought it for his infantry screen.

Adm Tudor had been an advocate of light armour screens for twenty years and had already submitted his own design to Churchill on 2 January, urging him to order 1,000. His 6ft high and 12ft long chrome steel shield for twenty-five men was mounted between a pair of artillery wheels infilled with steel sheet. The 1,000lb device knocked flat for transportation. Sueter conceded its superiority over the Vickers model, but further development lapsed until work on manually propelled and motorised shields was begun by the Trench Warfare Department of the Ministry of Munitions. An experimental version mounted on Diplock's track and carrying a machine gun was ordered by the Ministry that September.

Naval work on shields was halted by Churchill's vigorous reaction to Hankey's Boxing Day memorandum. The First Lord was tired of Kitchener's recriminations and was now openly contemptuous of military inertia concerning the machine-gun menace. He let the Admiralty loose to develop its own siege-breaking weapon and Sueter caught the blast. On Monday 18 January the First Lord told him that he wanted immediate and substantial trench-destroying experiments to be set in train by the Air Department. He had just ordered construction of an experimental Tritton/Bacon bridging machine but he wanted to see other lines of enquiry begun and carried forward at speed. Sueter, heavily preoccupied with aviation matters, recalled Churchill striding up and down the room while dictating a minute to him, punctuated by growls over his shoulder that 'We must crush the trenches in DAD. We must crush them in. It is the only way. We must do it. We will crush them. I am certain it can be done.'[10] That night Churchill minuted Tudor and Sueter:

I wish the following experiment made at once. Two ordinary steamrollers are to be fastened together side by side with very strong steel connections, so they are to all intents and purposes one roller covering a breadth of at least 12 to 14 feet. If convenient one of the back inside wheels might be removed, and the other axle joined up to it. Some trenches are to be dug on the latest principles somewhere handy near London in lengths of at least 100 yards, the earth taken out of the trenches being thrown on each side, as is done in France. The roller is to be driven along these trenches, one outer rolling wheel on each side, and the inner rolling wheel just clear of the trench itself.

The object is to ascertain what amount of weight is necessary in the roller to smash the trench in. For this purpose as much weight as they can possibly draw should be piled on to the steamrollers and on the framework buckling them together. The ultimate object is to run along a line of trenches, crushing them all flat and burying the people in them. If the experiment is successful with the steamrollers fastened together on this improved system, stronger and larger machines can be made with bigger driving wheels and proper protection for the complements, and the rollers of these machines will be furnished with wedge-shaped ribs or studs, which can be advanced beyond the ordinary surface of the wheel when required, in order to break the soil on each side of the trench and accentuate the rolling process.

The matter is extremely urgent, and should be pressed to the utmost. Really the only difficulty you have got to surmount is to prevent the steamrollers from breaking apart. The simplicity of the device, if it succeeds, is its virtue. All that is required is a roller of sufficient breadth and with wheels properly fitted with an unscaleable bullet-proof house for the crew. Three or four men would be quite enough, and as the machine is only worked by night it would not be required to stand against artillery. In a fortnight I wish to see these trials.[11]

Coincidentally, next day Col Louis Jackson, Assistant Director of Fortifications and Works, received the Tulloch/Swinton proposals. The contrast is striking. On the one hand the Navy Minister, clearly no engineer, was giving a Sea Lord and his Aviation Chief a bare fortnight to set up and complete trials for a land weapon of no relevance to the Admiralty. On the other, and simultaneously, two engineer officers close to the real solution were still struggling to get trials started by the Service that so desperately needed the weapon and so determinedly ignored the fact.

Briggs' engineering assistant, Lt Barry, reported on 20 January:

I have today visited Aldershot and inspected trials made with an American Holt caterpillar. The machine is, I believe, the most efficient form of tractor in existence, and the manner in which it goes over rough ground, soft ground, [etc.] is nothing short of marvellous. . . . With regard to the joining of two steamrollers together, it appears that if this were possible to do, and this machine was driven along a trench and did not break in half, the middle wheels would be supported by the outside wheels and it would not have the desired effect of rolling down the trench . . . steamrollers would be absolutely useless for this as they would immediately become bogged in any soft earth. . . . Any steamroller or tractor would be very hard to armour-plate sufficiently to give protection both to the driver and vital parts of the engine. This also applies to the caterpillar above. . . . The only method for really attacking Germans in their trenches seems to be to have an enormous machine with a plough attachment to it, with a roller behind it, which would walk along the side of the trench, smash in one side and then roll it down flat.[12]

Barry went on to set up the steamroller trial, coupling a pair of machines side by side and preparing trenches at Wormwood Scrubs. The heavy steamers broke apart three times within yards of starting. Barry continued with one machine. It was set at top speed at a 2ft high earth bank beside the trench. Having trundled over the damp ground on full power it baulked at the foot of the bank despite the 3in ropes bound round the driving wheels as makeshift strakes. Further attempts ended similarly and experiments were abandoned. Briggs and Barry thought the idea might work if a single giant machine were built twenty times larger than the trials rollers. They had become convinced members of Hetherington's 'big wheel' school and got out drawings of a stupendously proportioned steamer, but Sueter saw its futility and wisely dropped the whole idea of a trench plough or crusher. His report to Churchill concluded:

These experiments prove that the loading of a steamroller is too high for it to be successfully used over agricultural land, and that [for] a machine to perform this work [it] must be specially designed of a greater total weight and with very much greater wheel surface, and particularly much greater diameter wheels. A machine of this description would be very costly to produce and would probably be very difficult to bring into action. Also it could be easily mined.[13]

Barry's report was accompanied by a specification for the 'Revised Hetherington Proposal'. Briggs and Booth had reduced the land battleship to a still awesome 300 tons. Weight would be saved by adopting an open lattice girder frame 46ft high, 100ft long and 80ft wide. Armour 3in thick would protect the vital areas only. The three 40ft diameter wheels would give 17ft of underbody clearance. Top speed was 8mph. Although Sueter's thoughts were moving away from giant machines he put the proposal to Churchill at the end of January:

> It consists essentially of a platform mounted on three wheels (of which the front two are drivers and the stern wheel for steering), armed with three turrets, each containing two four inch guns, propelled by a 800hp Sunbeam diesel set [with] electric drive to the wheels. The engines as well as the guns and magazines would be armoured, but not the purely structural part which would be fairly proof against damage by shell fire if a good factor of safety is used and a superfluity of parts provided in the structure. . . . It can be destroyed by sufficiently powerful artillery [and] by land mines. . . . It would appear at first sight that the machine ought to be more heavily armed and gunned, but considerations of the disproportionate weight of the guns and of time of building have resulted in the proposal being reduced to the comparatively moderate one described.[14]

Churchill referred the scheme to his energetic and outspoken First Sea Lord, Adm 'Jackie' Fisher. Now seventy-three, Lord Fisher had rebuilt the Royal Navy and introduced the Dreadnought class before being recalled from retirement by Churchill in October 1914. Fisher in turn asked Vice Adm Sir Percy Scott, the Navy's gunnery expert, to look into the matter. Scott considered the idea of land battleships deeply flawed because such huge structures would be spotted and wrecked by heavy artillery long before they could be brought into action.

Sueter never had much faith in Hetherington's wheeled colossus theory. Scott's reaction persuaded him to drop it, though it was not to die so easily. The hard-pressed DAD was left with Barry's enthusiastic report on the Holt crawler – supported by Macfie – a hand-propelled sheet armour screen, and an ingenious little tracked one-horse wagon. Churchill was not going to be satisfied with anything less than a large fighting machine. Sueter decided to go for a tracklayer. He asked the War Office for loan of a Holt. They declined, so he turned to Bramah Diplock's Pedrail.

Sueter's submarine building experience led him to take a standard Holland class hull and halve its length. The 32ft section with a maximum diameter of 12ft gave him his general dimensions for a lightweight armoured and turreted landship with a moderately upturned bow and stern for a crew of eight. Armament would comprise one 12-pdr or two 6-pdr guns. Briggs calculated the project would produce a machine of 24 tons which was compatible with road-bridge loadings. Each track would be independently driven to give steering. The problem was that they needed a track length of the order of 20ft, far in excess of any yet made. There ensued a frantic search for literature on chain traction. Briggs found a 1911 copy of *Scientific American* which illustrated a heavy agricultural crawler with fairly long tracks. With these sketchy data they roughed out a design early in February 1915.

Churchill was unhappy with the dismissal of his steamroller idea. Sueter had produced nothing better and the First Lord was looking for a fresh lead from any quarter. It came at an informal dinner party given by his friend the Duke of Westminster at Grosvenor House on 14 February. The two campaigned together during the South African War and the 35-year-old Duke had joined the Armoured Car Division the previous November. Churchill thought him 'fearless, gay and delightful. Not good at explaining things or making speeches, but he thought deeply . . . and had unusual qualities of wisdom and judgement. I always valued his opinion.'[15] The Duke was enthralled with the experimental work. He had even offered Hetherington the engines from his racing boat *Ursula*. The dinner was his idea, to give Churchill an opportunity to meet Sueter's young Turks and hear their views at first hand. Sueter was excluded. Hetherington made a deep impression with his graphic description of the colossus crashing through woods and villages, trampling down trenches and crossing rivers. Here was thinking on a Churchillian scale. The First Lord recalled:

He spoke with force and vision of the whole subject, advocating the creation of land battleships on a scale far larger than has ever been found practicable . . . I went home determined that I would give imperative orders without delay to secure the carrying forward in one form or another of the project in which I had so long believed . . . I directed that he should submit to the Admiralty his plans which were for a platform mounted on enormous wheels.[16]

In Hetherington's submission to the Tank Awards Committee in 1918 he claimed he did not confine himself to the 'big wheels' proposal, saying that he gave Churchill 'a detailed description of the Diplock caterpillar track which I informed him appeared to give promise of development'.[17] Churchill told the Royal Commission on Awards in 1919 that he had no recollection of this: 'It was a wheel that night that we were talking about.'[18]

Hetherington's monolithic approach to the problem matched Churchill's temperament. (Two and a half years later Churchill was enthusiastically urging the construction of a 200-ton tank 'wide enough to go down a normal street'.)[19] He showed Hetherington's plans to Eustace Tennyson d'Eyncourt, his Director of Naval Construction, asking him if he would take on the design of a landship because its size and complexity equated to shipbuilding. D'Eyncourt was taken aback and asked for time to consider.

Sueter moved quickly. He learned of events at the Grosvenor House dinner party the next day, and instructed Hetherington to arrange a demonstration of the Pedrail Company's wagon on the following morning, 16 February, in Horse Guards Parade beside the Admiralty. A turreted Rolls-Royce was also to be displayed. Bramah Diplock and his co-director Reginald Brackenbury duly attended at 9 a.m. with their draughtsman James Lowe. Sueter persuaded Churchill to come out to see the wagon horse-hauled over the gravelled parade ground. Churchill pushed its 33cwt by hand and was astonished at the ease of movement. Sueter put his proposals for building a 24-ton machine on Pedrail tracks. It was very much a sailor's concept with its submarine-like prow and Sueter's explanation that necessary changes of trim on rough ground could be made by blowing water from one end of the machine to the other. Churchill was dubious, saying that it would need an airfield to turn in. Sueter told him that tighter turns could be achieved by locking one track while going ahead or astern with the other. An hour's earnest discussion followed, during which Sueter proposed the fitting of chaintracks to armoured cars.[20] The First Lord returned to his office unpersuaded.

In his memoirs Sueter put a heavy gloss on the outcome of the demonstration. He claimed that Churchill at once saw the superiority of a tracked machine over his own steamroller idea and Hetherington's three-wheeler. Sueter added that after much discussion the First Lord expressed his satisfaction that the turreted armoured cars could be built on chaintracks, and gave Sueter approval to build eighteen landships.[21] Churchill gave no such approval for several weeks, and from that day onward the First Lord effectively relieved Sueter of responsibility for what he called 'Churchill's problem'.

Three official attempts had been made to date to find a mechanical solution – the Admiralty's still untested self-bridging machine, its coupled steamrollers, and the Army's Holt. The first two were hopelessly impracticable and the day after Sueter's demonstration on Horse Guards, the Holt trial ended the Army's interest in a fighting chaintrack. Churchill's hopes now rested on a fresh start with d'Eyncourt and Hetherington. There were no other players on the field. He told the Royal Commission in 1919:

> I was not altogether satisfied that the subject was being handled by strong enough elements and by strong enough personalities in the Armoured Car Division. I thought it was absolutely necessary to break new ground . . . Commodore Sueter . . . knew what was in my mind and the sort of thing I was trying to get done. He was a very energetic officer doing his best to meet my wishes in every respect, but he failed altogether to solve the mechanical difficulties connected with the production of tanks. He failed to find anyone who could solve them. It was because of this that . . . I turned to Sir Tennyson d'Eyncourt.[22]

The hard-pressed Director of Naval Construction was about to find himself heading a landships project.

Five

THE SILENT SERVICE

How are our landships to be used if not by the Naval Brigade?[1]

Eustace Tennyson d'Eyncourt, Chairman of the
Landships Committee, 30 April 1915

C ol Crompton was stalled in a personal battle with the War Office. He had been trying since June 1914 to alert the Army to the need for cross-country motor vehicles, but his shots were bouncing off closed minds. The 69-year-old steam haulage veteran was by then a leading voice in transport circles. He had been Vice President of the Automobile Club of Great Britain and Ireland, now the RAC, in 1903 (when he had suffered the mirth of fellow members on being fined £3 for exceeding 12mph at Surbiton). After leaving the MTC in 1905 Crompton became the first President of the Institution of Automobile Engineers and Chairman of the Commercial Motor Users Association. His commercial ventures included the first contract spraying of British roads with gas tar, and his experiments with road dust inhibition and surfacing had led the government to create the Road Board in 1910 to improve highway construction standards. Crompton was appointed Engineer to the board.

The Army had no off-road motor vehicles save a handful of Hornsby crawlers. Its reliance on good roads for its motor transport was condemned by Crompton as misplaced optimism, but this was a situation of its own making which originated in 1910, when the War Office resolved to create a motor transport reserve. The choice lay between commissioning the design and construction of a fleet of purpose-built vehicles with their associated heavy ongoing costs of maintenance, replacement and development; or taking the cheaper 'carrot and stick' alternative of offering a subsidy payment to private hauliers for commercial vehicles which would be liable to requisition in time of war. The WO introduced a subsidy scheme, but it had to accept the fact that the vehicles were built for the less demanding use of commercial operators. The Army lacked the funds, as well as the conviction, to develop its own specialist vehicles.

Crompton now urged a radical change in the design of subsidy vehicles, including the adoption of larger-diameter wheels to cope with rough going. He also wrote that June to Gen Guthrie-Smith, the Director of Artillery, offering to design a chassis mounting for a heavy gun as a self-propelled unit on 6–8ft diameter driving wheels. Crompton waived any fee, proposing instead an honorarium of £500 and his name to be attached to the gun if successful. Six days after Guthrie-Smith wrote declining the offer, Germany invaded Belgium and Britain entered the war.

Crompton's old MTC colleague Col Holden was recalled from retirement and appointed Assistant Director of Transport. Crompton tackled him head-on. They were both members of a small coterie of serving and retired officers with expertise and progressive views on motoring matters. This influential group, which included Maj Donohue, orbited in loose formation around Whitehall and the motoring institutions. All three were council members of the Institution of Automobile Engineers. Capt Tulloch of Chilworth Gunpowder was another in that loop, incidentally supporting Crompton for re-election to the IAE council in 1913.

Crompton repeated his offer to Holden. The Colonel was a 'big wheels' man but he also wanted the other's views on chain traction. Holden dismissed it at once, saying he had no time for crawlers because they were susceptible to track damage from stones. It should be remembered, however, that he had been retired and out of touch with new track technology since the days of Hornsby's nutcracker problem, such as it was. The Army still lacked detailed knowledge of Holt's much superior system, the War Office having denied the MTC a sample machine. Crompton pulled no punches on the central issue. In an uncompromising letter of 7 September 1914 he told Holden:

At this war crisis it is necessary for everyone . . . to speak quite plainly irrespective of personal friendships. I cannot keep silent, feeling as I do the grave risks run by our Army of depending only, or principally on supply and ammunition columns composed wholly of small-wheeled motor lorries. . . . As you have for the last twelve years been practically the only mechanical engineer on the Mechanical Transport Committee and have advised that Committee on all technical matters, I am forced to conclude that it is due to your advice that a class of transport has been provided which is certain to fail in bad weather or on broken up roads . . . you think that mechanical transport is only intended for use on hard roads and that our Army would find such roads everywhere on the Continent. . . . To put it quite plainly to you, I think everyone will hold you responsible as technical adviser to the War Office for the type of wagon that is now in use and you will incur serious responsibility if you ignore what I now tell you is practically certain to take place under existing conditions.[2]

Crompton urged Holden to modify the subsidy lorries by repositioning the driving axles above the chassis to allow the fitting of 6ft 3in wheels. He continued to press his case and copied the correspondence to Gen Horace Smith-Dorrien, Commander of 2 Corps in France. Crompton's experience of Holden's judgement and a certain lack of drive adds point to Tulloch's warning a few months later when he cautioned Col Jackson that Holden would obstruct the Swinton/Tulloch scheme, as noted earlier in these pages.

Crompton had been consulting engineer to the Pedrail Company since 1899 when he tested Bramah Diplock's first four-wheel-drive steam tractor. Now Diplock showed him his latest tracklayer, the 1-ton Colonial wagon. It impressed the Colonel sufficiently to make him consider switching his gun from wheels to Pedrail tracks. He noted in his diary: 'It has a rather complicated set of double springs arranged between the chainway and the sleepers but runs with extraordinary small rolling friction over long and soft grass . . . difficulty is Diplock's arrogance – nothing can be altered.'[3] The inventor's stubbornness and Holden's rejection of chain traction persuaded Crompton to drop the idea. He later said that after caterpillars had been condemned by the artillery authorities he believed they would only accept the alternative of big wheels.

After more fruitless lobbying of von Donop and others, an old friend alerted Crompton to Wg Cdr Samson's road force and its mobility problems. The information came in November from Col Wilfrid Dumble, Crompton's late adjutant of the Electrical Engineers. A Canadian from Cobourg, Ontario, Dumble had retired from the RE in 1907 to manage the London General Omnibus Company where he remained until 1913. The 43-year-old Captain's war began with a lightning recall, promotion to temporary Colonel of Marines, and attachment to the Royal Naval Division. Four days later he was in France following an urgent appeal for buses in support of Churchill's naval units in Antwerp. London General supplied the vehicles and nominated Dumble to organise the expedition. He assembled the fleet, recruited their civilian crews and packed the buses with fuel, tools and spares. He and his seventy AEC 'B' Types reached Dunkirk on 24 September. Still in their red and white livery and with London destination boards and advertisements, they were the first of the 'Old Bill' buses to serve in France in many roles from troop transports to mobile pigeon lofts.

Following the evacuation of Antwerp Dumble was given command of all RN Divisional transport, remaining at Dunkirk to regroup and repair the forty-five surviving buses. He saw Samson's armoured vehicles struggling on clogged and ruinous roads, and suggested that Crompton with his wide experience of overland transport might find an answer. Dumble was ordered home to enlist the Colonel's help. (Crompton's daughter remembers Dumble entering their drawing room still covered with Flanders mud and full of his instructions to speak to her father without delay.) The news confirmed Crompton's fears.

The two Colonels attended William Tritton's howitzer tractor trials in December. Next day Crompton sent Dumble a paper setting out 'what I could do to help Admiral Bacon'. He badly wanted to join the party, but Bacon had just set Tritton on a new course of investigation, and in any case Tritton had a long-standing professional grudge against Crompton and would have resisted his inclusion. Crompton's opportunity came two months later when Dumble joined him at Thriplands, his Kensington home and laboratory, on 15 February 1915. Dumble described Tritton's bridging machine and asked Crompton's opinion of it. They discussed Churchill's instruction – it became a mantra – 'I want something that will straddle a trench and enfilade it with machine guns, and then you let men out rapidly and you take the trench.'[4] Crompton roughed out a scheme before writing on the 19th to Holden's superior, Brig Gen S.S. Long, Director of Supplies with responsibility for transport, saying that he had completed a design and suggesting a meeting over lunch at the Royal Automobile Club: 'I would take you away and deliver you safely back at your office after a proper interval for feeding and contemplative smoking accompanied by coffee and my instructive and entertaining conversation.'[5]

They never met; Long had other concerns. Crompton recorded the outline design in his diary. His 24-ton machine would attack the enemy trench head-on, driving half over the parapet to overhang it while machine guns in turrets raked the trench to either side before a storming party descended from a floor trap to mop up and hold the cleared section. He would take one of Tritton's howitzer tractors or an equivalent from agricultural engineers Marshall's of Gainsborough, Lincolnshire, and greatly extend its 12ft length fore and aft to provide a platform 36ft long and 11ft wide. The fully enclosed armoured hull would house forty-eight fighting men and a crew of two. The 8ft driving wheels would be widened to 3ft and the smaller steered wheels to 2ft.[6]

Like Swinton, Crompton wanted to adapt an existing machine to avoid long delay, but his design raised irreconcilable problems of stability and ground clearance. Churchill's tactics required a substantial raiding party to be carried inside the machine. Crompton had to create 250sq ft of floor space for them alone, plus provision for machinery, armament, ammunition, fuel and crew. He needed a low centre of gravity for stability and a reduced hull profile against artillery fire. All this was achievable only as a trade-off with ground clearance beneath the vastly cantilevered platform extensions. The wheels lay so far back that with only 18in of clearance the machine would have grounded on inclines greater than 1 in 8, the equivalent of a wheelchair ramp. This weakness was recognised in Crompton's suggested attack procedure:

Points in our own trenches must be . . . bridged or filled . . . a route selected and levelled, shell holes filled etc. by using this armoured fort for the work, at night time or day time if preferred, up to a point sufficiently near the enemy's trenches. After dark the fort will be manned by the garrison – machine gun, riflemen and working party. It will advance over the prepared ground and finally cautiously over the ground until the overhang of the front projects above the enemy trench so that it is open to machine gun fire. The flooring of the platform will be opened for a party to descend, finish off with the bayonet and then rapidly erect a framed tractor bridge or fill by faggots or similar means. The hauling rope will be carried forward and anchored as far in advance as possible. The hauling gear [winch] put in and the fort moved on.[7]

The big machines would be easy targets for German 77s during the preparatory ground levelling. Even by night their noisy activity could be flare-lit for the guns. This phase would alert the enemy to an impending attack and even mark the approach route of each carrier. Crompton's crude design and cruder tactics were suicidal, but they must be set against prevailing circumstances. The range of mechanical solutions was limited by urgency to the handful of machines currently available and to their adaptability to fulfil the tactical brief. If the brief itself ignored these realities, failure was inevitable. Almost nobody at home, in or out of uniform, knew anything of conditions at the front at that stage of the war. It was from this baseline and these conceptions – or misconceptions – that Churchill's landships venture would have to begin its uncertain progress.

* * *

The landships project was launched from Churchill's sickbed at 10.30 a.m. on Saturday 20 February 1915. Despite his influenza he had summoned five men to his room in the Admiralty building – Tennyson d'Eyncourt his DNC, Col Wilfrid Dumble, Capt Tommy Hetherington, and William Tritton of Foster's accompanied by a representative from Coventry Ordnance Works, probably J.H. Mansell. Churchill began by telling the contractors that he was cancelling the order for thirty self-bridging sets (which he had placed the previous Saturday), leaving only the experimental machine to be completed.[8] Tritton and Mansell then departed.

Churchill turned to Hetherington's scheme and discussed it at length with d'Eyncourt. The DNC was sceptical but Churchill appealed to him to apply the unique resources and experience of his ship construction department to the problem. D'Eyncourt, who had been responsible for design of the Royal Sovereign class of battleship and would later design *Hood, Nelson* and *Rodney*, was also immersed in the design and construction of naval airships. He could hardly refuse the First Lord's entreaties, however, and was appointed President of a three-man Landships Committee with Dumble and Hetherington. The Canadian's experience of managing London's largest bus fleet and his contacts in the motor industry had impressed Churchill as much as his breakneck organisation of the Antwerp expedition's transport. Hetherington was obviously an imaginative live wire and the DNC was utterly bankable. The committee's needs would be serviced by Murray Sueter's Air Department, but d'Eyncourt would report directly to the First Lord. On their way out Hetherington asked Dumble if he could identify a leading authority on heavy traction. Dumble at once named Crompton, and the three met that afternoon at Dumble's flat in Sackville Street where Crompton agreed to attend the first meeting the following Monday.

In seven days of sometimes surreal activity Churchill had ordered and then cancelled Tritton's bridge-layers, inspected and rejected a novel track system together with Sueter's 25-ton machine, and instead approved Hetherington's proposal for a 300-ton gunship on 40ft wheels. The Army's Holt trials had failed and any further interest from that quarter had died with it. Finally, the Navy's master shipbuilder had been talked into a seemingly impossible commitment to produce a fleet of landships.

Wary of Kitchener's wrath if he discovered yet another attempt by Churchill to expand his 'circus', the First Lord did not inform the War Office or, indeed, the Board of Admiralty. He knew of von Donop's decision to cease military experiments with chaintracks. He also knew that if word of his initiative got out the War Office would block it, tacitly supported by most of his own Sea Lords. Churchill resolved to lie low until a machine was ready for demonstration. Crucially, the Treasury must not get wind of it: 'I feared that they would in the ordinary course ask the War Office their opinion on the expenditure and I apprehended that the answer would be that the expenditure would not be useful to the Army, and that in any case it was not a matter for the Admiralty or for the First Lord.'[9] Perhaps wisely, Churchill struck out this sentence when, as Secretary of State for War in 1919, he was drafting his statement of these events for the Royal Commission on Awards to Inventors.

The committee first met on Monday 22 February in d'Eyncourt's office. He was joined by Dumble, Hetherington, Crompton and Macfie, the Holt enthusiast. Hetherington's giant three-wheeler was first considered. The respective merits of wheels and tracks were next examined at much length. Crompton, who confirmed that he had little knowledge of American tracklayers, was so impressed by Macfie's account of caterpillar haulage in the US that he decided to switch to tracks for his machine. He noted in his diary that d'Eyncourt favoured 'moderate wheels'.

Crompton tabled a slightly revised design of the wheeled fort which he had wanted to show Gen Long, Director of Supplies. He dropped all reference to preparing a path before an attack. An interesting proposal was added for winching the machine forward over bad ground under fire: from a powered cable drum behind the engine a wire rope was taken back as far as possible over the rear platform before passing through sheaves and being led forward beneath the machine to an anchor. The machine would winch itself forward almost its own length before the crab-like cycle was repeated, the anchor being repositioned by the crew each time from inside the hull. Rollers beneath the forward platform would ensure the anchor's flukes bit into the ground. A double set of winding gear could provide continuous 'drive'. Width was increased to 13ft and weight was cut to 23 tons. The hull would be clad in 8mm chrome steel. For transport on ship and rail the machine could be broken down for re-erection in six hours.[10] An alternative 126-ton super-heavy version would carry 5in armour, proof against field artillery, with an increase in width to 18ft. It would require five times the power of the lighter machine with its single Daimler 105hp engine.

The committee decided at first to build two small models – one wheeled, the other tracked, to determine which system should be adopted. Before the meeting ended these were scaled up to 25-ton machines to carry fifty men. Tritton would build the wheeled version based on his howitzer tractor (to be designated 'Self-Moving Cupola Type 'A''), while a lightly armoured crawler version of Crompton's design (Type 'B') was to be produced by a specialist in chain traction. Crompton's 126-tonner was noted (Type 'C'). Churchill approved, minuting 'As proposed & with all despatch.'[11]

Crompton was appointed technical adviser to the committee with instructions to produce alternative designs for the wheeled and tracked machines. He was given virtually a free hand, with no more detailed specification to work from than Dumble's verbal brief. He was an accomplished innovator. After founding his electrical engineering company, Crompton & Co., in 1878, he had introduced generating plant of very advanced design and began installing arc lighting to such major sites as Kings Cross station and Glasgow's St Enoch's and North British Railway stations. He was awarded the first gold medal for an electric lighting generator the following year. In 1887 Crompton introduced mains electrical distribution to West London. By 1889 only two licences for electric mains supply had been taken out in England and Crompton held one of them.

A drawing office was set up in the attic at Thriplands. Needing an expert on internal combustion engines and transmissions, he recruited his friend Lucien Legros, a meticulous and distinguished fifty-year-old engineer and past President of the Institution of Automobile Engineers. Legros had designed the first petrol-engined tram cars in England in 1895–8 and later engineered and built Iris motor cars.

Crompton turned to Pedrail Transport Ltd for tracks for the 'B' Type. He confirmed at the time that no other crawler system was in production in Britain.[12] Indeed, there appeared to be no tracklayer in the country save the

Army's Hornsbys and a pair of Holts. It is not entirely surprising that despite Macfie's entreaties the Landships Committee never considered a Holt machine, arguably the most efficient tracklayer of its day. Holden had only recently refused to lend one to Sueter. Any fresh approach to the Army or even to Holt's agents at that stage would risk disclosure of Churchill's hand and shutdown of the project.

Diplock and James Lowe, his draughtsman, showed Crompton the design work which they had begun on Sueter's 25-ton machine. A turret for a 12-pdr gun topped the DAD's torpedo-shaped 38ft hull. It was to be mounted directly over two broad Pedrail track bogies set in tandem, each 13ft long and independently driven and steered. The machine would have lacked steering if it had had only a single track. Crompton retained the layout but increased payload to seventy men and the gun was discarded. A low 40ft hull devoid of turrets straddled the two in-line tracks. The engines and control gear lay along its central axis and there was a two-man crew. On either side a narrow detachable wing overhung the tracks rather like an iron saddlebag, providing a pair of standing-room corridors for the assault party. The two tracks were set close to the extremities of the hull, the underside of which was angled upwards at each end in a cutaway to aid climbing. Its great length relative to an underbody clearance of only 18in left the machine seriously prone to grounding. The same problem would arise laterally from the platform's overhang if the machine rocked unduly over rough ground. Twin engines gave a top speed of 4.5mph. At 80ft, the turning radius can only be described as generous.

Crompton went to Lincoln on 26 February to discuss the wheeled 'A' Type with Tritton. The committee had approved the Colonel's proposal that Foster's howitzer tractor should be nearly tripled in length by extensions fore and aft to enable it to carry fifty men, with some means of trench crossing less complicated than the bridging machine's. Tritton still favoured his experimental 'bridger' as a lightly armed and crewed support weapon mounting two or four machine guns. He showed it to the Colonel and urged retention of its semi-tricycle layout for the troop-carrier version. Rather surprisingly, Crompton agreed despite the visible lack of stability with upwards of 12ft of laden extension platform behind the rear axle and some 24ft ahead of it perched over the in-line steering wheels. However, he seems to have had misgivings on arriving home, likening the design to a skate. Legros was sent to Lincoln with instructions to bring away drawings of the front-end layout. The scholarly and quietly spoken engineer received a chilly reception:

I found Mr Tritton working at a War Office [*sic*] scheme for bridging trenches, and that he had no belief whatever in the chain-track system. He received me rather rudely, wanting to know why Colonel Crompton and myself were butting into this when he was already working at a scheme for a War Office committee. He stated that he had experience in building and running chain tracks of his own make (termed Centipedes) and that caterpillar tracks were no good for such work as was in view, namely trench taking.[13]

Tritton shared Holden's opinion on chain traction and his view was possibly hardened by the lack of commercial interest in 'Centipede', his answer to the 'Caterpillar'. Centipede was a semi-track version of Tritton's very successful wheeled petrol tractor. Foster's appears to have built only one – to special order in 1913 for a Paraguayan sugar plantation. Unlike the rigidly locked camber of Roberts' track, 'Centipede's' track could be profiled from flat to any camber to suit ground conditions.

Legros returned home with a drawing of Tritton's first ideas. It was clear that the platform would have to be scaled down to carry thirty men at most, as the already lengthened tractor frame would distort under a greater load. He also brought a letter from Tritton which displayed not only his lack of enthusiasm for the troop-carrying idea, but also considerable personal hostility towards Crompton. In a statement to the Tanks Awards Committee in 1918 Tritton spoke about this meeting:

Mr Legros asked if I would place all my information at Colonel Crompton's disposal. I said NO [*sic*] and I gave Mr Legros a letter to take back to Colonel Crompton. I had already had many dealings with Colonel Crompton and I had all the work and he had the credit. . . . I very politely told him that if his committee or department wanted my assistance it was freely at their disposal.[14]

Tritton's and Crompton's paths had almost certainly crossed on two previous occasions. They were rival engineers during the electrification of London: the Colonel operated a power station in Kensington, and Tritton was appointed Chief Assistant Engineer with the Metropolitan Electric Supply Company in 1899. Tritton then joined Foster's as Works Manager in 1905 just after they had fitted a steam tractor with Diplock's third set of Pedrail wheels. The tractor went to Aldershot for trials that year with the MTC, of which Crompton was still a member. He was also advising Diplock, and Tritton would have met him in one or other capacity.

Crompton and Legros spent the morning of 4 March with Diplock and Lowe at Wyfold Street, preparing a drawing for what became the regular Friday Landships Committee meeting at 5 p.m. in the DNC's office. The very able Dale Bussell from Admiralty Contracts Department attended, doubling as committee secretary. Col Dumble had departed to join Sir W.G. Armstrong, Whitworth & Co. Ltd at their Openshaw gun factory in Manchester. Crompton's diary entry that day reads: 'Decided to press Caterpillar type landship very carefully.' He reported little progress with the wheeled 'A' Type, noting that Tritton was unable to fit a platform even for thirty men without overstressing the narrow chassis. Crompton and Lowe tabled the Mk I 'B' Type design. Their crawler presented a much lower hull profile and centre of gravity than Tritton's machine. Its floor trap exit was replaced by large armoured side doors which could be swung open to shield men while they cleared wire obstacles, details of which had been discreetly obtained from the Royal Engineers. Crompton was asked to finalise drawings for the 'B' Type and place construction contracts through Bussell. The heavy 'C' Type was dropped. Churchill minuted 'Press on.'

At Sueter's request, Diplock had got Lowe to complete an elevation drawing of the DAD's original turreted design. Lowe had hurried over to Thriplands that morning and secured Crompton's approval for it to be produced at the meeting. It was Sueter's final throw. His half-submarine design was rejected.[15]

This marked the end of Murray Sueter's creative involvement with landships, though he retained administrative control of the committee. Sueter had been the first by a few days to commission the design of a tracked trench destroyer. His concept machine was, significantly, a modestly crewed gun platform rather than the lightly armed troop carrier which the Landships Committee was now pursuing.

Because of the problems with Tritton's machine, Crompton was instructed to approach other firms, including Foden's, with an invitation to design and construct a big-wheeler. He had privately concluded that it was pointless to continue with wheels and Tritton's attitude rankled. Crompton left Foster's to pursue a wheeled solution on their own. He spent the next day at Foden's lorry works at Sandbach, Cheshire, arranging for the firm to take on the framing and final assembly of his 'B' Type. The limited resources of Diplock's Pedrail company meant that construction of the track assemblies would have to be contracted out through the Admiralty. There were problems too with the twin transmissions. Crompton wanted the machine to be drivable from either end, as fast in reverse as in forward gear. He was trying to adapt automobile gearboxes which were incapable of such work. Without identical ratios in forward and reverse he would have stripped standard boxes, so purpose-built transmissions were ordered from locomotive builders McEwan, Pratt & Co. Ltd of Burton on Trent, Staffordshire. As for engines, Legros, who was now working full time at Thriplands, had earmarked three Rolls-Royce armoured car units. Foden's appointment as lead contractor was approved on 12 March. Track design would be sub-contracted to Pedrail.

Foster's abandoned work on the tricycle 'A' Type. Its frame was inadequate for the load. With a flourish Tritton instead showed the committee a model of a radically new design on 19 March. The 'Foster Trench Tractor' was an articulated big-wheel landship. A 20ft tractor and its 28ft trailer were each mounted on a single axle between a pair of 15ft wheels. The trailer could carry a powerful gun or, Tritton claimed, transport an assault party of seventy men – exactly the complement planned by Crompton for the 'B' Type. To expect to pack so many fully armed men into the narrow trailer's 150sq ft was wildly optimistic. A fixed turret on top of the trailer provided an arc of fire directly rearwards, the gun being blinded in all other directions by the wheels or the tractor ahead. Steering was from the trailer via a manually operated brake on each wheel. Tritton must have known that the design was unstable at only 8ft 6in wide, and the huge bulk of the set would make it an easy target. He later admitted that the 36-ton monster with its 105hp engine was underpowered and 'inherently bad'.

Tritton promised to put the first machine on the road within three months at a cost of £2,000–3,000 subject to swift approval. He ended with a swipe at Crompton's 'caterpillars', alleging that they were liable to 'scrounching' – his word for the nutcracker tendency of adjoining track plates to grip wire and stones with resultant damage. Inexplicably, d'Eyncourt accepted the design without comment, seeking permission next morning to order one each of the two types. Churchill called him in before summoning Hetherington,

Crompton and Legros for the first of several meetings at the Admiralty that day. They ended with an evening session at which the First Lord increased the numbers to twelve Pedrail crawlers with the necessary twenty-four Rolls-Royce engines plus three spares, and six big-wheel machines. He marked the folder 'Most urgent. Special report to me in case of delay. Estimates of time and money.' Expenditure totalling £70,000 was approved on 26 March.[16]

Churchill wrote across the file cover in his customary red ink 'Proceed as proposed and with all despatch. On account of secrecy this may be taken as full sanction.' 'Secrecy' included concealment from the Treasury. The committee's expenditures were charged to (or interred in) Admiralty vote 8 111 B – an obscure fund covering auxiliary machinery for contract-built ships.

The landships contractors were wired at once to proceed, with contracts to follow. Government munitions contracts were generally based on payment of approved costs plus 10 per cent, an unavoidable formula for new work entailing unknown expenditure, though it encouraged cost inflation by the supplier. Dale Bussell had little choice as no working drawings were available from which to estimate quantities and labour. Delivery of the first big-wheeler was expected by the end of June; the first Pedrail machine was to follow a fortnight later. Meanwhile, Foden's were running into a serious labour dispute. Crompton and Foden had attended a fruitless meeting of the Labour Conciliation Board on 23 March. By the time Bussell's confirmatory telegram reached Sandbach three days later the factory was already crippled. Of the workforce of 1,100, 400 were on strike and threatening to move to better paid mining and munitions jobs. After a dispiriting visit on 14 April Legros contacted Dudley Docker's Metropolitan Carriage, Wagon & Finance Company in hopes of finding alternative capacity there. He was directed to Metro's subsidiary, The Patent Shaft & Axletree Co. Ltd at Wednesbury which was able to take over the work. Available pressing and drop-forging capacity was very short nationally by then, but Shaft's Old Park Works could undertake this and similar work for the Pedrail machine, and the company was appointed main contractor.

The committee engaged Crompton as its design and consulting engineer. He and Legros were to work full time for four months backdated to 1 March, Crompton at £130 and Legros £72 per month. Sueter withdrew some of Crompton's earlier freedoms: all questions of design were to be considered in committee; Crompton could no longer give firms instructions unsupported by official orders; Hetherington would assist him and oversee construction, submitting all drawings and purchasing requests through Boothby.

A search for armour began. Hetherington and Stern went over to Paris on 2 April to interview M Berjery Dérocle, inventor of a compound which he claimed to be bullet-resistant if used as a filling between two sheets of steel plate. They brought back a sample which was tested at Woolwich. The gelatine was packed into a 38mm gap between two plates, respectively 4mm and 2mm thick. Test firings literally shot Dérocle's idea to bits. Legros now toured the Sheffield plate mills which were overwhelmed with orders.

Crompton's hull was of unitary construction to keep down weight; he omitted structural framing. Its final design depended on the size of available sheet armour, the wider the better, to minimise joins. Legros was looking for hardened steel plate, but because of its relative thinness it required exceptionally heavy pressure in the rolling mill. Unfortunately there were few pairs of rolls in the country able to turn out such plate larger than 4ft × 2ft. Vickers (and Wm Beardmore in Glasgow) could go to 6ft × 4ft. The plate also had to be rolled dead flat to ensure rivet holes married tightly at the joining of sheets, and needed to be finished to true edges to minimise the need for grinding, a difficult and slow operation on hard steels. Legros had to reveal his purpose during visits to John Brown, Hadfield's, Flather's, Firth's and Vickers, and found them all anxious to help.

He learned that the Germans were now reversing the normal rifle bullet to improve penetration. In that position its lead filling first came into contact with the plate and for a millisecond it welded the nose of the round to the surface, absorbing some of the shock before the hard core punched on through. Legros was asked for a German rifle and ammunition for trials. When he wired Wormwood Scrubs he was assured that he was covering old ground, they had all the results and no test was necessary. However, the RNAS trials data only covered Beardmore's plate and the findings did not hold true for steels of variable hardness from other mills. The misunderstanding led to a later increase from 8mm to 12mm in the thickness of the landships' flank armour, imposing a severe weight penalty and resultant power loss.

* * *

Unknown to the Admiralty, Kitchener ordered heavy armoured cars to be built in support of a fleet of 700 London buses which were earmarked for requisition, should an evacuation or other emergency arise in the capital.[17]

Several vehicles were built at Woolwich Arsenal on AEC 'B' Type bus chassis. The turretless hull fully enclosed the engine and driver compartments, with an open-top fighting platform behind. Sliding shutter rifle ports surrounded the cab and platform in place of mountings for fixed weapons.

Woolwich did not tap into the Navy's recently acquired knowledge of light armour until the cars were built, at which point Sueter was contacted and asked if his expert on the subject could come over to the War Office. Briggs was away so Hetherington went, probably on 12 April.[18] The newly promoted Major found himself before Kitchener, von Donop and Guthrie-Smith. Hetherington favourably impressed 'The Chief' who questioned him closely on the RNAS tests and much else before sending him on to Woolwich to inspect the finished cars. Hetherington found the plate was only bullet-proof at ranges over 300yd, useless for armoured car work, and reported accordingly. The War Office was aware of Sueter's experiments with thin armour and could have obtained the necessary data at any time.

*   *   *

Pedrail's broad sleeper track gave a performance over wet ground which was exceptional even by the standards of conventional crawlers. The devil lay in the system's complexity and the need to scale up track length to 18ft from the Colonial wagon's 6ft. No practical machine anywhere had got near that and every Pedrail component would have to be redesigned to support greatly increased loads and the higher demands of the engines. Legros was having difficulty finding available plant for some of the work. A 2-ton stamp was needed for the slippers carrying the track feet, which neither Vickers nor Firth's could release from other government work in hand.

Diplock began to miss deadlines for finished drawings, and without working drawings the builders were stalled. They could not leave plant idle, so the tightly scheduled time slots for landship assemblies were threatened. Diplock resented Crompton's insistence that Lowe should move full time into the Thriplands drawing office and, pressed to complete the drawings in ten days, he replied on 12 April that he hoped to finish them in three or four weeks. Crompton and Legros hurried over and discovered gross errors in the design of the foot carriers which meant that they could not be riveted up. Diplock gave way and Lowe moved to Thriplands next day, but a cloud of doubt had formed over Pedrail Transport Ltd.

Crompton was also becoming concerned at the lack of communication with the military and the continuing vagueness of his design brief. He needed specifications for armour and armament, and as he made clear in a progress report of 9 April, he could not get far without more information on proposed tactics. Churchill's near obsession with a monster machine had been scaled back to reality by d'Eyncourt who had set a 25–30-ton design limit. The committee was, however, left with the First Lord's tactics as originally interpreted by Dumble and Crompton, and implicitly accepted thereafter by Churchill and the others. They were trying to pack a substantial assault party and light support weapons into an overlarge machine to be run right up to the enemy trench; the alternative was Sueter's less technically challenging gunship, heavily armed but lightly manned to provide close fire support for attacking infantry. The committee was pursuing the motorised equivalent of a medieval siege tower.

Hetherington and Lt Albert Stern, his transport assistant, accompanied Crompton on a visit to the front on 21 April, intent on seeing captured German trenches at Neuve-Chapelle. Crompton put up his Crimea medal for the occasion. They reached Boulogne at noon and motored on to the RNAS base at Dunkirk where they were met by the Duke of Westminster, who had taken over the Villa Mugusta on the Plage. Unfortunately the trenches had been recaptured and there was little to see from an observation tower. Next morning they drove to GHQ at St Omer, stopping *en route* to measure canal bridges and road curves. On arrival the Admiralty party was told that no information could be given to them without clearance from the War Office and they could not enter the battle zone. Hetherington recalled that the Staff dismissed the landships idea as a joke and a waste of public money. The trio was ordered home. They had planned a six-day inspection; instead they were back in London thirty-eight hours after setting out. They had been within feet of the office of the one man who could give them the information and encouragement they needed, but Swinton was unaware of their mission.

However, it was clear enough to Crompton from his observations that the crawler's 80ft steering radius would have to be halved to get it up to the front. He began work next morning, a Friday, and the routine committee meeting was postponed to noon Saturday. The Colonel abandoned the rigid Mk I Pedrail in favour of an articulated machine – a scheme Tritton had already decided upon. The difference between them was Crompton's preference for independent power to both platforms of his turretless 34-ton set. Fifty-six men would be carried in the side aisles and eight more on platforms fore and aft. The 8mm armour plate was increased to 12mm to resist reversed bullets. To help offset the extra weight the panel height was reduced to 4ft 6in, compelling the troops to be seated and further lowering the hull profile.

Tactics were also altered. Enemy trench lines were interrupted by frequent traverses which would prevent the landship's machine guns from raking long sections in enfilade fire. Instead of driving head-on over no-man's-land before mounting the parapet and overhanging the trench, they would cross in a zig-zag approach and halt broadside to the trench to deliver preliminary fire with grenade throwers. These should disable long stretches of trench prior to releasing the storming party. Later, Crompton further refined these tactics to provide a rolling barrage of mortar fire from the machines, moving slowly parallel to the trench and 100yd back from it. The armoured side panels were top-hinged for quicker exit. When they were swung open, hinged base plates fell to form a skirt around the machine, giving added protection for any wire-clearing party working under the ship's lee. Loopholes for rifles and machine guns encircled the hull. The committee approved Crompton's proposals for his Mk II 'B' Type Pedrail. He had completed the basic design with his three draughtsmen in 24 hours.

* * *

A lightweight US chain tractor arrived at the Wormwood Scrubs depot in late April. It proved to be a lucky break. The iron windfall came from the Killen Strait Mfg Co. of Appleton, Wisconsin, whose London agent had written to the director of Admiralty contracts advising that a machine had arrived and that William Strait was in town and would be glad to give a demonstration. Dale Bussell saw the letter and alerted Crompton. After booking a viewing the Colonel searched the country for other American crawlers, while continuing to give Holt's machines a wide berth.

Strait brought his tractor to the Clement-Talbot works on 27 April. With a tricycle layout like the much heavier Holt, the machine took its drive through a short rear-mounted pair of caterpillars, but in place of a wheel up front it was fitted with a small steerable track. The little Strait was well designed and engineered. It greatly impressed Crompton, although Hetherington's mud pit was too much for it and an armoured car had to haul the machine out. All three track girder frames pivoted at one end with a shock-absorbing spring at the other to reduce the jarring of unsprung machines. Interestingly, the rear face of the driven tracks was angled upwards and rearwards to help the tractor climb obstacles in reverse gear. This neat and novel arrangement of Strait's was reflected in the front profile of the first tank, which almost certainly had its origins in his Wormwood Scrubs demonstrator.

Crompton arranged the purchase of the machine for £800. He had a platform fitted and test-laden to see what the axles could stand. Strait's London agent, H.H. Chipman, had actually contacted Crompton early in January to extol the virtues of the tractor, though it seems no machine had been shipped over.[19] Crompton was still a convinced wheels man and did not respond. His new interest in American crawlers coincided with doubts concerning Diplock. Chipman's invitation and Bussell's prompting were indeed timely.

The next day, 28 April, in the heavy rain which seemed to dog tractor trials that year, Crompton, Legros, Hetherington, Stern and Wilson drove to marshes in the Thames estuary. A US Bullock tractor was put through its paces close by J.B. White's cement works at Swanscombe. The 8-ton machine, a semi-track crawler steered through two front wheels, was considered to be quite advanced. It successfully hauled 5 tons of stone though the wagon was sunk to its axles. In a follow-up letter to John Palmer junior, Bullock's London agent, Crompton was sufficiently carried away to reveal the purpose of the exercise:

I am about to put a proposition before my Committee that I be allowed to order from you two of your Californian Creeping Grip Tractors for the purpose of providing them with an armoured platform . . . for carrying . . . thirty men across a fire-swept zone near the trenches. . . . Our eventual object, however, would be to purchase from you portions of your Creeping Grip chassis enlarged from any of your existing patterns as shown on the enclosed drawing. The enlargement is in the direction of length and is mainly for the object of allowing the tractor to traverse wider ditches or depressions than is possible with your present type . . . I have been preparing designs of two such chassis which are to be coupled together by substantial coupling, in such a manner that they will provide an almost continuous platform for sixty or seventy men. . . . We are also providing arrangements to make a joint between the two chassis sufficiently rigid to make the two frames into one continuous girder for crossing shell holes or depressions up to 10ft in length.[20]

* * *

Following the icy reception at GHQ, Crompton again raised the matter of the information vacuum in which the committee was working. He addressed a long memorandum to d'Eyncourt on 29 April detailing the progress of design and tactics as evolved by his team, and his pressing need for confirmation that they were on the right path. He lacked the most basic information, including the nature and defences of enemy trenches, the preferred tactics and radius of action of the machines, how they should be armed and what means of throwing bombs, and whether night attacks were planned. Crompton requested a conference with engineer officers at St Omer. Knowing the War Office would only delay matters, he wrote direct to Gen Sir Horace Smith-Dorrien who was commanding the reorganised 2nd Army in France. The letter went by courier next day:

> I, the old Colonel of the Electrical Engineers, am now employed by the Admiralty to prepare designs for . . . trench attacking devices . . . twelve of one kind and six of the other have been ordered, and are now well in hand. . . . As you know me sufficiently well you could help me if you asked Sir John French to allow me to come to you to confer with yourself, your CRE or other officers best fitted to help me with advice. I can be at Dunkirk within 24 hours of receiving a telegram.[21]

Crompton showed d'Eyncourt the letter a few hours after its despatch. He had again revealed the Admiralty's hand to GHQ, never quite having grasped that Churchill had no intention of passing any landships to the Army. D'Eyncourt told the Colonel that Churchill had read his memorandum and had declared that it was up to the naval people themselves to secure the information. He emphasised to Crompton that he only approved the letter as a private communication, adding '. . . how are our landships to be used if not by the Naval Brigade?'[22] This should not have come as a surprise. Murray Sueter had addressed written instructions on procedures to Crompton and Hetherington a month earlier, making clear that three new squadrons were to be formed to operate landships as part of Boothby's armoured car force.[23] Crompton's abortive tour had not been cleared in advance with the War Office because Churchill presumably hoped he could bluff his way to the front without revealing his mission.

Smith-Dorrien's reply on 3 May made clear that he could do nothing. Three days later the General was on his way home, having resigned his command after objecting to senseless losses arising from French's orders during the second battle of Ypres. The C-in-C's acceptance was conveyed to Smith-Dorrien by Gen William Robertson, French's Chief of Staff, "Orace – you're for 'ome.'

Crompton's diary records that he 'made a clean breast of my fears respecting Diplock' at the landships meeting on 7 May. He was losing confidence in Pedrail's ability to service the contractors, and the crawler demonstrations had undoubtedly been an eye-opener. Compared with the complexities of the Pedrail system, remarkable as its performance was, the American tracklayers were mechanically simple, robust, and in production. US plants had the resources to design quickly and build scaled-up track assemblies.

The committee decided to limit construction of tracklayers to two coupled sets for evaluation – a Mk II Pedrail type and a Mk IIA on Bullock tracks. Two Creeping Grip machines and spares were ordered. Bullock's was also asked to lengthen two pairs of tracks and frames from the current 5ft to 9ft 8in centres, for which they promised delivery four months from receipt of drawings. Crompton's one-time chief technical assistant, 32-year-old George Field, was to go out to Chicago to give design support and supervise the track work. He was also to assess the capacity of Bullock's and others to build complete landships. Field was a very competent engineer, an automobile specialist with his own small factory. He had designed a light car, and co-designed with Crompton his 1908 steam gun tractor. The two men had produced the British Standard Fine screw thread.

The Bullocks were to be coupled on arrival in England before undergoing trials as a single articulated unit. Crompton had to devise a linkage and spent much time with Wilson grappling with the loads imposed on it by his two 14-ton chassis, both 22ft long, when each was driven through acute angles relative to the other. The coupling would additionally have to lock the two half-ships into a rigid girder-like whole when crossing trenches to prevent the lead unit from dropping its nose and ramming the far side. On top of these extremely demanding functions, it must transmit lift from the rear half-ship to raise the front end of the leading chassis several feet before attempting to cross wide shell holes or mount a parapet.

Though unimpressed with the twinning format, Wilson produced a design and model for a coupling on 25 May. Crompton accepted it and asked him to supervise the preparation and trials of the machines. The Bullocks would be coupled back to back, the rear of each having been fitted with a heavy 6ft high space frame. Between the two frames a very stiff universal coupling was set low down, on either side of which were powerful hydraulic rams to aid steering. It was more brute force than science. The steering technique entailed throttling back the lead half while accelerating the rear after setting the lengths of the twin rams appropriately. These would nudge the front half in the required direction, the universal joint acting as a fulcrum. The turn would be followed through with further applications of throttle and ram settings from the rear unit. The technique would all become very theoretical when the respective chassis were lurching over broken ground, each in a constantly changing plane relative to the other.

The locking together of the two ships as a rigid whole was to be achieved by a pair of winch-controlled cables carried over the top of the space frame and shackled well forward on the other chassis, which had a corresponding assembly. Either half-ship could bodily haul the front end of the other to hold it straight and level, or increase lift to raise it some 3ft off the ground preparatory to climbing a low trench parapet. The rear half would then drive forward on full power, ramming the raised lead unit up the mound. A plough fitted to the front half would push the remaining soil or sandbags off the crown of the parapet on this thrust. Other considerations apart, the exposed tackle was vulnerable to battle damage which could cripple the set, effectively breaking its back, but Crompton explained why he favoured coupled units:

A long series of calculations made by Legros and myself on our drawings of the jointed ships, have confirmed my opinion that the jointed principle by which one half of the ship forms the support to enable the other to be partly lifted over an obstacle or gap, is a sound one for these large compound vehicles. Moreover as the two halves of the vehicle are symmetrical the two coupled together form a double-ender train, which can be run equally fast or manoeuvred equally well in both directions, and thus obtain the great advantage of advancing or retiring out of the danger zone without the delay of turning round.[24]

Up at Lincoln a full-size wooden mock-up of Tritton's articulated big-wheeler had been erected in a corner of Foster's works. The outlines of the 15ft wheels were chalked on to timber framing. To reduce fighting weight to

36 tons the overall length of the March design had been cut from 48ft to 37ft by shortening the trailer which was now identical in size to the tractor. Each hull sat almost entirely within the circumference of its two wheels. The hulls had also become double-deckers but the claimed capacity of seventy men was still highly optimistic. Tritton's linkage operated broadly as Wilson's, with two winched chains above a universal coupling, but without space frames the stresses were even greater.

The mock-up was inspected by Hetherington and Wilson on 16 May. It was obvious that the design was profoundly flawed. Soon afterwards Tritton went down to the Barlby Road depot for a review meeting chaired by Hetherington who told him the machine was likely to be a serious obstacle to military traffic near the front, particularly if knocked over by shellfire. Worse, the foreshortened trailer's flanks were now wholly screened by its wheels and as a result the only free field of fire was a narrow arc rearwards, necessitating a battlefield 'U' turn to bring the armament to bear. The meeting, attended by Crompton, Legros, Wilson, Stern and Lt Symes, their armour specialist, considered placing the tractor behind the trailer to secure forward fire. This idea was rejected because the tractor unit had no steering, which also meant the set could not be reversed.

Tritton suggested that to improve its offensive capability he could decouple the machine and let the trailer unit operate as an independent fighting module, cable-linked to an electric power source on the remote tractor. This would entail a complete redesign but the RNAS team was enthusiastic. They saw possibilities for silent night approaches and increased payloads. Unmanned machines could be packed with explosive and, with locked steering, despatched at enemy positions before being detonated electronically. There appears to have been a collective retreat from reality that day. It is hard to believe that those present could have contemplated such a scheme had they been allowed to see the battlefields.

The committee asked Tritton to put his proposals in writing. His letter of 5 June to Crompton explained that he was abandoning both the twin-chassis format and 'big wheels' traction in favour of an 'armoured wagon or fort' on 8ft wheels.[25] He offered two types, both using the Daimler 105hp unit, either as a standard petrol-engined machine of just over 14 tons with complete freedom of movement, or a petrol electric ship linked by a mile of cable to a tractor-mounted dynamo. The cable drum could be carried inside the machine or on an armoured trailer. Tritton recommended the latter with an integral drum, its weight of nearly 18 tons dropping to less than 15 tons by the time the cable was paid out. The petrol version would allow 56sq ft of floor space for armament, ammunition, crew and stores, as against 82sq ft for the petrol electric. Tritton acknowledged the risk to crew and ship if the cable was shot away and was planning to plough it 12in deep as it was laid. The fact was, however, that he had reverted to the howitzer tractor chassis as the basis of design. Foster's were effectively back where they had started three months before.

The Landships Committee was unimpressed, cancelling Foster's order and closing down all work on wheeled ships on 8 June. Ironically, the very next day Tritton found himself at the Shoebury ranges with the cancellation fresh on his mind as he watched his Portable Bridge Machine fail its much-delayed trials. He claimed in 1918 that he had received an order, later cancelled, to build seventy trench-crossing fighting machines to a design drawn up on 3 June 1915. He even gave the drawing number, 101V.[26] The Bovington Tank Museum has a copy which confirms this as the Portable Bridge Machine with a box-like armoured hull fitted with one forward-firing machine gun. The author has found no hint of any such order, actual or contemplated, in War Office or Admiralty files. Tritton only secured Churchill's February order for thirty machines which was, of course, cancelled by him days later.

Crompton wrote a friendly private letter to forewarn Tritton of the committee's decision and to assure him that it would do its utmost to put other experimental work his way. They were now left with the Pedrail and Bullock systems, and the Colonel was seriously concerned about the lack of contact with Army professionals who could give direction to the project and remove much blind guesswork. He was also questioning the pursuit of troop carriers to the exclusion of gunships. He had tried to meet Maj Gen Sir Percy Girouard, a member of the WO Munitions Committee and late Director of Railways to the South African Field Force, with whom he had served, but Girouard broke the appointment. Next day, 20 May, Crompton had unburdened himself to d'Eyncourt in a carefully prepared letter:

> Every day I feel more and more that the First Lord's original idea of providing moving forts to carry short range guns or mortars is of increasing importance. Both our classes of landships [i.e. wheeled and tracked], therefore, have in addition to the duty of transporting men . . .

the second and very important duty of serving as rapidly moving gun platforms carrying short range trench attacking guns or mortars.

This morning I have received a letter from my own patent agent, a skilled engineer, a sergeant in the London Scottish, who has been for some time in the trenches; he says that we want more than anything else a means of throwing grenades. . . . In these days when it is evident that the latest idea is to fire away almost unlimited amounts of high explosive shells from a distance . . . I believe that the same work could be done by our landship at one tenth of the cost in ammunition and human life. My idea is to make them thoroughly efficient for both these duties, and I still harp on my original idea and wish to confer at Army Headquarters with Sir John French, Sir Horace Smith-Dorrien and others of my old friends including Colonel Fowke, the C.R.E. whose opinion will be of maximum value to me. I am perfectly certain that when they know what we are aiming at they will be at one with us to develop the use of these landships.[27]

Crompton's assertion that Churchill had originally wanted gunships is not supported either by events or by Crompton himself in his statements to the Tanks Awards Committee in 1918.[28] He may have felt it would strengthen his case to suggest otherwise in this instance. It made little difference; his letter probably never reached the First Lord. Churchill had been fighting another, and more personal, battle – he tendered his resignation to the Prime Minister next day.

Six

COMBINED OPERATIONS?

The caterpillar system is no bloody good for the job.[1]

*William Tritton, Managing Director, Wm Foster & Co. Lincoln, 3 March
1915. Tritton built the first tank later that year – on 'caterpillars'.*

While Crompton begged for an end to secrecy and confusion in his small sphere, Churchill was driven from the Admiralty and Asquith's government collapsed. The forcing of the Dardanelles by the Navy, which Churchill had urged in January 1915, had progressed through a succession of failures into a joint Services catastrophe for which much of the later responsibility lay with Kitchener and the government. In mid-May the already grim situation turned from shock to anger with the revelation in the press of the acute shortage of shells and armaments generally. Adm Fisher's emotional resignation over the handling of the Dardanelles campaign followed. The two events triggered a crisis at home. With Jackie Fisher gone, the Sea Lords refused to continue to serve Churchill. They detested his military adventures in France which they viewed as self-indulgent diversions from the war at sea. Conservative pressure forced Asquith's hand and brought Churchill's letter of resignation on 21 May. It did not save the Liberal government which was driven into a national coalition under Asquith. Churchill was replaced by the Conservative Arthur Balfour on the 27th.

Sueter's shield was gone. His Air Service, Armoured Car Division, Anti-Aircraft Corps and the landships project came under sustained fire from three of the four Sea Lords. Only Adm Tudor remained firmly on side. Sueter recorded his superior, Cdre Lambert the Fourth Sea Lord, remarking that 'Caterpillar landships are idiotic and useless. Nobody has asked for them and nobody wants them. These officers and men are wasting their time and are not pulling their proper weight in the War. If I had my way I would disband the whole lot of them. Anyhow I am going to do my best to see that this is done and stop all this armoured car and caterpillar nonsense.'[2] Fisher's successor, Adm Sir Henry Jackson, told Sueter in the presence of the other three Lords that all these activities were little wanted. He left Arthur Balfour in no doubt of the Navy's wish to get rid of Winston's entire 'circus'.

Lambert requested the transfer of the armoured cars and landships to the Army. Balfour approved, wanting to distance himself from what he called 'Winston's fad'. D'Eyncourt alerted Churchill who appealed personally to Balfour to withdraw the landships order. He suggested instead the formation of a joint naval and military committee to carry the project forward and offered to preside. Sueter also stood his ground, finding an ally in Balfour's Naval Secretary, Cdr Charles de Bartolomé. Between them they prevailed on the new First Lord to retain d'Eyncourt's committee until it had constructed one machine. Balfour was glad to let Churchill continue to keep an eye on the project, and agreed the formation of a specialist squadron for experimental work in support. Lt Cdr Redmond McGrath commanding 14 Armoured Car Squadron was instructed to select twenty men for this duty. No. 20 Squadron was formed and led by him early in June as part of Boothby's force. The Squadron would expand to become an important tank test and transportation unit.

Crompton was able to repeat his plea directly to Churchill at the 8 June landships meeting during a sombre review of progress. Churchill cancelled Foster's research programme, and was sufficiently impressed by the Colonel's case and the marked lack of progress to call for background information to enable him to write to French. Sueter feared Balfour would yield to pressure and shut down the landships project if a machine could not be put on the ground quickly. All depended on Crompton's tractors but trials were still weeks away, and d'Eyncourt was confessing himself too preoccupied with warship construction to spare more than an occasional meeting on trench-taking. Early in June Sueter instructed Boothby to join the committee and force the pace. He also sent in Lt Walter Wilson and Hetherington's assistant, Lt Albert Stern.

From that moment onward until the end of the war Wilson and Stern in their differing ways would hugely influence the direction and quality of tank development. If Murray Sueter had done nothing else for the coming weapon, he deserves the highest praise for those two appointments. Stern was installed as secretary on 16 June, freeing Crompton and Bussell of this work. He had been ordered to reorganise the committee on business lines and he began as he intended to continue. The 36-year-old RNVR Lieutenant was a successful banker. His dynamic and assertive personality and steamroller style often flattened those who stood in his way, but he got results. The DNC took to him at once. Stern wrote a new procedure with d'Eyncourt's approval which, *inter alia*, accused Crompton of routinely bypassing the committee in placing Admiralty orders and giving out decisions on new designs and inventions. The old Colonel responded with a courteous objection; he certainly cut a few corners to avoid delays, not helped by the weekly intervals between meetings of the committee. Stern for his part soon became notorious for ignoring Admiralty procedures.

Stern and his staff (PO Percy Anderson plus a writer) needed an office. Two days after his appointment he rented a room at 83 Pall Mall from the Commercial Motor Users Association, at his own expense. The Admiralty Office of Works sent word that this was not permissible and allocated him a stuffy room under the roof at Winchester House in St James's Square 'for the next few weeks'. The Lieutenant having instantly rejected it, the room went to a luckless rear admiral. Further procedural steps by the Admiralty were met with Stern's reply that he had placed an armed guard on the door with orders to shoot intruders. He was left alone, still paying the rent six months later.

Crompton and Legros had their contracts extended to the end of August. Metropolitan was about to begin construction of the twin chassis for the Pedrail machine and another set for its Bullock equivalent, when on 11 June the company asked to be relieved of the work, saying it involved too much detailed supervision and scarce resources. Metro was persuaded to reconsider, but only on its own terms. Its formidable chairman, Dudley Docker, detested state interference in industrial enterprise. Throughout the war the company refused to accept a condition attaching to munitions contracts which obliged suppliers to open their books to inspection to prevent excess profits. Docker feared that businessmen seconded to the newly created Ministry of Munitions (MoM) would acquire sensitive commercial information from these inspections which could be exploited by his competitors after the war. Instead, Metro offered certification by its own auditors as sufficient evidence of compliance.

The landships contract allowed Metro a 10 per cent profit on approved costs, subject to inspection and verification by the Ministry. The Admiralty would supply two Rolls-Royce engines at its cost for each landship. Metro had insisted that the value of these free units, worth £1,260 per ship, should be treated as its costs to reflect the fitting entailed.[3] When this was refused the company asked to be released from the work. Crompton advised Dale Bussell to allow the mark-up because Metro was the only firm with presses available for the Pedrail assembly and the company now had valuable knowledge of the machine. Bussell relented and Legros told Metro the point was conceded, but the company still refused any inspection of records. The contract was withdrawn by the Admiralty in July at the request of the War Office. As it happened, Diplock's working drawings were so far from completion that Crompton was in no position to order a start.

The drawings were not coming through because Diplock was experiencing great difficulty in scaling up the tracks from the little wagon. In mid-June he had to scrap newly completed drawings of the foot assembly and start again, and his roller-chain specification had not yet been agreed with the Coventry Chain Company. Crompton's concerns now were the delayed drawings, the special lengthening of the Creeping Grip track, the hunt for a replacement for Metro, and preparations for the Bullock tractor trials. Each of the first three was a potential showstopper. He and Legros were working night and day to progress the work, the old Colonel making sure, however, to get in a regular evening game of squash with Stern and others in the basement courts at the RAC Club.

In the United States Lt Field had arrived in Chicago to find that the designer of the Bullock tracks was no longer with the company. No one else there was competent to prepare drawings for track lengthening. He was also disconcerted to see Bullock's assembly techniques – men were sledge-hammering track shoes into mesh with the sprocket teeth; he was assured this was routine as the pitch of the links had always been incorrect. Field asked for a standard 'Giant' to be towed behind a tractor to observe track steerability. It skidded most of the way round an 80ft circle, the tracks trying to go straight on. After calling to see Killen Strait's designers in Milwaukee, Field cabled Crompton that he thought the standard Bullock's 5ft track length was about as long as was feasible, and Strait's company could produce better work. Crompton's reply called for two sample pairs of lengthened tracks and frames from Killen Strait to the same specification as the Bullock order. It ended: 'Your expenses [$100 weekly] considered extravagant please economize.' Crompton and Strait were designing an experimental plough attachment for the tractor to throw up protective parapets and night-dig shallow jumping-off trenches. For security purposes their Western Union telegram exchanges were disguised as farm machinery messages, Crompton's cover organisation being the Australian Ploughing Co.

McEwan, Pratt & Co. at Burton on Trent were well ahead with the new transmissions for the Bullocks. They were additionally charged with the construction of the steering and coupling gear, and preparation and staging of the trials. The two Creeping Grip machines reached Burton on 16 June, red with rust, ex-deck cargo. McGrath's 20 Squadron took up residence near McEwan's works to dig trenches and remain in support. Wilson, who had been liaising with Tritton on the big-wheelers, joined them from Lincoln as trials officer. Work began on preparing the course.

*   *   *

In France Col Swinton had continued to put about his scheme for armoured trench fighting machines, though with caution lest he be ordered to drop it. He let a number of opportunities pass until late May when he met Capt Ralph Glyn, a well-connected Liaison Intelligence Officer between the War Office and GHQ in France. As Swinton explained his ideas, Glyn said he had heard rumours that the Navy was doing something or other with armoured shields. He promised to find out what was happening and back in London he visited the Admiralty. His timing was good. Churchill had just departed and the Sea Lords were preparing to jettison unwanted cargo in the Army's direction. Following Glyn's call, Adm Tudor contacted Maj Gen Scott-Moncrieff, Director of Fortifications and Works, informing him in confidence on 30 May that the Navy had ordered eighteen landships. With a hint of rebuke he went on:

> They are being built on the principle that this is essentially a war of machines, and machines and armour protection hardly appear to have been utilised to any great extent on shore as yet. Personally I have had a fad for the last 30 years that steel screens on two wheels pushed by men would be better than sending flesh and blood unprotected against trenches and entanglements. A Capt Glyn has been over here from the D.M.C. [Director of Military Cooperation] about this business and we have shown him models and drawings. If you will send over a representative I will let him see them also.[4]

Tudor detailed the ideal 'Mobile Armoured Shield', his text well salted with nautical terms. It profiled the familiar troop-carrier format for seventy men and two or three machine guns. He thought the machines could advance at night between the beams of blinding searchlights while infantry on the flanks pushed small wheeled shields until they reached the enemy trench. The boat-like hulls incorporated independently steam-driven port and starboard 'drive belts', while the main weight was carried on steel runners along the keel. Steering was by slowing the port or starboard track. A high bow was fitted with wire-cutting shears.

Glyn returned to the Admiralty with Scott-Moncrieff. There Tudor and d'Eyncourt showed them Crompton's model and drawings of the articulated Mk IIA on Creeping Grip tracks. They next called on Crompton who begged for immediate military advice and support. The brief discussion was to be Crompton's only dialogue on landship design with any Army representative. Scott-Moncrieff reported his findings to Maj Gen von Donop, the Master General of Ordnance, on 10 June: 'This design seems to get over the difficulties which had proved so insoluble to us in our WO investigation.'[5] He urged the immediate formation of a joint naval and military landships committee to include a general staff officer with the necessary tactical experience. Von Donop agreed and the Admiralty was invited on 21 June to concur and appoint representatives. The military members would be Scott-Moncrieff, Col W.D. Bird (the Director of Staff Duties), Col Holden of the Holt trials, and Maj E.L. Wheeler RA. The Admiralty approved, offering the services of d'Eyncourt's committee but insisting that as the landships project was clearly a military matter it should now be taken over by the War Office. To the relief of the Lords Commissioners the WO promptly agreed the transfer.

Scott-Moncrieff gave d'Eyncourt the Army's first reaction to the landship's design, writing on 16 June:

We think there should be at the bows of the landship on either side, one 2 pounder Pom-Pom to deal with machine guns in emplacements. That armament should be supplemented by two machine guns placed further back somewhat on the lines of the broadside fire of ships. Loopholes for musketry fire would be required everywhere of course. The above represents the view of the G. Staff here but it may be modified in detail.[6]

The War Office was simply calling for increased firepower and passed no comment on the machine's structure and size. It implicitly accepted the tactical purpose of the design – to convey an assault party and give covering fire.

Swinton took the opposite view. He realised that parking a machine packed with troops alongside a trench while attempting to neutralise it was to invite obliteration over open sights. He wanted a fighting platform with a ten-man crew. Unknown to Scott-Moncrieff he had submitted to FM Sir John French on 1 June an impressive summary of the machine which he had in mind. His memorandum, 'The Necessity for Machine Gun Destroyers', covered tactical deployment, performance and armament.[7] It began with a review of the situation in France, pointing to the great numbers of machine guns employed by the enemy, the resultant economy in German defensive manpower, and the losses for minimal gain suffered by the Allies. Some of his ideas were prophetic. He proposed a caterpillar-type petrol tractor proof against steel core armour-piercing and reversed bullets, armed with two Maxim machine guns and a 2-pdr quick-firing gun. It should be able to cross 4ft trenches, climb 5ft parapets in forward and reverse, and have a speed of 4mph. Swinton visualised the machine as resembling a Hornsby caterpillar, possibly with a third track out front as a forecarriage, Holt style.

Swinton stressed the need for secrecy in manufacture and for absolute surprise in a first mass attack. The machines were to be brought up to railheads and dispersed by night to final positions spaced 100yd apart in pits just behind the front line. A preparatory bombardment of the entanglements fronting the enemy trenches early in the night would, he thought, cut their wire, later bursts of rifle fire keeping wiring repair parties in their trenches. The dawn attack would see the destroyers climb ramps over the British parapets before driving straight for the enemy positions. Any pre-marked machine-gun emplacements were to be run down; opportunity targets would include enfilade fire on reaching the trenches. By then the destroyers were expected to have attracted much of the remaining hostile fire, allowing the infantry to advance 'practically unscathed'. And so the advance would continue, while supporting artillery-directed fire at enemy batteries.

Swinton's paper was passed to Maj Gen Fowke, Engineer-in-Chief to the BEF. Fowke had shown no interest in his submission the previous October and was not going to change his mind now. He challenged Swinton's belief that such a machine could be built. He considered present caterpillars were too slow and too heavy. The crew would be at least 10ft above the ground (Swinton's description implied no such thing) and nearly every bridge in the country would need strengthening: 'I therefore think that before considering this proposal we should descend from the realms of imagination to solid facts.'[8]

In reply Swinton made the fair point that until an experimental machine had been built it was premature to condemn it out of hand. In any case the War Office had seventy-five Holt tracklayers on order right then. As to height, he visualised 'a heavy motor lorry with caterpillar attachment carrying a large metal tank'.[9] As to weight, the tracks would greatly reduce ground pressure but the destroyers could be partially dismantled for road movement if necessary.

Glyn was back at GHQ on 7 June. He had told an astonished Swinton that the Admiralty was indeed conducting experiments and actually building landships. Knowing that Fowke's negative views could yet lose the day, Swinton sought an authoritative counter. He tried to see Lord Cavan whose 4th Guards Brigade had fought all over the Western Front. The General was not at Brigade HQ when Swinton called. Over the roar of a battery of howitzers nearby he gave a shouted explanation of his visit to Cavan's Staff Captain. The General wrote in reply the same day:

I welcome any suggestion in this extraordinary war that will help to take an enemy's trench without a cost of 50% of the leading company and 75% of that company's officers – for this is what the present day assault amounts to – even with every precaution. . . . The great and serious trouble is that one cannot tell, especially now in high crops – whether the enemy's wire is cut – or not. Here comes in your 'Juggernaut'. We know if 5 'Juggernauts' have passed through that the wire is no more. This is a certain saving of hundreds of lives and a fat legacy to 'moral'. I think it should be possible to pass Platoons up actually hanging on to the back of the 'Juggernaut' itself, without waiting for its enfilade fire up and down the hostile trenches, as this is easily overcome by good traverses. . . . I hope very much indeed your idea may have a good trial. . . . [10]

It was a timely endorsement, though Cavan came to view tanks as a disruptive threat to military conformity by the time he was appointed Supreme Head of the Army as CIGS in 1922. Swinton's memorandum next passed to the recently formed BEF Experiments Committee which evaluated the many suggestions for new weaponry now reaching GHQ. It concluded that his proposal had considerable tactical value and recommended that an experienced vehicle-maker should comment on the possibility of producing trench destroyers. That clinched it. On 22 June French forwarded Swinton's paper to London with a powerful endorsement. It contradicted the reaction of the War Office to current landship design and marked a major advance in its evolution. Twenty-four hours earlier, the War Office had approached the Admiralty proposing joint action to build the weapon. The production team, their design objectives and the end users were coming right at last.

Swinton was recalled home on 19 June for a few days to relieve Hankey who was abroad. Fearful that any private lobbying might compromise the official train that he had set in motion, he confined himself to meeting Col Bird, the Director of Staff Duties, who confirmed Glyn's account.

Churchill chaired the first joint conference of the two Services at the Admiralty on 29 June. It was agreed that the Army should address tactical aspects, armament and performance requirements, while the DNC's team would carry on with design and construction. The War Office passed control of the project to Maj Gen Sir Stanley von Donop, as Master General of Ordnance. The joint committee arrangement would continue with Scott-Moncrieff as President. Churchill's attendance was invited. The Army Council had been wrong-footed and driven into acceptance of an inter-Services role; it was now up to them to determine the function, tactics and performance requirements of the landships.

Churchill lacked executive power, but while Asquith's coalition government settled in, his drive and experience were of value. He supported Balfour at the Admiralty and had been given a seat on the new Dardanelles Cabinet Committee which replaced the War Council. In a perceptive appreciation of the war situation circulated on 18 June Churchill fiercely condemned the lack of progress in mechanical warfare. French losses in Gen Joffre's May offensive totalled 220,000 men. The BEF in the Ypres salient and elsewhere had suffered the loss of 4,000 officers and 96,000 men since 22 April. The ground gained by both Armies was a mere 8 sq miles. He continued:

The French cannot afford to lose men at this rate for no return. . . . It is remarkable that during eight months of trench warfare, ingenuity seems to have had so little success in discovering means of offence and advance. We are now somewhat readily accepting the proposition that high explosive shells used in unprecedented and extraordinary quantities will achieve decisive results. This has certainly not been proved by the results so far attained by the French offensive. . . . The method is effective for clearing a few miles of ground; but its applicability to the reconquest of Flanders and the advance through Germany is doubtful.

The problem of crossing two or three hundred yards of open ground and of traversing or destroying barbed wire . . . ought not to be beyond the range of modern science if sufficient authority had backed the investigation. The absence of any satisfactory method cannot be supplied by the bare breasts of gallant men.[11]

* * *

While the Bullock machines were being readied, the Landships Committee had decided to put on a show at Barlby Road immediately after the joint Services conference on 29 June to demonstrate progress. The only available hardware was the little Killen Strait tractor (which was now a testbed at the Wormwood Scrubs depot), a turreted Rolls-Royce armoured car and two of Diplock's 1-ton Pedrail wagons on which sheet armour had just been mounted as infantry screens. Stern tried and failed to get the Bullock machines driven down from Burton for the event; he forgot or ignored the need for authorisation, bypassed Boothby and got himself a reprimand. Churchill postponed the demonstration to Wednesday 30th to ensure the presence of David Lloyd George, the newly appointed Minister of Munitions. Among others who attended were the Duke of Westminster, Sir Frederick Black (the Director of Munitions Supply) and Maj Gen Sir Ivor Philipps from the Ministry, Maj Gen Scott-Moncrieff, Col Holden, and Louis Jackson – now a brigadier-general and Head of Trench Warfare at the MoM, who had so stoutly supported Swinton and Tulloch on the Holt trials.

Hetherington had become expert at throwing Strait's tractor into and over obstacles on the Talbot recreation ground adjoining the works. Lt Oliver Thorneycroft had fitted a scissors-like torpedo net cutter to the front of the tractor, which Hetherington now drove into a cat's cradle of tensioned barbed wire prudently strung precisely at cutter height. Dummy shell holes and small piles of railway sleepers were crossed by the machine which rose at crazy angles to the sky, throttle wide open and emitting a gratifying thunder from the straight-through exhaust. Stern had brought along Wilfred Stokes with his new trench mortar for a closing *feu de joie*. Stokes got five shells into the air in eleven seconds, all falling inside a 12yd circle. Lloyd George immediately ordered 1,000 mortars. It was obvious that the Strait machine was too light for landship work but Hetherington's bravura performance made an adequate case for keeping going. Scott-Moncrieff promised to produce a landship performance specification the following day, but Churchill was not reassured. Convinced that the project would waste away if left with the War Office, he encouraged Lloyd George to take it on and nurture it at his Ministry of Munitions.

The Killen Strait machine became the world's first tracked armoured vehicle when, shortly afterwards, Lt Symes fitted it with a turretless Delaunay Belleville armoured car hull. Symes was by now a valuable member of the team and had growing expertise in all things armour. He had just been commended for developing an armour-piercing bullet. The conversion was on Boothby's instructions following a short visit of inspection to Gallipoli in May. He wanted the machine to join the armoured cars out there but the imminent disbandment of his force intervened. It ended its days as a tow tractor at the RNAS Barrow Airship Station, having accompanied Boothby there when he took command in September 1915. He sent back a Pierce Arrow lorry in exchange.

The months of enforced second-guessing ended for Crompton with the arrival of the Army's specification two days after the demonstration. The requirement was for a lightly crewed fighting machine – the big troop carrier was not wanted. Another major and urgent redesign was necessary.

SECRET. CATERPILLAR MACHINE GUN DESTROYER.

Suggested conditions to be adhered to in design, if possible. These are tentative and subject to modification.

Speed: top speed on flat not less than 4mph. Bottom speed for climbing 2mph.

Steering: to be capable of being turned through 90 degrees on top speed on the flat. . . .

Reversing: to travel backwards or forwards (equally fast?).

Climbing: to be capable of crossing backwards or forwards an earth parapet 5ft thick and 5ft high. . . .

Bridging: all gaps up to 5ft in width to be bridged directly without dipping into them. All gaps above 5ft in width to be climbed (up to a depth of 5ft with vertical earth sides).

Radius of action: to carry petrol and water for 20 miles.

Capacity: Crew and armament. To carry 10 men. 2 machine guns. 1 light

Q.F. gun. Note by DFW. For each pair of machines: 6 – 2 pounders, 4 – Maxims and 25 men are considered better by G.S. [General Staff].[12]

Eight tons were allowed for armour, ammunition, armament and crew. Save only for Scott-Moncrieff's footnote on armament, these data originated word for word from Swinton's June memorandum. The Army had accepted his fighting landship and tactics. Crompton saw little difficulty in meeting the requirements, though crossing gaps between 6ft and 17ft wide presented problems for a coupled ship. To climb vertical faces up to 5ft high would require the rear half to raise the front half 20°, a kingpost having to be added to his cable linkage to heighten the support of the stays.

Crompton roughed out plans for a Mk III on the lengthened Bullock tracks. The Pedrail system was set aside but he held fast to the principle of a coupled machine. Each half-ship would now shed its troop-carrying wing sections. Instead of an oversize superstructure straddling a pair of in-line tracks, a narrow 21ft long and 5ft wide box body was set low between the tracks. A stepped roof profile allowed for two turrets, one above and behind the other, each mounting a 2-pdr QF gun. Two machine guns were fitted in the bows. Turning radius was reduced from 40ft to 30ft. Weight remained unchanged at 14 tons. Machinery was below floor level, accessible internally from hatches. Crompton rented a Kensington stable at 12 Drayton Mews and construction of a full-scale matchboard mock-up began there on 9 July.

It soon became clear that Swinton's rejection of troopship tactics in favour of a more realistic gunship would further delay Crompton's already slow progress. The committee had lost Metropolitan, and Tritton was out of the picture. D'Eyncourt had got away with a US farm tractor once, but a purpose-built trials machine was sorely needed to demonstrate progress to the War Office and the upper reaches of the Admiralty. Boothby was not alone in questioning Crompton's coupled ships approach, telling the Colonel:

I am not very happy in my own mind about the landship with the joint in the middle. I believe the forepart will drop into the trench and the drive of the after part will give a downward movement driving it further in. Do you not think a [single chassis] six wheel unit might be better, the fore and aft units being caterpillars on bogies and the centre unit either a wheel or caterpillar?[13]

Boothby's point was that two adjoining axles or track frames should be on the ground at all stages of a trench crossing to keep the machine from dropping.

His month with the committee drove d'Eyncourt to give Sueter an ultimatum; unless the Wing Commander was withdrawn he would resign. He said Boothby was involving himself in matters of design and increasingly challenging his authority as chairman. Boothby was removed on the understanding that a single Bullock half-ship would immediately be prepared for trial over trenches, and that Crompton's experiments with articulated machines would be stopped unless there was an early breakthrough.

Stern asked Wilson: 'If you were put in charge of this job who would you sooner work with, Colonel Crompton or Mr Tritton?' Wilson replied: 'If Tritton and I are put on the job we would soon produce a machine that could do something.'[14] Tritton was familiar with the issues and had demonstrated his ability to produce 'design and build' work at speed. D'Eyncourt and Stern decided to transfer both functions to Lincoln.

Crompton was told only that he should invite Tritton to take over the Metro contract. He expected to have full drawings for his Mk III twin-hull machine by 'about the end of the month'. Tritton accepted, and called to see d'Eyncourt on 15 July. They took a taxi round to Thriplands expecting to collect some finished blueprints. The Colonel could only produce a sketch of the machine, and makers' drawings for the engines and McEwan's gearboxes. Tritton sent William Rigby his leading draughtsman to Thriplands on the 19th with instructions to produce detailed drawings strictly to Crompton's designs, initiating nothing himself. Rigby returned on the 24th with one print. Tritton cabled the DNC that he had received 'a mere sketch and quite unfit for our purpose, we have no instructions, drawings nor details as to the various mechanisms we have to incorporate. We are therefore at a standstill pending full particulars.'[15] Relations between the two men had deteriorated further since Crompton's criticism of Tritton's proposal to power his ship electrically.

Tritton had received a telegram from Stern on 21 July asking Foster's to prepare to build up to twelve landships. The committee met next day. It was decided that Tritton should build a single half-ship as an independent unit before proceeding further with the twin-hull Mk III. Crompton was shaken by what amounted to a vote of no confidence in the coupled design, and by his failure that day to persuade the committee to place an immediate order for one. He was asked to devise steering via wheels or tracks for the solo half-ship, and produced a heavy trailing two-wheeled frame with Ackermann steering.

Tritton met d'Eyncourt and Stern at the Ministry on 30 July. Stern had been phoning Lincoln for progress reports almost daily, always to be told there were no drawings so they could not start cutting metal. Tritton was informed that Crompton and Legros would be retired and their designs abandoned. Foster's was to receive immediate design responsibility, with Wilson in attendance as Admiralty superintendent. They were to start again, using the extended Bullock tracks and the howitzer tractor's Daimler engine and transmission to cobble together an experimental machine in three weeks if possible. Tritton thought he could rivet up a hull in boilerplate in fourteen days. He cabled Lincoln: 'Whole landship job handed to us with Wilson as overseer. He and Legros coming to Lincoln. Ask Starkey [chief draughtsman] start two more draughtsmen if possible will wire later on after further interview with d'Eyncourt this afternoon.' Crompton's work was at an end.

The DNC finalised the order next day, telling Tritton his people were to work day and night to complete it. This marked Tritton's first official involvement with tracks, the system he had so often condemned. He had told Legros in March 'The caterpillar system is no bloody good for the job' and repeated these sweeping sentiments to him while *en route* to the Bullock trials. However, his objections, based on the nutcracker action of some early chaintracks, lost much credibility when a year later he told d'Eyncourt that: 'All makers of Centipede type of vehicle have avoided this [nutcracker] type of construction.'[16] Soon after the war Tritton produced a book promoting Foster's pioneering activities with the tanks. He made no reference to their work for the Landships Committee prior to August 1915, saying only that he was first sent for by d'Eyncourt on 30 July when the DNC 'admitted' to him that they had made no progress.[17]

The Bullock trials began in August, primarily to test Crompton's linkage, establish the performance of coupled machines over differing obstacles, rehearse the new tactics and find methods of clearing barbed-wire entanglements. McEwan, Pratt & Co. was an internationally respected firm building small diesel locomotives. Robert McEwan, the Managing Director, and Maj Ernest Baguley of parent company Baguley Cars Ltd gave enthusiastic support. The Major had recently come home from France to be invalided out of the Army. (Shortly after the trials he lodged a claim for an invention relating to them, the details of which are unrecorded. The claim was refused by Bertie Stern.)

The first experiments with a single Bullock Giant began on 10 August. Boothby had rejected Wilson's first trials site in McEwan's yard as being too visible to the public despite plans for temporary screening up to 18ft high. Instead they had rented a secluded field nearby in Sinai Park at Shobnall. The official party was joined by numerous sightseers from a local hotel as guests of Wilson and his brother Percy, who had followed him into the RNAS in May. The tractor was fitted with a torpedo net cutter and first tackled a wire and steel cable entanglement. Anything it failed to shear was flattened. It was then reversed over a narrow fire trench where one of the tracks fell into a traverse. The differential, which was non-locking, came into play, the other track ceased to drive and the machine had to be winched out. Track tension had to remain slack to allow for the binding effect of mud. Consequently when crossing a trench the unsupported lower arc sagged badly, while under lateral pressure on a slope the machine could ride right off its tracks. It was not a promising start.

The two big tractors were first coupled back to back on 19 August. It quickly emerged that when the linkage was tensioned to hold the two half-ships rigidly together for trench crossing, the set became unsteerable. The coupling also became over-stressed if one of the chassis took a severe tilt relative to the other.

When Crompton was asked to modify the half-ships as separate fighting units, the question of how to get them over trenches without nosediving was carefully avoided by the committee. The proposed solution was so painfully ineffective that nobody claimed it. A rectangular iron frame like a flat roof canopy was built over one of the tractors, set some 6ft above the platform. Three heavy poles each fitted with a broad base-plate were suspended from either side of the frame to hang just clear of the ground. It was hoped that when the ship surmounted a trench parapet and rocked over into its descent, the lead pair of crutches or 'elephant feet' could be swung forward to rest on the far side of the trench. With its nose suspended over the gap the machine was theoretically free to drive across on the heels of track still in ground contact. The remaining feet were intended to keep the machine upright during the manoeuvre. The idea was a total failure, amusing only in retrospect. It was indicative of mounting desperation at Burton.

*　　*　　*

Lloyd George's Ministry of Munitions was in the process of taking over almost all armaments production from a shocked and truculent War Office. It was created in June to tackle the munitions shortages which had become a public scandal. The quietly able Christopher Addison MP joined as Under Secretary. He and Lloyd George were to build a formidable national machine for war production.

Lloyd George moved quickly after the Killen Strait demonstration, securing Balfour's formal agreement on 17 July to hand responsibility for the landships to his ministry rather than the War Office. Scenting that it might be accused of duplicity, the Admiralty wrote an emollient letter to the WO and the MoM coolly confirming the transfer. The WO was slow to respond, but eventually von Donop accepted the situation with good grace on 17 August, secure in the belief that the Army retained the right to approve final design for all munitions. The splitting of design control and production between the two ministries was unsustainable but the Army Council held out until 25 November, only capitulating after being ordered by the government to let go. Responsibility for design, patterns, specifications, testing of arms and inspection then passed to Lloyd George's ministry. The Army remained responsible for specifying munitions performance requirements and for their storage and distribution to the troops.

Balfour agreed to keep the Landships Committee going with d'Eyncourt in the chair until the first machine was produced to the DNC's satisfaction. It would report to E.W. Moir, Director of the MoM Inventions Department, which would take over fully at that point. The War Office committee under Scott-Moncrieff was ongoing. 20 Squadron had been attached to d'Eyncourt's team since 7 July. It would transfer from Wormwood Scrubs to the Ministry's experimental ground at Wembley Park, where it would be shared with Louis Jackson's Trench Warfare Department. D'Eyncourt ensured that Stern, the Wilson brothers and Kenneth Symes remained on board by transferring them to the squadron. Symes was working with Beardmore's and Vickers, researching armour and designing turrets. Boothby placed Hetherington in command of the Squadron, McGrath stepping down to become his deputy.

Col Hankey had been unsuccessfully lobbying from London to get Swinton on to the new BEF Experimental Committee (the 'Monkey Tricks Committee') to inject more drive. He had the ear of the Prime Minister and was able to put to him an alternative proposal. Swinton was recalled on 18 July to become Hankey's deputy as Senior Assistant Secretary to the CID. The two officers had, of course, served together there before the war. Swinton was unable to get away to visit d'Eyncourt until the 30th. The DNC briefed him guardedly before realising his visitor was a genuine landships supporter. Swinton described his meeting with Stern next day as like lighting the fuse of a mine, and Stern recalled their first words:

> 'Lieutenant Stern', he said, 'this is the most extraordinary thing I have ever seen. The Director of Naval Construction appears to be making land battleships for the Army who have never asked for them and are doing nothing to help. You have nothing but naval ratings doing all your work. What on earth are you? Are you a mechanic or a chauffeur?' 'A banker', I replied. 'This', said he, 'makes it still more mysterious.'[18]

The dynamic banker and the visionary soldier struck sparks from each other – there was a Livingstone and Stanley quality to their meeting. More importantly, the struggling landships venture had secured a powerful new friend at court.

Seven

LANDSHIPS

Balata died on test bench yesterday morning. New arrival by Tritton out of pressed plate. Light in weight but very strong. All doing well, thank you. Proud Parents.[1]

William Tritton, telegram, 22 September 1915

6 August 1915 was a black day for Col Crompton. He learned that morning that his son Nigel had been wounded (he was killed in action three months later); and a curt letter from d'Eyncourt instructed him to produce all landships orders issued from Thriplands. The DNC wished to inspect and initial them before they were passed to Foster's which was now the contractor 'for the whole of the work'. Crompton was instructed not to give further orders without d'Eyncourt's approval. He was informed that he and Legros could expect their contracts to be terminated at the end of the month. It was a dismissive communication which the old-school Colonel never forgot: 'I complain of the way I was treated by Sir T. d'Eyncourt. As one engineer to another he showed a total absence of engineering etiquette, carrying on with two people at once, which I resent very much indeed.'[2]

In his restrained letter of acknowledgement Crompton gave an encouraging report on preliminary tests at Burton. He expressed his doubts about Tritton's ability to spare time to take the job to completion, adding 'we have had a hard and difficult part to play. Boothby and his men have always pulled against us, the designing engineers.'[3] The Colonel vainly sought backing from Churchill, who expressed surprise and annoyance and promised to make enquiries.

George Field was recalled from America. On the voyage home he summarised his findings. He thought Strait's angled track should be adopted to aid climbing. Alternatively a separate front-mounted pair of frames should swivel to follow ground contours. As for Crompton's double ship,

I should prefer double engined single ship with one engine on each side. . . . From my interviews and discussions I have completely abandoned the idea of the double ship as impracticable, it being unwieldy and difficult to steer. The effect of the back half on the leading half when the leading half is at an angle is to push it further into an awkward position and throw undue strain on the couplings. . . . I consider that a machine carrying a moderately heavy gun and travelling at about 8mph of far more utility than a man-carrying machine; it could also be armed with Maxims. The use of epicyclics is essential if changing gear is required; else machine must come to rest before change can be made. The double engine will do away with all the complications required for steering.[4]

Field encountered general hostility on his return to 83 Pall Mall, particularly from Stern who was dismissive of his suggestions and work in America. By then any associate of Crompton's was yesterday's designer. Field had made provisional arrangements in the US with Bullock's, Killen Strait, and the Federal Bridge Company and the Waukeshau Engine Company, both of Milwaukee, to build complete landships at the rate of 100 per week in all. This early opportunity to tap into America's immense engineering resources was discarded by the Landships Committee which feared loss of control at such a distance, and was probably doubtful of securing adequate shipping capacity. The MoM was already placing huge munitions contracts with US suppliers to equip Kitchener's seventy new divisions by the following spring. George Field joined 20 Squadron before transferring to the RFC in 1916.

*   *   *

Crompton and Legros worked out their last weeks monitoring the trials and doggedly progressing the coupled ship design. The Mk III twin turret half-ships were replaced by a Mk IIIA with a single forward turret, reducing overall height to 7ft 6in. Crompton was perennially concerned to cut height to reduce exposure to gunnery, shed weight and improve stability. His final design proposal was handed over on his last day of service. On Field's recommendation Crompton's Mk IV machine was to be mounted on Killen Strait tracks, reducing height to 6ft and weight to 12.5 tons per half-ship. The Colonel intended to clad the hull with a protective sheath of light steel plates spaced off the underlying armour.

It was all for nothing. Six months – much of a fighting season – had passed. If a fleet of some 150 landships was to materialise and crews and engineers were to complete training by the start of the 1916 campaign, then working drawings for a credible design should have been coming off the boards in July. The committee had proved numerous options to be impractical but had put nothing but agricultural machinery on the ground.

Crucially, however, it was pursuing a tracked solution, for which credit must go to Macfie, Sueter and Crompton. A mass of research data had been accumulated by Crompton and Legros but it proved of little value. Their professional approach throughout had been meticulous, almost academic. They had produced a series of over-ambitious proposals to meet two opposing tactical requirements, Churchill's and, latterly, the Army's. If instead of troop transports they had been instructed from the start to produce the gun platform which the Army eventually requested, might a practical prototype have emerged by this time? Regardless of the consequences of Churchill's questionable and technically demanding tactics, the outcome by late August 1915 is unlikely to have been markedly different.

Churchill later denied that he had ever asked for troop transports. His replies under cross-examination by counsel for Crompton and Legros before the Royal Commission on Awards to Inventors in 1919 were evasive:

q. At that time [March 1915] the idea was to have a machine which would carry a number of men into the enemy's trenches?
a. That was not my original idea. I essentially dwelt upon it as an engine of war which was to fight, to roll down wire, and to sweep the trenches with machine-gun fire, and which the troops were to use as a *point d'appui* to manoeuvre with, rather than using it as a carrier to carry a definite body of troops into the enemy's lines. As a matter of fact there is utility in both those ideas, and both were developed as the war went on.
q. At any rate Sir Tennyson d'Eyncourt's idea at that time was a machine which would carry a large number of men. The plans were for that?
a. He knew what we wanted to have done. There was a great latitude as to the road which might be taken. He presented two definite methods of arriving at a practical solution.[5]

It is hard to square these responses with contemporary records. Churchill unequivocally supported the big troop transporter throughout his stewardship of the Landships Committee. The assertion that having set up the committee he left the choice of battle tactics to a master shipbuilder strains credulity. Crompton told the Tanks Awards Committee in 1918: 'My main instructor was Mr Churchill himself. He always said "I want something that will straddle a trench and enfilade it with machine guns and then you let men out rapidly and you take the trench".'[6] As to d'Eyncourt's having presented 'two definite methods of arriving at a practical solution', the second method – a lighter heavily armed machine – was only produced at the request of the Army after Churchill's departure. There was no visible latitude for the committee to vary the brief, hence Crompton's cautious letter to the DNC in May proposing the second version, and its rejection.

The Colonel asked if he and Legros could continue their involvement with the project in an advisory and honorary capacity. Their offer was accepted but they were never again consulted by the landships team. D'Eyncourt's last word on Crompton was addressed to Swinton: 'He never really produced complete plans which could be worked to.'[7]

It is now appropriate to catch up with other events before returning to Tritton, Wilson and the committee.

*   *   *

Lt Robert Macfie attended no further meetings of the Landships Committee after the first in February 1915, but it was there that he spoke so persuasively for tracked traction. Crompton, to his credit, scrapped the big-wheeler at once and took up the idea, but Macfie was shocked that Crompton had selected the Pedrail system to validate tracklayers. Macfie devised his own crawler loosely based on the Holt. The big difference was the machine's purpose – this was to be a gun platform. In a 13 April memo to Boothby, Macfie had visualised two columns of landships penetrating beyond the trench lines, allowing a horde of cavalry and horse artillery to dash through to seize command and communications centres:

I am aware that machines are proposed which will be armoured against rifle and Maxim fire which are to carry parties of soldiers to the trenches, whereupon doors are to be opened and the men pour out. I would submit that this plan fails to deal effectively with the enemy's artillery, and that further, only the front line of enemy's trenches can be dealt with in this way.[8]

Macfie persuaded Murray Sueter to let him convert an old 5-ton Allday lorry chassis to chaintracks for evaluation. Messrs Nesfield & Mackenzie, a small engineering company in Uxbridge Road, West London, were already making anti-aircraft gun mountings for Sueter, who instructed them on 22 April to work to Macfie's orders. Six weeks later Albert Nesfield told the DAD that he could no longer tolerate the Lieutenant's violent abusiveness to him and his employees despite their best efforts. He asked for Macfie to be replaced, but received no reply. Nesfield described Macfie's Allday design as comprising two pairs of tracks, the front pair being steered. A certain amount of work had been done on the conversion and a miniature electrically driven model had been made. Nesfield had also been designing his own landship on a single pair of tracks, each independently powered for steering. The arguments between the two centred on their respective designs, specifically the means of steering. Macfie maintained that Nesfield's turning mechanism with only one track in drive would tear off the braked track.

As Nesfield demonstrated a small model on 1 July to Hetherington, Crompton and other officers at Wormwood Scrubs, Macfie entered the room and pounced on it, claiming it was his. Soon afterwards the armoured car squadrons began to disband and Macfie's bits and pieces were removed to the Barlby Road depot. His presumably revised drawing dated 19 August has recently been found among Stern's papers.[9] He planned to fit one pair of tracks, the Allday's power train being retained with short drive chains taken from the rear axle to shafts on the track sprockets to either side. The very heavily armoured hull was a rectangular and turretless steel box with an arrowhead front. The interesting thing about Macfie's track frames is their angled and upturned nose, much as George Field had sketched six days earlier while sailing home from the USA. Directional control relied on a towed two-wheeled frame with Ackermann steering, exactly as Crompton had proposed for his Mk III on the lengthened Bullock tracks only a week or so before Macfie made his drawing.

Stern and the committee were no longer interested in Macfie's theories. His standing in the RNAS never recovered from the dispute over the model. Stern considered him 'a very troublesome fellow' and 'a most impossible man to work with'.[10] Macfie resigned from the Service that November, later accusing Hetherington, Stern and others of conspiring to rob him of his design, from which he wrongly claimed the tank was built. To anticipate events for a moment, soon after the tanks became public knowledge in September 1916 Macfie found backers to finance the commercial production of his machine.

He visited Stern that December, seeking his help to secure the necessary priority for purchase of 15 tons of steel for a prototype. Stern told Macfie that he would first need to see his drawings which he said would be fairly treated. When Macfie replied that Stern had not treated him fairly over his earlier drawings, which he claimed Stern had commandeered, the meeting ended abruptly.[11] Macfie mounted a campaign of vilification of Nesfield and past colleagues which only ended in 1919.

*   *   *

Swinton's ally Tom Tulloch joined the Supply Branch of the Ministry of Munitions. He told his Holt trials colleague Louis Jackson that he deplored the general lack of military imagination which invariably left the initiative to the Germans. He believed the War Office could still improvise twenty or thirty of the trench destroyers which he and Swinton had urged in January – nothing less would do the job. Jackson agreed but had a different machine and weapon in mind. His section of the WO Department of Fortification and Works had just been taken over by the Ministry of Munitions and renamed the Trench Warfare Department. He and Capts W.H. Livens and F.H. Vincent went too, taking assorted kit with them including a heavy flame-thrower with an 80ft reach. Jackson wanted to mount the projector in a machine on Crompton's abandoned and part-completed Pedrail tracks. It was the second of several attempts to harness Diplock's systems for war.

Jackson salvaged Crompton's dies, templates, drive chains and other material for a test machine. The Colonel provided drawings and data for the main erectors, bridge-builders Stothert & Pitt of Bath. Twelve self-propelled flame-throwers each carrying 5,000 gallons of petrol were to be built, subject to trials, and fifty smaller Pedrail machines of 500-gallon capacity. The bigger machine's twin 100hp engines from Aster Engineering of Wembley each powered a Pedrail in-line bogie. It took a strong man to hand steer them. When the well-engineered but desperately low-slung No. 1 chassis was driven out of the shed by Maj Walter Wilson on 7 June 1916, it just managed to climb a 4in thick railway sleeper before lurching a few degrees until the 33ft × 9ft frame grounded. Official trials were delayed until August. *En route* to the experimental ground at Porton the free-running roller beds developed weaknesses and the Pedrail feet proved unsuited to rough roads. The machine was then fitted with an unarmoured tram-like body before failing further tests on Salisbury Plain. This interesting vehicle lay at Bovington until, sadly, it was scrapped in 1923.

Diplock died in August 1918 just three months after his brother passed away, probably from the influenza pandemic which killed thousands that year. Reginald Brackenbury kept the business going until its liquidation in 1921.

*　　*　　*

By the time Swinton arrived in Whitehall in July 1915 the control of d'Eyncourt's small team had become dangerously split between the Admiralty, the War Office and Lloyd George's Ministry of Munitions. He contacted Tulloch who advised a round-table conference to clarify departmental objectives and responsibilities. Swinton was no longer a distant Colonel with a mad fixation. All doors were now open to him and he was more than Donald Hankey's deputy. The Prime Minister had been persuaded by Hankey to let Swinton concentrate on weapons development in general and landships in particular.

Swinton convened an inter-departmental conference on 28 August in the War Cabinet offices at 2 Whitehall Gardens. Scott-Moncrieff took the chair. It was agreed that the War Office would continue to specify operational requirements, the Admiralty would control design and experiment for the time being, and the Ministry of Munitions would eventually take over the whole work of the 'land cruisers or armoured caterpillar motor cars'. The need for secrecy and for large numbers of skilled men to build, crew and service the machines was agreed. 20 Squadron would be increased to 600 men drawn from Boothby's recently disbanded force. Louis Jackson's Trench Warfare Department would find them plenty of construction and experimental work until they were needed.

Tulloch entered a reservation strongly objecting to any aspect of landships work passing to the MoM. He said the preliminary experiments by d'Eyncourt's committee would provide the data necessary to reach a decision on the weapon's future. If it was decided to take it on from there, all responsibility should pass to a small full-time directorate with wide powers, dedicated solely to the development and production of the fleet and its recruitment and training. The Inventions and Trench Warfare Departments were unsuited to this work, he said. Logically it should go to the War Office to be managed as a specialist branch like the Flying Corps – but Tulloch was three and a half years ahead of the event. Churchill minuted 'Agree. Capt Tulloch's view strikes me as most important and ought not to be overlooked.'[12] Adm Tudor would urge a similar course after the first demonstration of the tank.

Tulloch had not changed his opinion on scale. He remained convinced that the Army needed a giant machine, proof against field-gun fire; it had to be able to smash through the enemy's first, second and reserve lines and destroy his heavy guns in a single strike. Tulloch wanted to see a 500-ton articulated and steam-powered land battleship. Churchill agreed. More rationally, von Donop received a report of the conference and was asked if he would use his good offices as Master General of Ordnance to obtain 100 naval 6-pdr guns for the first landships. His pained reply was predictable:

I am not prepared to take any responsibility for the decisions arrived at by this conference and I cannot give any information as to the possibility of supplying the guns and ammunition until I am provided with the designs of both. . . . I view with dismay the manner in which this subject is being dealt with. A War Office committee was appointed for it, the C.I.D. is also dealing with it, a conference decides [sic] on what should be done – they are called Admiralty landships – the personnel is to come from a Naval organisation and I am asked about the provision of guns and ammunition the patterns of which I have not seen and about which I have not been consulted.[13]

Von Donop was right in one respect, too many people in and out of uniform were involved with the project and calling the shots, but he also bitterly resented the Ministry of Munitions taking over his responsibilities for ordnance production. Ernest Moir had been provoked into making a formal complaint to Lloyd George, alleging that the MGO was, in effect, damaging the war effort.[14]

Relishing his new appointment, Swinton sprayed the War Office with ideas reflecting his inventive mind and sense of humour – he specialised in Greek puns. He proposed that the floor surface of the 'Armouredillos' should be profiled with deep ridges which would become horizontal firesteps when the floor tilted to perhaps 45° as the vehicles breasted trench parapets. The gunners would otherwise skid down the steel deck just when maximum fire was required. For the same reason Swinton recommended that instead of fixed mountings, the machine guns should be hung from the roof in slings. The gunners would be suspended in bosun's chairs. To repel boarders at ranges too close for fire through the revolver ports he suggested an external ring of nozzles discharging atomised acid spray. As one of the objectives of the weapon was to draw enemy rifle and machine-gun fire away from advancing infantry, Swinton also wanted landships to carry in front of them a large noticeboard inscribed with a snappy insult, such as:

GOTT STRAFE DEUTSCHLAND

but having a few letters displaced as:

GOTT SETRAF DUSTECHLAND.

'The misplacement of the letters if cleverly done will just suffice to make every German who sees it try to read it instead of shooting at our infantry. This device may appear ludicrous but it is based on sound psychological grounds.'[15]

Swinton was becoming a focus and clearing house for all manner of landship matters. Tulloch was convinced the ships would receive considerable protection from artillery if a double skin of armour was adopted. He offered Swinton his services together with those of an expert from the Explosives Loading Company of Faversham which he had jointly set up in 1912. (Until the war it was the only factory in the country to specialise in loading shells with TNT. It supplied the government with 100,000lb of TNT from stock in August 1914.) The idea was examined by Crompton and later by Wilson and Symes before being dropped.

Maj Henry Guest, Secretary of the BEF Experimental Committee in France, forwarded a scheme to Swinton devised by Maj A.I.R. Glasfurd of 27th Infantry Brigade. He visualised a Pedrail-based fleet of armoured machines the size of 2-ton trucks which would rely on surprise to penetrate enemy defences without a preliminary bombardment. The difference lay in their primary armament. Glasfurd wanted to fit cyanide projectors with a 120ft reach.[16] Swinton circulated the Major's paper to the Committee of Imperial Defence for consideration, but it got no further.

From France Capt J. Rose asked Swinton 'Has the idea of NOISE [sic] ever been mooted? I mean noise on a great scale such as a big syren or buzzer. Nothing is more nerve shattering at close quarters and all orders would be upset if a syren could be carried and let loose on arriving amongst the enemy.'[17]

* * *

Tritton and Wilson had left London on 4 August with d'Eyncourt's instruction to produce an experimental machine from readily available parts, including the lengthened Bullock tracks, for delivery in three weeks if possible. Tritton thought he could do it in two using the howitzer tractor's power train once more. To avoid the distractions of working from Foster's and going home nightly, Tritton booked himself into Lincoln's White Hart Hotel and converted the first-floor Yarborough Room to a drawing office. He went into semi-retreat there with his chief draughtsman Mr Starkey. Wilson also put up at the hotel and divided his time between Burton and Lincoln, spending long evenings with Tritton. The day's sketches were destroyed each night for security. They broke off to attend the Bullock trials on 10 August to see wire-cutting experiments. Cut or uncut, Tritton maintained that the wire would cause a track failure, but he was wrong. Legros, who was present at the trial, considered that day marked Tritton's belated conversion from big wheels to chaintracks.

Wilson was more colleague and partner than official supervisor to Tritton. Construction of what became known as the 'No. 1 Lincoln Machine' or the 'Tritton' began on 11 August in a corner of the Wellington Foundry, completing on 8 September. The machine was a simple boiler-plated box body with dummy roof turret. Tritton had fitted a heavy rear-mounted steering tail, much like Crompton's earlier version. A tiller bar steered the two 4ft 6in wheels through linkages to each hub, the tiller being cable-connected back to the driver. Against the advice of Mr James, Hornsby's Chief Engineer, Tritton wisely installed brakes on the differential's drive shafts for secondary steering if the wheeled system failed (it usually did). James feared the brakes would absorb excessive power and the linings would quickly burn out (they did).

The machine never moved out of Foster's yard on the Bullock tracks as they were received from Chicago. The flanges on the rollers mounted the specially lengthened tracks and ran the vehicle right off them. Tritton made some modifications, after which it was driven on 19 September to Cross Cliff Hill where, largely concealed under a tarpaulin, it was demonstrated before d'Eyncourt, Moir, Swinton, Hetherington and Stern. Swinton was shocked to see a large crowd, mostly Foster's employees and their wives, lining the boundary fence, but Tritton and his directors appeared unconcerned. The 16-ton machine just managed to climb a 2ft parapet before casting a track while crossing a 4ft 6in trench. The flanges of the track rollers had peeled right off. It took two days to get the machine back to the works where mild steel rollers were made up and tried with no better result.

Lt Field also saw the machine sliding about on its tracks and noticed that:

the tracks were fitted . . . in such a manner that it was impossible to utilise the specially designed bracing members in spite of the fact that they had been received by the Lincoln people and full instructions issued for satisfactory erection. The rocking of the tracks was uncontrolled also, and the tracks were therefore improperly erected. [I] pointed this out, but was informed that 'a whole lot of junk had been received of which no use could be made, besides which, it was not required'.[18]

Field had detailed knowledge of the special bracing which he claimed was never fitted. The track was certainly assembled by Foster's at breakneck speed. Time was saved by mounting the engine at the rear with the drive-end forward, consequently if a forward gear was selected the machine would have moved backwards. Swinton had absolutely no difficulty putting it about that the machine was a failure and had been abandoned.

The War Office had not formally confirmed its requirements for trench crossing and climbing, but it was clear from the start that the Lincoln Machine's track length and front profile were inadequate for such work. Knowing this, Tritton and Wilson had begun to consider an alternative in mid-August. The hull would have to be at least 20ft long as against its predecessor's 14ft. They expected severe problems with track override and power loss from the weight of additional armour; ground clearance and stability were other difficulties. It seemed unavoidable that the turret and armament would have to be at roof level to provide an all-round field of fire, but a high hull would be dangerously top-heavy. How to reconcile these factors?

Wilson thought the unthinkable. Instead of extending the low track frames, which would not help climbing, he suggested running the track right around the hull with a steeply angled front end. The armaments could then be mounted on either side between the upper and lower runs of track, instead of on the roof. He sketched a low lozenge-shaped machine. Because the design's tracks were integral with the hull, separate frames were avoided and weight reduced. The bottom arc of each track was the footprint equivalent of a giant wheel but without its unwanted mass. The track's curvature also limited the number of shoes in ground contact, thus reducing drag when steering, saving power and tightening the turning radius. Wilson bolted a removable half-round gun casement ('sponson' in naval parlance) to either side of the hull; they projected like bay windows and added 3ft to overall width. (Responsibility for introducing the sponsons was later contested between Tritton and d'Eyncourt.) The 26ft long hull stood 8ft high and 13ft 9in wide over the sponsons. The machine was first called the 'Wilson' and later 'Big Willie' or 'Centipede' after Foster's 1913 crawler, though there all resemblance ended. Later it simply became 'Mother'. Maximum speed was expected to be 2mph.

A day or so later, on 23 August, Tritton visited d'Eyncourt to report progress on the No. 1 Lincoln Machine. It was so obviously inadequate that he felt compelled to reveal the far from complete new design, sketching it on scrap paper. He returned to Lincoln with instructions to build a test vehicle with all speed. Tritton apologised to Wilson for his impromptu disclosure, but the cat was now out of the bag and they had yet to overcome the most threatening problem of keeping the machine on its immensely long tracks. Stern arrived on the 26th with WO performance requirements: the weapon must cross trenches 5ft wide, climb a 4ft 6in parapet (previously 5ft) and climb a 1 in 1 slope.

Tritton and Wilson wrestled with track design for the next four weeks. In place of the Bullock system they considered multiple roller chains, or even a mat-like track of densely woven wire strands on to which driving teeth could be riveted. Standard rubber and webbing Balata belting was briefly talked of until Tritton's firemen turned their hoses on a suspended length, the wet fabric shrinking and deforming the belt. D'Eyncourt was horrified at the idea, sending Lt Symes up from London on 21 September to dissuade them from its use. By the time he arrived an all-steel track had been devised by Tritton, its links riveted to armour-plate shoes which were profiled with a supporting lip to prevent sag. Spring flanges on the rollers held them fast under lateral pressure to prevent them riding off the track. The design proved so reliable that it remained basically unchanged for the rest of the war. That evening Tritton sent the Admiralty an historic telegram from the White Hart.

Balata died on test bench yesterday morning. New arrival by Tritton out of pressed plate. Light in weight but very strong. All doing well, thank you. Proud Parents.[19]

A full-size wooden mock-up of 'Mother' was hastily made and sent by road to the Wembley experimental ground where it was kept out of sight under guard in a small circus tent. It was viewed on 29 September by representatives from the War Office, Ministry of Munitions and d'Eyncourt's committee, with Lt Col R.N. Harvey, Maj J.T. Dreyer and Maj Henry Guest from the BEF

Experimental Committee. Swinton stood on a packing case and talked them through the key features. They were well pleased with what they saw.

Armament was hard to come by and had to fit the limited sponson space. Their preference was for a 6-pdr gun but Brig Gen Guthrie-Smith, the D of A, had earlier told Swinton none could be spared from aerial defence. He refused Swinton's suggestion that he order more, saying he would look a fool if the war ended next day.[20] A 2.95in mountain gun had to be turned down because there were only four in the country. Von Donop could not supply fifty 2-pdr Vickers-Maxim automatics (a larger pom-pom) in less than five months. One of each of these last two guns had been fitted on the model for comparison, but it was finally agreed that the machine should carry a 6-pdr 57mm QF naval gun on a pedestal mounting in each sponson, one Vickers-Maxim machine gun firing forward, and four Lewis or other automatic rifles projecting from loopholes to secure all-round fire. Thanks to d'Eyncourt and the Admiralty 100 Hotchkiss 6-pdrs were forthcoming. An eight-man crew was also agreed, duties to be decided later. Every member was to be trained to drive and to fire the guns.

Albert Nesfield had called to see Swinton four days before the viewing. He produced his small working model with bicycle chaintracks which, though not carried across the roof like Wilson's, broadly resembled the track alignment on 'Mother'. After watching the machine climb books in his office Swinton took him over to the Admiralty and left him with the DNC. Nesfield continued to press his claim as the 'inventor' of the successful track until the end of the war and beyond.

*   *   *

An early indication of War Office thinking on the number of machines to be built appeared in an exchange of minutes in mid-September 1915 between von Donop and Gen W.D. Bird, the new Director of Staff Duties, who thought perhaps fifty would be required. Days later six divisions of Haig's First Army went over the top at Loos into largely uncut wire after an inadequate artillery barrage and the first use of gas by the BEF. Modest gains were paid for with appalling losses totalling nearly 60,000 British casualties by the time the campaign ended on 14 October. After the failures of guns and gas, the landship would be the last shot in Britain's munitions locker with any chance of achieving a breakthrough. Tritton and Wilson could not have realised at the time how great was the burden of responsibility they carried. The Army's future demand for tanks would be measurable in thousands.

Getting the materials together took Foster's a further month before construction of 'Mother' could start on 28 October. Security at Lincoln was unorthodox but effective. Instead of swearing his workforce to secrecy Tritton encouraged ridicule, letting the work be seen as the Guv'nor's crazy idea. Its purpose was further obscured by treating the hull and chassis construction as two quite separate orders, and assigning different job numbers to each on drawings and factory worksheets. The hull was designated a 'Water Carrier for Mesopotamia' and to those in the boiler shop the structure was simply 'that bloody tank'.[21] Paperwork for the engine, transmission and track assembly was marked 'Demonstration & Instruction Chassis' destined, if anybody asked, for the Royal Marines Artillery at Eastney Barracks, Southsea, where Foster's howitzer tractors had gone.[22] The first of the Tritton tracks was completed and bench-run on 22 November. Shortage of materials delayed its mate but both tracks were made up at 12ft centres and fitted on 3 December to the Lincoln Machine, now purely a testbed and renamed 'Little Willie'. They performed well in Burton Park on the 8th.

Asquith wound up the Dardanelles Committee in November in an attempt to dampen criticism of inefficiency in the direction of the war. Churchill's exclusion from its successor, the smaller Cabinet War Committee, brought his resignation from the government on the 11th. Nine days later he was a Major in the trenches. Sir John French had offered him command of a brigade after time to familiarise himself with local conditions, but in the meantime Churchill was attached to the 2nd Battalion of the Grenadier Guards, going into the line on the 20th. When he came out he submitted a characteristically radical memorandum to French. His *Variants of the Offensive* proposed several novel means of attack as alternatives to the 'bare breasts of men'. It opened with *The Attack by Armour*, and after considering the advantages of hand-held shields and composite screens mounted on caterpillars, he examined fighting tracklayers:

About seventy [caterpillars] are now nearing completion in England, and should be inspected. None should be used until all can be used at once. . . . They are capable of traversing any ordinary obstacle, ditch, breastwork or trench. They carry two or three Maxims each and can be fitted with flame apparatus. Nothing but a direct hit with a field gun will stop them. . . .

If artillery is used to cut wire, the direction and imminence of the attack is proclaimed days beforehand. But by this method the assault follows the wire cutting almost immediately, i.e., before any reinforcements can be brought up by the enemy, or any special defensive measures taken.[23]

Much of Churchill's thinking appears naive in the light of subsequent events – his continuing faith in manually pushed shields, the value of torpedo net cutters for wire, a reliance on night attack – but his intention was to inform and redirect tactical planning at GHQ and in that he had some success. We have already noted Tritton's reference to a nebulous seventy caterpillars ordered and cancelled at around this time.

A parliamentary question to the Under Secretary of State for War on 8 December explicitly revealed the nature and purpose of the landships. James Hogge, Scottish Radical and self-confessed 'special investigator', asked whether Ernest Moir, the Director of Munitions Inventions, had reported to the War Office 'on the use of mobile forts propelled by caterpillar tractors for use in traversing ground honeycombed by trenches; and if so, has he reported favourably on their utility?' Harold Tennant replied for the WO that no such report had been received. Hogge was dangerously well informed. The Committee of Imperial Defence ordered that the press should be warned off and asked for measures to be taken in the House to avoid such questions in future.

Swinton's guiding presence was providential at this time. Scott-Moncrieff and his team were slow to give d'Eyncourt practical support even when requested. Hetherington later said that as soon as Swinton involved himself they got what they wanted. Without him they would have been ignored by the Army. On 17 December Swinton alerted the joint committee to the imminent arrival of the first 'Land Cruiser' and the need for a definite policy on production, personnel and finance. Tulloch's influence is visible in Swinton's key recommendation calling for production to be controlled by 'one business man of proved capacity, preferably one who has been connected with the experimental construction up to date'. They clearly meant Stern.

The second inter-departmental conference followed on the 24th, Scott-Moncrieff presiding. It opened with a somewhat surprising statement from the Ministry of Munitions that it did not after all want responsibility for supply of armoured land cruisers, believing them too complex to fit into its munitions portfolio. Tulloch's influence was at work here. He and Lt Col Symon were the only MoM representatives present. Tulloch had been pressing since August for the Ministry to disengage, believing that landships production would suffocate and be sidelined under bureaucratic and competitive pressures there. He had Swinton's support and the tacit agreement of the War Office which resented the increasing powers of the MoM. Tulloch's call for a free-standing directorate under the auspices of the WO was much more appealing.

Next the suggestion was made, tongue in cheek, that the Admiralty might take on production, but Rear Adm Morgan Singer pointed out that the machine was hardly a naval craft. It was decided that an inter-departmental Supply Committee with wide powers should be formed as soon as the Army Council confirmed acceptance of the finished machine. It would be sponsored by the War Office with Stern as President, three WO members, including Swinton, and four from the Admiralty. D'Eyncourt and Tulloch would act as technical consultants. The committee would take its instructions on supply and design direct from the General Staff at the War Office which would provide initial funding for fifty landships. The WO would simultaneously form a detachment of the Machine Gun Corps comprising 75 officers and 750 other ranks. Members of the much enlarged 20 Squadron would have the opportunity to transfer to the Army and join the detachment.

D'Eyncourt was concerned to maintain secrecy by dropping all reference to landships. In a departmental minute of 4 November he had renamed them 'Water Carriers', and the Landships Committee became the 'DNC's Committee'.[24] The machines suffered the acronym 'WCs' until Swinton was asked at the conference to find an alternative. That evening he and Lt Col Dally Jones toyed with words descriptive of the ship's hull. 'Container', 'Reservoir', 'Cistern' were discarded in favour of 'Tank', and this name was written into the report. Perhaps Swinton knew that Foster's already used it, perhaps not. It was a good choice, as blunt and inscrutable as the machine. Kitchener read the report and minuted:

> As soon as a machine can be produced, the first thing the Secretary of State for War considers necessary would be to test its practical utility under field conditions; without such a test we may be wasting material and men uselessly.[25]

A skilled labour shortage hit Foster's shortly before assembly of 'Mother' was due to start. The Wellington Foundry lacked protected status as a war plant and its tradesmen were leaving to work elsewhere on designated production where they would qualify for a War Badge, identifying them as priority workers. Tritton's repeated requests for badges were ignored until Stern went round to the War Badge Department in Abingdon Street and threatened to send in 20 Squadron with an armoured car to take a supply by force. He signed for a sack full.

'Mother' first moved under its own power into the yard on 7 January 1916, fracturing several track shoes. The shoes had too hard a temper, but Wilson took a chance and had them removed for annealing in one of Foster's furnaces. The machine was 5ft longer and slightly wider over the sponsons than the wooden mock-up. Visitors from London that day included Maj Hugh Elles RE, a General Staff Officer (Operations) at GHQ. He was there on the orders of Sir Douglas Haig who had replaced Sir John French in December as C-in-C. After reading Churchill's *Variants* paper on Christmas Day, Haig had instructed Elles to take a briefing from Churchill before inspecting the machine and reporting back to him personally.

The tank returned to the yard on 12 January, climbing heaps of pig iron and scrap with ease. Next day it was driven at a sedate 3mph to Poppleton's Field nearby, crossing ditches and flattening hedges on the way. Wilson, Stern, Hetherington and Symes took turns at the controls, driving across a pond and other obstacles.

Stern and Hetherington motored up from London to Lincoln on the 19th with a load of solid armour-piercing shell. 'Mother' moved that night to a remote corner of Burton Park for live firing next day. D'Eyncourt wanted to know the recoil effect of the 6-pdr on the sponson, hull frame and crew. Hetherington fired the first shot, having bet Wilson £50 that the shock would collapse the hull. There was a misfire and while they were bent over the breech the gun fired spontaneously. Nobody was observing the fall and they feared they might have hit Lincoln cathedral. Two hours of walking and spade work recovered the shell, still in the field. The machine proved stable when further rounds were fired. A 5ft wide trench and a steep bank were crossed without difficulty. It was a deservedly triumphant day.

A full-dress demonstration nearer to London was planned, but the Wembley ground was too public. With Lord Salisbury's permission Stern and d'Eyncourt settled on the home park at Hatfield House. It had taken the Navy eleven months and cost just under £35,000 to put 'Mother' there. The first of His Majesty's landships was ready for inspection.

Eight

PREPARATIONS FOR BATTLE

Embark in the chariots of war and slay the malignants with arms of precision.[1]

Winston Churchill's exhortation to cavalrymen to transfer to the tanks

Operation 'Puddleduck' (only Swinton could have named it so) saw 'Mother' and 'Little Willie' heavily sheeted and railed down to Hatfield, unloading at dead of night on 27/8 January 1916. Departure from Lincoln had been threatened by railway officials concerned that the big tank's tracks projected beyond the sides of the wagon. Wilson reminded them there was a war on.

The machines were driven to Hatfield Park over closed roads. At the test site Swinton and Hetherington had devised a course prepared by 20 Squadron and members of the Herts Volunteer Regiment. It reproduced British and enemy trenches and wire with a no-man's-land between. For added realism sappers had blown a replica shell hole and dammed a stream to create a swamp, leaving Lord Salisbury's private golf course with two additional hazards.

Working parties completed preparations that day, watched by wives and girlfriends from cars on the estate road. The tanks stood shrouded but in full view 200yd away. To dispel curiosity Swinton and another officer walked along the line of cars and, with frequent glances at the tanks, loudly expressed the hope that the 'motor pumps' would be powerful enough to drain the new swamp. An informal trial of 'Mother' on Sunday 29 January was watched by many who had been involved in the project. Foster's had stencilled across its grey hull 'HMLS Centipede'. 'Little Willie' was the reserve machine. Those present included Adm Tudor, Gen Scott-Moncrieff, Brig Gen Louis Jackson and Dr Addison (from the Ministry of Munitions), Col Maurice Hankey (who received his knighthood soon afterwards), Capt Tulloch, and

Col Crompton who was unimpressed. Col Holden (also about to be knighted) and Cdre Lambert, the hostile Fourth Sea Lord, declined invitations. The run went well, Murray Sueter loudly proclaiming that 3,000 machines should be built immediately.

The official trial was held after lunch on Wednesday 2 February. Lord Kitchener paid a surprise visit that morning, watching with Tritton as 'Mother' gave a special performance. The Secretary of State's reaction to the tank that day was recorded variously by those who were there as contemptuous or convinced. Tritton recalled that afterwards he and Kitchener sat on a fallen tree and talked alone for over half an hour. 'K' raised all possible objections to the machine – perhaps, Tritton thought, to draw him out. Kitchener's last words when they parted were: 'It is a pretty mechanical toy, but without serious military value.'[2] Tritton wrote this down immediately afterwards. Kitchener stayed for the afternoon display but left before it ended. Swinton overheard him say the war would never be won by such machines; they would be knocked out by artillery.[3]

Lloyd George was also at Hatfield Park and recorded in his memoirs that he experienced the same reaction from Kitchener. However, he received a letter some fourteen years after the war from Gen Whigham who had accompanied Kitchener to the trials. Whigham wrote that 'K' had been so impressed with what he saw that he told Gen Robertson the tank was far too valuable a weapon for such public display, and left early with Whigham and Robertson to convey that he would waste no more time on it. On their way back to London Robertson told Whigham the reason for their hasty departure and swore him to secrecy. Whigham added that Kitchener subsequently 'had great expectations of them . . . and referred to them more than once in course of conversation. His one fear was that the Germans would get to hear of them before they were ready.'[4] Whigham repeated this account in the national press in 1937. Robertson recorded that even before they left the trial ground Kitchener approved his proposal that 100 tanks should be ordered immediately.[5]

Lloyd George observed that if Whigham was right, it was unfortunate that Kitchener never saw fit to tell him, the Minister of Munitions, at the time. Relations between the two Ministries were strained, however, and the MoM had declared only five weeks earlier that it had no wish to become involved with tank production. Kitchener's disinterest in the landship weapon prior to Hatfield is unquestionable. But if Whigham and Robertson are to be believed, he then underwent a Damascene conversion. There is some significance in his actions that day and the next. Despite the immense demands on his time, Kitchener chose to spend the morning of the trials in a private appraisal of the machine and close questioning of its co-designer. Instead of hurrying back to Whitehall, he remained for much of the official demonstration before making a somewhat theatrical exit with the CIGS and his deputy. He told the War Committee next day that he had been 'impressed by the trials'.[6]

With an eye to funding for production, Hankey and Stern shrewdly cultivated Reginald McKenna, the Chancellor, giving him a good lunch at the United Services Club before driving him to Hatfield in Stern's Rolls. Arthur Balfour's sixty-seven years did not stop the First Lord of the Admiralty from going round the course in 'Mother', though he was persuaded to disembark before the last and widest trench. The demonstration was a complete success despite an overheating engine.

The representatives from GHQ were led by Maj Gen R.H.K. Butler, Haig's Deputy CGS, who asked Stern when he could have some tanks and what alterations were possible. The two questions became a military mantra, repeated with increasing emphasis for the rest of the war. Stern told him that save for changes to loophole positions, no modifications were possible if deliveries were wanted that year. McKenna promised all necessary finance if the Army adopted the machines. Swinton accompanied the King to a private trial on 8 February, after which His Majesty had a ride and was much impressed.

The French Military Attaché and members of the French General Staff, to whom invitations had been sent, were notable absentees from the trials. 'Mother' remained at Hatfield a further two weeks on their account before being removed, still unseen by them. This is curious because within a day or two of the tank's departure, French Army representatives attended the first demonstration of their own armed and armoured tracklayers.

Col Baptiste Estienne commanding the 6th Divisional Artillery was Swinton's Gallic counterpart. Since seeing Holt crawlers hauling British guns, Estienne had been trying at intervals for the past year to persuade the C-in-C of the French Armies to develop fighting tracklayers. He finally secured an interview on 12 December 1915 with the Sub-Chief of Staff at GQG (French General Headquarters). Unknown to Estienne, the armaments firm of Schneider et Cie of Le Creusot had demonstrated a fully tracked 'Baby' Holt and the bigger semi-track version to the President and senior officers in June that year. Schneider's was instructed to arm and armour the Baby for use primarily to cut and crush wire, its track length being inadequate for trench crossing. Tactically it could prepare clearways for a rush of advancing infantry. In December, therefore, Estienne found himself pushing an open door. He was sent to Schneider's where he gave the designer, M. Eugène Brillié, the benefit of his experience of trench warfare. Design changes followed and two pre-production machines were first demonstrated on 21 February 1916. Four hundred machines – *tracteurs Estiennes* – on extended tracks were ordered on the 25th for delivery within ten months. They were armed with a short 75mm gun and two machine guns and could cross trenches up to 5ft 10in wide. It is interesting to contrast this confident adaptation of the Holt with the lamentable reaction of Scott-Moncrieff's committee to the Holt machine twelve months earlier.

Back in London, reaction to the Hatfield trials was positive but not unqualified. The attack potential of the machine was accepted, as was its ability to flatten wire. Doubts centred on its vulnerability to gunfire, especially when the element of surprise was lost after its first use; the lack of concealment; its low speed and liability to draw fire on troops in its vicinity; and the difficulties of night operations with tanks. However, the Army Council wrote to the Admiralty on 10 February to ask that its very warm thanks and appreciation be conveyed to d'Eyncourt and his committee for their work in evolving the machine, and to Mr Tritton and Lt Wilson for their work in design and construction. 20 Squadron was praised for its contribution.

The most conspicuous absentee at Hatfield was the tank's sponsor Winston Churchill, who was still in France and commanding the 6th Royal Scots Fusiliers. D'Eyncourt sent him the news:

Dear Colonel Churchill,

It is with great pleasure that I am now able to report to you that the War Office have at last ordered 100 landships to the pattern which underwent most successful trials recently. Sir D. Haig sent some of his staff from the front.

Lord Kitchener and Robertson also came, and members of the Admiralty Board. . . . The official tests of trenches etc. were nothing to it. . . . Wire entanglements it goes through like a rhinoceros through a field of corn. . . . I strongly urge ordering immediately a good many to the pattern which we know all about. As you are aware, it has taken much time and trouble to get the thing perfect, and a practical machine simple to make; we tried various types and did much experimental work. I am sorry it has taken so long, but pioneer work always takes time and no avoidable delay has taken place, though I begged them to order ten for training purposes two months ago. I have also had some difficulty in steering the scheme past the rocks of opposition and the more insidious shoals of apathy which are frequented by red herrings, which cross the main line of progress at frequent intervals. The great thing now is to keep the whole matter secret and produce the machines altogether as a complete surprise.[7]

The letter was reproduced in Col J.F.C. Fuller's *Tanks in the Great War*. Tritton took great exception to it, writing in his own copy of the book 'Surely the most despicable letter ever written!! EHTD merely asked Tritton and Wilson to "do something". He did not give five hours consideration to the whole job.'[8]

                              *   *   *

Mindful of Foster's limited capacity, Stern had already arranged production with the Metropolitan Company. He and Wilson had satisfied Metro's Chairman Dudley Docker and Technical Director Maj John Greg that tanks were a manufacturing proposition.

Stern habitually ignored official procedures when negotiating government business. After Oxford he had cut his trading teeth in New York's financial centres before returning home in 1901 on the death of his father to become a successful partner in Stern Brothers, the family bank. Now, he quickly established a rapport with the tank builders who respected his blunt approach and willingness to take decisions with minimal reference back. Stern agreed the impossibility of costing the work until a machine was completed. They fixed a provisional price per tank of £5,000, to be adjusted on delivery of the first machine. Stern claimed this saved the country £5.5m by the end of the war. All was now ready for construction to start. They awaited Haig's response.

Kitchener invited Stern to take the chair of the Tank Supply Committee, as agreed at the December conference. Lloyd George performed a smart U-turn and approached him with a similar invitation from the Ministry, saying it was no longer a matter for the War Office. Grasping this splendid bargaining opportunity, the Lieutenant banker told the Minister that he was willing to undertake the volume production of tanks in six months' time providing he was given special powers. Lloyd George assented and made his peace with Kitchener. Bertie Stern's semi-autonomous committee would be joined by d'Eyncourt, Wilson, Symes and Bussell from the old Admiralty team, Swinton and Lt Col Wheeler RA for the War Office, and Tom Tulloch and Lt Col Byrne for the MoM. They were later joined by a senior Staff Officer from the WO, and Frederick Skeens, a senior draughtsman and gunnery specialist from the DNC's department who had earlier worked with Crompton on turrets.

Tommy Hetherington had been nominated for the committee at the December conference, but never joined. He had influenced the course of events twice in the tank's long gestation. D'Eyncourt and Stern may have felt he had little more to offer following its birth, but Churchill ensured that he received official recognition when in 1918 Hetherington was appointed CBE 'for services in connection with the origination of the tanks'. After handing over 20 Squadron to McGrath in April he joined the RNAS Board of Survey for airships, later becoming Chief of the RNAS Survey Department.

* * *

Haig's observers at the Hatfield trials reported back at GHQ, and on 9 February the C-in-C informed the WO that thirty or forty tanks should be ordered at once, as he understood this number could be produced without interfering with other war material. He wanted to know what additional numbers could be delivered by mid-July. To aid security Haig asked that all concerned should receive official notification that the invention had been discarded, leaving only a small core 'in the know'. When he approved the draft he added a final note in his own hand:

Secrecy is of the highest importance in order to get full advantage from the use of these machines [Haig's emphasis].[9]

The trifling quantity requested by Haig contrasts starkly with the 400 demanded by the French two weeks later. Swinton argued for an increase to at least 100. He reminded the Director of Staff Duties of the importance of fielding a large number of machines on the first occasion that the weapon was deployed, the element of surprise being lost thereafter. 'I would point out that it is eight days since members of the Army Council and representative officers from [GHQ] witnessed the trial of the machine, and that this period translated into output . . . corresponds to an out-turn of something like 20 machines, and every week which elapses before the order is placed will result in a similar delay.'[10] The War Office ordered 100 machines on 12 February.

Minutes after receiving the order that Saturday morning Stern and d'Eyncourt burst into Lloyd George's room with a ready-prepared authority constituting the Tank Supply Committee. They caught him on the point of departure for the country. Lloyd George recalled: 'They presented a pistol at my head in the shape of a "charter" . . . for immediate signature by me.'[11] It would give Stern and his organisation wide powers and freedom of action. The committee would be attached to the MoM as an executive body working directly under the Minister. It was free to communicate with any government department, manage its own finances and place orders direct with contractors. The committee's decision would be final in all matters of manufacture and inspection, and the Ministry was to grant all facilities for supply of labour and materials. All payments were to be made on the sole authority of certificates issued by the committee, without further question. It was to arrange immediate construction of 100 tanks and £50,000 was to be allocated for experimental work.

Lloyd George initialled the paper. He later discovered that Swinton was waiting outside on the road ready to puncture his tyres if he attempted to leave before signing the charter. That afternoon orders were phoned and telegraphed to Metro for 75 tanks, Foster's for 25, and Daimler's for 120 of its 105hp engines. Walter Wilson would supervise tank construction in Lincoln and Birmingham. Armour plate would be rolled by Beardmore's in Glasgow and Cammell Laird and Vickers Ltd in Sheffield. Kenneth Symes was to supervise armour production and research, and set up an inspectorate for all parts and assemblies, leaving engine inspection to the Admiralty. It was an historic day – and the fulfilment of Churchill's hopes at his bedside meeting almost exactly one year before.

Two days later the War Office approved the formation of a Tank Detachment. Swinton was appointed to command the unit – one of the Army Council's more inspired decisions. It was impressed on him, however, that this was a home appointment. Having trained his force, he would pass it on to local commanders on its arrival in France. The policy was flawed, and overlooked an inevitable lack of understanding by field commanders of the strengths and limitations of a complex new arm. Their incomprehension extended to operational planning. Swinton urged Scott-Moncrieff to arrange for a senior engineer officer to inspect the entire front and identify sectors where ground conditions were best suited to tank operations, but such vital staff work was neglected for a further nineteen months with severe consequences. Without Swinton's foresight and attention to detail the tank's evolutionary progress would most certainly have faltered.

The new arm was attached to the Motor Machine Gun Service (MMGS) of the Machine Gun Corps. It would train at their Bisley depot near London until it got its own ground. Personnel were to be drawn from the MMGS which had recently been equipped with motorcycle combinations mounting a machine gun. These batteries were intended to increase the firepower and mobility of the divisions in France, but the static conditions had forced a reduction in numbers and provided a pool of men of the right calibre for tanks. Although they could be told nothing of the new weapon they were to be given, their commanding officer Lt Col R.W. Bradley and some 700 other ranks transferred *en bloc*. Members of 20 Squadron were invited by Swinton to transfer too, but the Army was offering artillerymen's pay scales which were inferior to their Navy rates, and McGrath's men stood fast. Stern and most of his officers did transfer to the Army, which for the rest of the war refused to award them rank commensurate with their responsibilities. This compromised their dealings with the military elsewhere, especially in France where their lack of rank hampered communication. Stern and Wilson became temporary majors, and Kenneth Symes a temporary captain.

Swinton began work at Siberia camp, Bisley, on 16 February. The new unit initially adopted a company structure and fifteen were authorised, each comprising two sections of six tanks. On completion of basic training Swinton planned to form them into three battalions of five companies each, an organisation not matched elsewhere in the Army. GHQ objected in mid-May, saying they wanted a more elastic format, the company to be the tactical unit, each with twenty-five tanks. This meant altering the entire organisation on which the detachment had been working at Bisley. Swinton re-formed to six companies, A–F, each of four sections of six tanks, the twenty-fifth being a company spare and crew. A section would be divided into three subsections of two tanks each. A mobile workshop would travel with each company.

For security reasons Swinton dealt directly with Gen Wilkinson Bird, Director of Staff Duties at the War Office. The same considerations took the detachment through several name changes. It became the Armoured Car Section of the Motor Machine Gun Service (mid-March); Motor Machine Gun Corps 'S' Detachment (29 March); Heavy Section, Machine Gun Corps

(1 May). Haig was refused permission in October to change it to the Tank Corps, accepting instead Heavy Branch, Machine Gun Corps (16 November). He finally got his way on 27 July 1917. The Tank Corps was granted the prefix 'Royal' on 18 October 1923. To avoid confusion we will stay with 'Heavy Section' for the time being. This title was suggested on 20 April 1916 by Lt Col P.E. Lewis of the Adjutant-General's office.

Stern used bluff and his charter to acquire two fifth-floor rooms in 'Armaments Building' (the Hotel Metropole), headquarters of the Ministry. His small team had moved in on 15 February when he was appointed Director, Tank Supply Department MoM. Swinton needed a base for his almost daily contacts around Whitehall. He got no help from the Army and so became a squatter with his orderly-room sergeant in one of Stern's pair, sharing a TSD typist. This was by no means the only example of military indifference towards its new arm.

*   *   *

Pending arrival of the first machines, an intensive training programme was started in gunnery and two types of machine gun. The Naval Gunnery School on Whale Island answered Swinton's call for help by laying on a series of introductory firing courses over water. Land firing was more of a problem. When he was refused use of the ranges at Shoeburyness Swinton resorted to the Bisley small-arms facilities adjoining his camp. On the first day's shoot his men had got off ninety-seven rounds before the range officer ordered them off after recording six ricochets into the Chobham Hills. Swinton finally secured the RA ranges at Lark Hill on Salisbury Plain. His treatise *Notes on the Employment of Tanks* was completed in February and set out in masterly detail the characteristics and proposed tactics of the weapon. It was an essential reference for staffs and field commanders and formed the basis of all training, but some of its key points were ignored in France until the Cambrai battle in November 1917.

It was agreed that a number of tanks should be permanently fitted with twin Vickers machine guns in each sponson in place of the 6-pdr Hotchkiss QF gun. Swinton designated these all-MG machines 'female', and the 6-pdr tanks 'male'. Fifty more tanks were ordered on 21 April at his urging, the overall total of 150 Mk I to comprise equal numbers of male and female types. Metro got most of the new batch, with Foster's adding five to their twenty-five, and seven going to near neighbours Robey & Co. of Canwick Road, Lincoln.

Robey's got off to a promising start, bolting together a set of hull side-armour plates to form a drilling jig. However, Wilson soon concluded the firm was frightened of the work, reporting in May that staff appeared uncertain how to proceed with assembly of the first hull. The work was transferred to Foster's in June, though Robey's continued to make track and other components.

Maj Hugh Knothe of the Army Service Corps joined the Heavy Section in April as its mechanical transport and engineering specialist. He had commanded a fleet of Holt caterpillar tractors for an artillery brigade in France, and now went straight to Lincoln with orders to crawl all over 'Mother' until he knew every rivet. He then produced detailed equipment inventories for three mobile workshops. Mistrusting his expert assessment, the War Office referred it to GHQ. An approval came back with the suggestion that two 4.5in lathes might be substituted for one 9in lathe – as asinine as asking for two 8in shirt collars instead of one 16in. Fortunately the Heavy Section relied more on the Tank Supply Committee than the War Office for its equipment needs.

Bertie Stern claimed that any telephoned request to his people was met before the caller rang off. Swinton thought he was hardly exaggerating. He asked for two full-size dummy tanks as training aids, specifying that one side was to be an exact replica in boilerplate. The interiors were to include shell racks, wooden guns with correct breech action, and all the painful protrusions. Swinton wanted the mock-ups to be given a slow pitching motion by a man turning a handle outside, which would also actuate a series of small hammers beating on the boilerplate to simulate striking bullets. By the time one dummy had been built the real thing had arrived. It later became routine for new types to be preceded by a few made up in boilerplate for training use. This was considered for Mk I by riveting up scrap hull templates, but delivery of the first production machines was imminent.

The Heavy Section needed an isolated secure tank training ground. Swinton sent a major with mapping experience to scour the country, finally homing in on Norfolk and Lord Iveagh's shooting estate at Elveden near Thetford. Fortunately the WO Lands Branch supervisor was a professional – and still civilian – surveyor with a bracing approach to the requisitioning process. He shook Swinton with the promise that he would be free to occupy the estate within a week, several necessary evictions notwithstanding. Lord Iveagh overcame his initial shock and became a firm supporter of the detachment.

At the end of April Home Defence Force Pioneers moved in to dig and wire a very realistic battlefield over 1.5 miles wide in expectation of the first tank arrivals in mid-June. All approach roads were closed and the 11-mile perimeter was ringed with guards from the Home Defence Corps armed with ball cartridge. Signs warned the curious to keep away from the 'Elveden Explosives Area'. The work went on inside a separately guarded inner perimeter. Explosives were used to blow craters in the training area, fuelling local suspicions that a tunnel was about to be driven under the Channel to surface in Germany. In less than ten days the Great Eastern Railway Company built a spur at Culford Lodge (Lodge Farm) directly into the secure area. It was taken off the single-track line between Thetford and Bury St Edmunds, and served a 700ft siding with an end ramp for tank loading. It was operational early in July.[12]

*   *   *

Swinton gave much thought to communications. The RE Experimental Wireless Establishment produced a compact set of about 200-metre wavelength and a range of 3 miles for tank use. Metro had been ordered to build seventy-five pitched-roof covers of heavy wire netting for fitting on top of the tanks to deflect bombs and it was hoped these could double as a wireless aerial, though the signal proved to be inaudible inside a moving tank. Nevertheless, by the end of July 1916 six WT sets and operators had arrived. GHQ decreed at the last minute that no wireless was to be installed for fear of radio interference, and the sets were withdrawn.

A telephone link was fitted in each Section Commander's tank with 1,000yd of cable on a rear-mounted drum. Tritton produced an ineffectual attachment to plough the cable in, but following repeated line breakages the system was abandoned. A signals procedure from tanks to infantry and aircraft was instead devised using flags displayed from the roof hatch, or lamps at night. Some tanks carried pigeons for transmitting messages back to command posts. The fitting of an armoured 'mailbox' on the tail of each machine was considered for communication with accompanying infantry. Another infantry aid was to be a bullet-proof ammunition locker bolted to the rear of the tank to carry 2,000 rounds of small-arms ammunition in magazines in canvas buckets.

Swinton commissioned 10ft captive balloons to be flown at 1,000ft behind the lines to help tank commanders find their bearings when withdrawing from action. Coloured balloons could be hoisted up the mooring cable for signalling purposes. A scaled-down basket with dummy artillery spotter was slung beneath each balloon to further provoke the enemy but the equipment was withdrawn on instructions from GHQ which feared it would draw fire. Murray Sueter's balloon unit had given technical advice and his Anti-Aircraft Mobile Brigade later used the balloons for gunnery practice.

As an alternative to wire roof covers, Kenneth Symes produced cladding in 4mm and 6mm soft plate as a second skin. Twenty-five sets were ordered and all but two were shipped to France, but never fitted.

* * *

Swinton met Sir Douglas Haig in London on 14 April. The C-in-C was preoccupied with the coming Somme offensive. He noted in his diary that Swinton had told him 150 tanks would be provided by 31 July, to which he replied that that was too late, 50 were urgently required for 1 June. Swinton's postwar account of the meeting differs. He says he had to tell the C-in-C that there was 'just a possibility that some might be shipped by the 1st August, and that if sufficient were delivered during July, the crews for seventy-five might be trained by August'.[13] Swinton's response was dangerously optimistic. GHQ had ordered the first machines just eight weeks before. (The first production tank reached Elveden on 18 June. The fiftieth arrived a month later, but almost all lacked sponsors.)

Even at that early date Haig was preparing to waste his first and only opportunity for total surprise with the new weapon by throwing a mere handful into its battlefield launch. Swinton was appalled, reporting the conversation to Hankey who in turn appealed to Willie Robertson, the CIGS:

My Dear General,

I very rarely offer a suggestion on purely military questions, partly because I don't consider it to be my job, partly because I know that professionals don't want to waste their time with the views of amateurs. . . . I only depart from my rule in this case because my suggestion concerns matters with which I have lately been very closely connected.

Briefly, my suggestion is that Sir Douglas Haig should be asked to do all in his power to avoid being committed to anything in the nature of a decisive infantry attack until the 'caterpillar' machine gun destroyers are ready . . . and to put all possible pressure on [Marshall Joffre, French C-in-C] to do likewise. The reasons are as follows. If my information on the subject is correct, a very large proportion of the casualties in the great attacks are inflicted by machine guns. The 'caterpillars' have been designed for the express purpose of dealing with these. A very large sum of money has been spent on them and a great number have been ordered. . . . If, only a few weeks before they were ready, we had lost a very large number of infantry (such a figure for example as Sir Douglas Haig mentioned last Saturday) in attacks unproductive of material results, it would be most unfortunate. It might even happen that in the few weeks immediately preceding the arrival of the 'caterpillars' our Army might have become so exhausted that no attack could be carried out for some weeks or months, by which time all prospect of their employment as a surprise would have been lost.

In short, I am convinced that it is of overwhelming importance to the morale of the Army and the nation, to the higher command of the Army, and to the cause of the allies as a whole that our attack should be a success, and I suggest that this new weapon, containing we hope the element of surprise, may just turn the scale. . . .

I had somehow got into my head that something of this kind was intended, but Sir Douglas Haig's estimate on Saturday of the losses he anticipated during June and July has (perhaps erroneously) led me to fear that his big effort will immediately precede the completion of the 'caterpillars'. . . . I do venture to ask that you will give this letter your consideration.[14]

Robertson forwarded the letter to Haig. Hankey foresaw, and Haig had just confirmed the expectation of very severe losses of men in the coming offensive. Hankey noted in his diary two weeks later that 'the Army want a regular orgy of slaughter this summer'.[15]

Fears that the first tanks would be thrown piecemeal into the battle were not new. Swinton's February paper had emphasised that 'these machines should not be used in driblets' but held back until all were available for a great combined operation with the infantry.

After consulting Stern, Swinton had to report on 26 April that no tanks or crews would be ready by 1 June. They expected to have a few incomplete training machines by 1 July with full completion of all 150 by 1 August. 'This', Swinton said, 'is the cold truth.' In mid-June the forecast was put back to 50 fully assembled tanks by 1 August and the remainder by early September. In fact, all 150 were only completed at the end of October.

Lloyd George received confirmation of French tank production from M. Paul Painleve, his opposite number in Paris. Painleve wrote on 2 May that the machines were based on American 'caterpillar' tractors, capable of crossing trenches 2 metres wide. They were to be armed with machine guns or mortars throwing a heavy HE charge up to 800 metres. Col Estienne visited Elveden in June, eager to assess the British design and compare notes with Swinton and his officers. He was honoured with a tree-felling demonstration, one of Swinton's precious machines being risked for the occasion to push it over. Estienne returned home to press for Anglo-French collaboration in the mass production of tanks for 1917, the French to specialise in fast light machines to complement the slower British heavies. His strongest plea was for the BEF to avoid premature disclosure of the weapon to the enemy before the French tanks were ready, when the two allies could simultaneously launch a powerful surprise attack and really damage the German Army.

Estienne's vision was not realised. Haig and the General Staff viewed their untried tanks as infantry support weapons for strictly local engagements. Any breakthrough by their heavy tanks would be exploited by massed cavalry, not by speedy little French *chars d'assault*. Hugh Knothe at Elveden was reminded of this in his attempts to include a motorised supply column in the Heavy Section's own war establishment. He pointed out to GHQ that ammunition and fuel supply for tanks coming out of action was critically dependent on motor transport and on drivers experienced in working with the section. They would have to navigate alone, reach dumps and rendezvous much closer to the fighting than normal, and so be specially trained in map reading, the use of unditching equipment and so on. Lt Gen Burnett-Stuart of the General Staff refused. 'These engines [i.e. tanks] will be an adjunct to an offensive in trench warfare and are not likely in an action to get further away from their starting point than a distance of three miles, supposing them to start from a point one mile behind our front trenches.'[16] He added that tank companies would have to rely for resupply on borrowed transport from the infantry formations to which they were attached. They would depend on the willingness of hard-pressed infantry officers to release wagons and drivers for their fuel, ammunition and rations.

Seven hundred sentries in three cordons surrounded the tank park at Elveden. Those in the outer ring had no idea what they were guarding. 'Mother', with sponsons but minus guns, arrived from Lincoln on 4 June. Trainees saw the awesome beast at last. The first production machine reached

Elveden on the 18th; Swinton had twenty by 10 July, with the first sponsons arriving a week later. Armstrong, Whitworth built the male sponsons and gun mountings, and Metropolitan the female. David Fletcher of the Tank Museum at Bovington has noted that whereas on 'Mother' the rear doors in the sponsons were hinged on their inboard side to open flat against the hull, this was reversed on production machines where the hinges were positioned outboard to enable the opened door to part-screen crew members exiting under fire.

To mislead the curious, the battleship-grey hull of every tank from Lincoln carried an inscription in Russian in 12in Cyrillic lettering – 'With care to Petrograd'. On arrival Knothe's men obliterated this and stencilled a WD number to either side at the rear in yellow 6in letters. If word of the machine's purpose should reach the enemy, at least the numbering sequence would suggest a gathering armada – male serials began at 701 and females at 501.[17]

Gen Kiggell at GHQ had written to the War Office nominating Royal Academician Solomon J. Solomon, now a lieutenant-colonel with the Royal Engineers, to undertake 'the painting and disguising of tanks. It seems that if a loose mat or roof covering . . . will meet the purpose, the mats themselves can be constructed and painted differently on both sides so as to materially conceal them from the air.'[18] This was not how Solomon saw his brief. He arrived at Elveden at the end of May. Armed with several tons of paint, he set up a studio in a barn and turned out machines in bilious pink, enhanced with generous splotches of green, brown and grey-blue. The combination was more suited to sunset in Sherwood Forest than the battlefields of France, and the scheme was dropped when winter mud did the job without further creative effort. For the rest of the war British tanks were normally painted a uniform mud brown, though this did not extend to roofs which remained untreated. Solomon, the genial society artist, became a camouflage expert in other fields.

With the arrival of the machines Maj Knothe's team moved camp nearer to the Culford Lodge siding. It became a specialist unit, the 711 MT Company, ASC, quickly growing to ten officers and some 300 men. They operated from temporary workshops in the open and in all weathers, making good factory defects, repairing breakdowns, unloading tank trains and providing drivers and driver training in unremitting labour, often around the clock. Detraining was carried out at night because the siding was in view of the main line. It was dangerous work; the tanks drove off with 2in to spare on each track. The whole area became a quagmire. Most of the early drivers came from the ASC Tractor Depot at Avonmouth. The first batch were ex-long-distance lorry men who on seeing the tanks decided that they knew almost nothing of internal combustion engines and were returned by Knothe as incompetent. Those who followed settled in well, though leave was almost unobtainable and rations were short for many weeks.

There were two establishments at Elveden – the Training Centre and 'The Area'. The former covered gunnery and all training without tanks. The Area was a high-security zone for driver and other hands-on training. The reader can join a group of driver trainees for the next few paragraphs, or skip ahead.

◆　◆

A tank is jacked up on baulks of timber to allow the tracks to run free before the men are introduced to its mysteries in crew-size groups of eight. As the sponsons are missing they can see, through the big cutaways on either side of the hull, the mass of the Daimler engine centred amidships. Ammunition racks almost fill the rest of the white painted interior, official capacity being 160 rounds of 6-pdr shell plus 1,500 of small-arms ammunition in special tin boxes for male tanks, and 7,800 of SAA for females. (Crews unofficially stockpiled more on the narrow aisles.) Other stowage is provided for such battle luggage as a spare machine gun, MG barrels, tools in underfloor lockers, towing cable, water, grease guns, drums of track and engine oil and grease, four Pyrene fire extinguishers, signals flags and rockets, protective crew kit, first-aid kit, two days' rations and much else.

It is explained that four men are needed to drive the beast, plus a gunner and loader on each 6-pdr in the sponsons, or machine-gunners as applicable. An automatic rifle with pistol grip is mounted between the driver up front on the right, and the commander beside him whose slightly higher seat gives him better control of the weapon. The driver takes care of ignition, throttle, footbrake and clutch controls and a primary gearbox providing two forward speeds and reverse. He cannot steer ('swing' in the jargon) the tank unaided. The commander operates two steering brake levers controlling the respective tracks. Either man can reach the differential lock behind him. Immediately behind the engine a small platform covers the gearbox. Most of the space further aft is filled with the differential and its cross shafts, from each of which a secondary two-speed gearbox delivers the final drive to the track-driving sprocket on that side. To avoid two sets of complicated gearchange linkage back to the driver, the left- and right-hand secondary boxes are each manned by a gearsman who awaits the driver's signal. These auxiliary gears are essential because the primary box cannot withstand the loads on its own.

The combination of primary and secondary gears gives four forward speeds. Unfortunately, reverse is a higher ratio than the lowest forward gear – the crew can drive into trouble and find they cannot back off. A radiator fills the rear bulkhead. The engine is flanked by foot-wide gangways, the roof only some 5ft clear above. Two gunners will have to crouch and fight in each shallow sponson while avoiding a lurch on to the hot engine behind.

The instructor mysteriously 'trips his mag' and tickles the carburettor before putting four trainees aboard to turn a large cranked starting handle behind the engine. They heave at the handle to an accompanying sucking and blowing from the pistons and valve gear and the click click click of the magneto impulse starter before, with luck, the first muffled thud precedes a roar as the six cylinders fire up. With instructors at crew positions a shouted demonstration follows in a thickening haze of exhaust fumes, accompanied by some exaggerated coughing among the novices. Having gone through his gears the driver signals to the two gearsmen behind – even shouting is now useless – by hitting the hull with a heavy spanner and then holding up one or two fingers to indicate the required secondary gear. While he carefully manipulates the clutch the gearsmen ease the large pinions into mesh. A lesson on manoeuvring techniques follows.

There were four steering options, all with drawbacks. The first employed the steering tail alone, with the tank's differential unlocked. The simple frame of the 1.5-ton tail was mounted between the tracks at the rear, trailing two 4ft 6in iron wheels. They were steered by the driver via cables to a hand wheel in his cab. The pivoting tail could be raised hydraulically if the tank was to steer on its tracks alone. When lowered, eight powerful coil springs from the tank exerted lift to the fore end of the pivoting frame, imposing an opposite downward force on the flanged wheels at its rear to maintain grip over rough terrain. In the event the tail was almost useless on soft ground and was largely ignored as a steering aid. Its secondary function was as a counterbalance when crossing trenches, keeping the nose up for another foot or so of travel to the far side. Similarly, on breasting a sharp ridge the tank's extended tail allowed the machine to rock forward rather than crash-dive.

The remaining steering options required the tail to be lifted clear of the ground. The hydraulics proved unreliable and could take from 5 to 20 minutes to achieve this, so it was just as well that crews customarily 'kept our tails up'. The commander's track brakes served for slight directional changes, the differential remaining unlocked as the tank swung in the direction of the braked track. Steering on the brakes avoided the hazards of stops for complex gear changes, but the smell of overheating Ferodo linings gave warning that they soon burned out.

For bigger 'swings' the tank had first to be halted, adding to the dangers under fire. The driver would lock the differential and instruct the secondary gearsman on the inside of the required turn to engage neutral (signal – loud spanner blow on the hull and clenched fist). He then selected first in his primary box and signalled the other gearsman to do likewise (one finger). As the driven track made the turn, the commander hand-braked the other. A final option involved stopping and turning 28 tons of tank through the secondary gearboxes alone, after selecting differing ratios in each. The manoeuvre might succeed on a concrete hardstanding but otherwise risked wrecking the gear shafts. Halts for steering changes were frequent when weaving around shell holes and took up to 10 minutes a time, wearing the nerves under fire. 'Overswings' were common, necessitating a repeat operation to correct the error and bring the tank back to the required degree of turn.

◆ ◆

Instruction was one thing, but custom and practice came only with experience in the field. If the ground was wet, crews exposed to shellfire were careful not to sleep under their machines for protection; men had been crushed overnight as tanks settled down in the soft earth. Most engines ran better once they had boiled, but were difficult to restart when hot. Fuel quality was atrocious – drivers avoided throttling down too much as the engine tended to fire in the exhaust at low revs, sending sheets of flame from every joint which periodically started roof fires of reserve petrol kept in tins, tarpaulin covers, camouflage nets and crew kit stowed aloft. Roofs were cleared before going into action. Later, the tanks were fuelled with aviation spirit for fighting, while the often dirty and very low 45 octane MT spirit was retained for normal use. A ledge part-way up the Daimler engine's casing was ideal for frying bacon, bully beef and bread. Its loss when Ricardo power plants were introduced for the Mk V was keenly felt. Cold starts could be nightmarish. Some drivers resorted to injecting hot petrol direct into the cylinders. An old Lewis gun magazine and an empty Fray Bentos bully beef tin or other suitable receptacle were both filled with petrol and ignited. As the flames died in the magazine, the driver placed his boot over the tin to extinguish its contents and with a pair of pliers as handle it was hurried across for injection with a syringe. The practice never reached the instruction manual.

Manhandling and marrying newly delivered sponsons to battered tanks was an unexpected problem. The machines at Elveden had been pressed into immediate service for driver training, but lacking sponsons many of the hulls had flexed and distorted around the large apertures. When the sponsons arrived in July it was found that a number of the twenty-six securing bolt holes had gone out of alignment on many tanks. The preferred solution was to sledgehammer a drift into whatever aperture remained, the alternative of drilling 8mm of nickel steel armour having even less appeal. Knothe's fitters never forgot the experience.

The width of the tanks had to be reduced for rail movement to avoid exceeding the railway loading gauge. This meant removal and separate stowage of the 35cwt sponsons and their armament, a wretched and dangerous task. Metropolitan supplied a heavy trolley for each pair. The procedure for removal was first to run the tank up on to three rail sleepers beneath each track. The trolley was then manhandled into position with its floor beneath the sponson. A pair of girders were bolted between two vertical 'A' frames which in turn were secured back to the roof of the tank. When unsecured, the sponson was suspended from the girders and lowered to the trolley. When both sponsons were aboard, twenty men on drag ropes hauled the trolley up the train's loading ramp and along the line of wagons. On detraining, the two teams of ten had to race down the usually greasy ramp to avoid being run down by the laden trolley careering after them.

With the arrival of the sponsons at Elveden, gunnery training from moving tanks began. The buildings of North Stow Farm in the centre of the training area were taken over as a stop butt for live firing. It had barely started when the War Office ordered cessation because many shells had ricocheted up towards the north boundary with risk of injury to the public. The embargo was lifted when Swinton pointed out that he would be sending a new weapon and crews to war having never fired a shot on the move.

The training tanks took a pounding which revealed their weak points. When they 'bounced' heavily, the structure flexed so much that the secondary gears could disengage. Belly plates were too thin and could be pressed inwards to foul the flywheel and seize the engine, or even distort the engine bearers if the tank straddled a tree stump or grounded ('bellied') over a firm ridge. Tracks constantly broke from sheared links. Pinions and track

Col E.D. Swinton.

Maj Tom Tulloch.

William Rigby.

Sir William Tritton.

David Roberts.

Rear Adm R.H.S. Bacon.

Sir Eustace Tennyson d'Eyncourt.

Cdre Murray Sueter.

Lt Walter Wilson *(left)* and Maj
Tommy Hetherington.

Wg Cdr Frederick Boothby.

Wg Cdr Charles Samson *(right)* and
Lt Bill Samson.

Col Bertie Stern.

Howitzer tractor trials, Lincoln, December 1914. This is the bridge that caused Adm Bacon to suggest a fighting self-bridging version.

Tritton's Automatic Portable Bridge, April 1915. The modified howitzer tractor is under test in Foster's yard in Lincoln. Maj Tommy Hetherington is at the right-hand bridging control wheel.

Admiralty pattern Rolls-Royce armoured car, France, 1914. Note the exposed fighting platform and driver's hood.

Cdr Samson's 3-pdr QF naval gun on a 'B' Type London bus chassis, France, 1914.

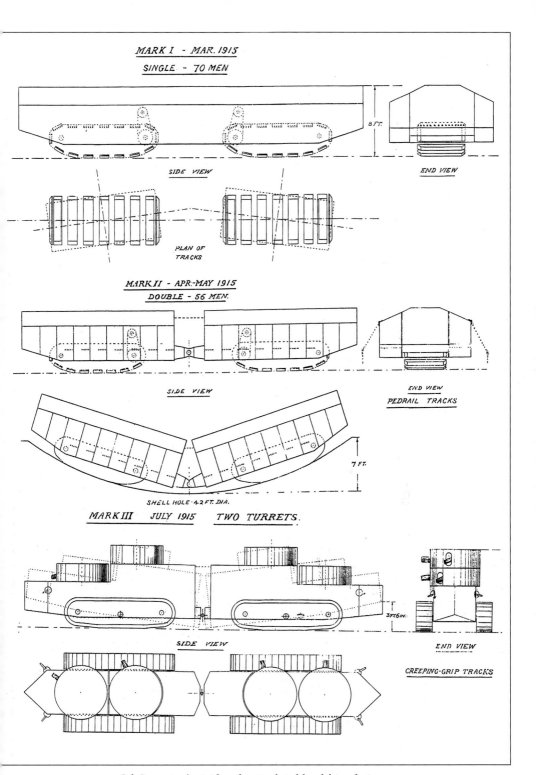

Col Crompton's rigid and articulated landships designs.

Bullock tractor with experimental 'elephant feet', August 1915. The legs were an unsuccessful attempt to aid trench crossing.

Experimental twin-bogie Pedrail tracks, 1916, built from parts salvaged from Col Crompton's landship. His Mk I chassis and running gear would have looked like this, although 7ft longer and with upturned ends.

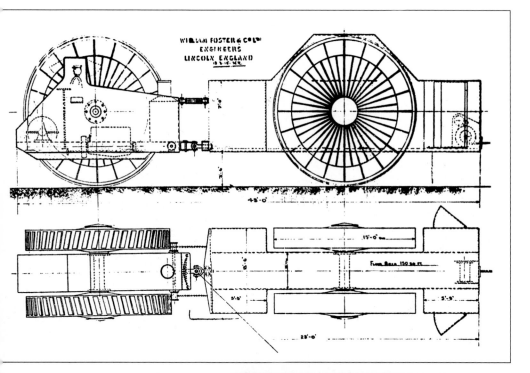

Tritton's Trench Tractor, drawn 3 March 1915. The 8ft 6in wide articulated landship is on 15ft wheels. Its instability is very evident. Note the double coupling to maintain rigidity; and the driver's head.

Mock-up of Tritton's Trench Tractor, Lincoln, May 1915. Lt Wilson is on top, Tritton on the driver's turret. The wheel profile indicates its scale.

Trials at Lincoln, 19 September 1915, of the No. 1 Lincoln machine on the extended American tracks which failed. The hull is shrouded to maintain secrecy.

'Little Willie' on Tritton's successful tracks at Burton Park, Lincoln, 8 December 1915.

Holt tractor on the Guillemont–Martinpuich road (nearly), October 1916. By the Armistice the War Office had bought 1,651 of these sturdy US-built Holts for gun haulage.

drive sprockets failed to mesh fully, causing severe wear of pinion teeth and numerous failures. The heavy spring-loaded tail suffered endless problems with Hornsby's hydraulics, a weak iron frame and poor general design. The machines devoured fuel and lubricants, getting through 2 gallons of petrol and half a gallon of heavy track oil per mile. A day's training consumed 4 gallons of engine oil, half a gallon of gear oil and 20lb of grease per tank. But crude as the vehicles undoubtedly were, they held the promise of a battlefield revolution and the Heavy Section knew it.

* * *

The Somme offensive opened on 1 July 1916 after a week of numbing bombardment. It was the British Army's blackest day. By sunset with little ground gained, nearly 60,000 men had fallen. A third of them were killed. Some 1.7 million shells had left much of the German wire uncut. Five days later Lloyd George was appointed War Minister following Kitchener's death in June aboard *Hampshire*. He was succeeded at the Ministry of Munitions by Edwin Montagu MP, Financial Secretary to the Treasury.

As losses continued to mount and the campaign stalled, Haig spoke of a renewed push in September. He believed the enemy was weakening and he was determined to throw in the handful of completed tanks come what may. The Cabinet was alarmed. Stern and d'Eyncourt made their own representations, emphasising that crews were not ready and most of the tanks would be the mechanically worn training machines. The DNC pointed out that when the enemy first saw tanks he would quickly produce a counter-weapon. The most dangerous antidote would be fire from light QF guns concealed in dugouts ready to be hauled up on sighting the advancing machines – he was proved absolutely right. Montagu went over to plead with Haig against the premature disclosure of the only half-decent prospect of a future breakthrough.

Robertson put all the arguments to Haig at Lloyd George's request, writing on 25 July that if orders were placed now the BEF could expect 500 tanks in the new year instead of perhaps 150 in September. He ended: 'In the meantime every possible step is being taken to expedite the preparation of the tanks so that a small number may be available at the earliest possible date should you decide to employ them in that way.'[19] It was not Robertson's intention that the C-in-C should feel undue pressure from the War Office.

Haig replied that it was now or never before the following spring, and he would not hesitate to use tanks if necessary.

Swinton cautioned Bird that the huge casualty rate would soon bring a call for more tanks. He warned that the order should be placed immediately, before current production ended and the skilled labour and plant were committed to other work. GHQ would also have to decide whether to stay with the Mk I or introduce a type which was proof against field guns, for which a design had been prepared by Stern's committee. Brig Gen Burnett-Stuart replied: 'Before any judgement can be formed it will be necessary to see at least 20 tanks fully equipped and manned, functioning in accordance with some definite tactical scheme. It will also be necessary to view the French experiments . . . with their tanks.'[20] He asked how long a decision could be delayed without breaking continuity of production, to which Swinton replied 'immediate'. Continuity had already been broken as regards guns, gun mountings, gun ammunition, engines and accessories, but so far the skilled workforce had not been broken up.

A demonstration was staged on 21 July at Elveden in response to Burnett-Stuart's comment. Swinton was reluctant to release machines from an already tight training programme but reassurance for a doubting staff in France overrode all other priorities. He threw in every tank that was in serviceable condition. Twenty-five advanced across the mock battlefield firing at or overrunning MG positions and creating much noise and smoke. The large gathering included Robertson and Lloyd George, though unfortunately the party from GHQ arrived moments before the end of the demonstration. It was adjudged a success. Robertson instructed Swinton to order a further fifty tanks.[21] To his credit Robertson won approval to double this to 100 at the next meeting of the War Committee on the 27th. The two batches of fifty were designated Mks II and III respectively, each type divided equally into male and female versions. Foster's was to build twenty-five Mk II males, the rest went to Metro.

Butler, Haig's DCGS, and Swinton had agreed on 22 July that the first section of six tanks and a workshop should be on the sea within two weeks, the remainder to follow in lots of two sections at weekly intervals. The hard-worked machines at Elveden were in rough shape and Knothe thought it might take two months to get them all battle-ready. His mechanics lacked experience and special tools for such jobs as track removal. Key accessories were also missing, but Stern guaranteed to complete the work in ten days. His appeal to Metro for volunteers brought an immediate response from forty men who were billeted by the police at Thetford. They were fed courtesy of the Great Eastern Railway which installed a restaurant car on the tank siding until the work was finished.

*   *   *

Stern's Tank Supply Department had driven Mk I production forward and was already developing new machines and equipment. His small team of fourteen specialists at Armament Buildings was working flat out on such diverse activities as design of a tracked self-propelled heavy gun and the development of a supertank resistant to field-gun fire. Final design of Mk I details had included loopholes, gun mountings, shields and recoil systems to fit the sponsons, means of escape, reinforcement of belly plating, extra roof protection and production of double-skin armour. They also examined camouflage measures, additional ammunition stowage, improved engine cooling, and overcoming the repeated failure of hydraulic systems. In addition they sourced and monitored the production of a vast inventory of material ranging from ammunition, armoured telephone cable, armour plate, communications equipment, compasses, first-aid packs, gun sights, machine guns, periscopes, pistols, prismatic binoculars, telescopes and tarpaulin tank covers, to items in particularly short supply such as cooling fans, exhaust systems, magnetos and radiator tubes. They were competing for priority allocation of skilled labour, especially fitters, gear-cutter operators and turners. There were the essential routines covering negotiation and award of contracts, organising factory by factory inspection of components and assemblies before acceptance, staff recruitment, accommodation and training. Logistical planning was centred on tank transport by rail, the transhipment of the machines to sea ferries and onward movement in France. Scarce flatcars had to be found in England and France, loading and offloading procedures devised, and special equipment including sponson transport trollies and lifting gear obtained. Provisioning for the 6-pdrs called for a specially reduced charge to suit the modified gun, and consideration of the relative values and quantities of black powder and other propellants, pointed shells, fused shells, high explosive and case shot for 75,000 rounds of gun ammunition. Proofing of the guns and production of range tables followed.

Lt Norman Holden joined the department in July as Stern's deputy. The two would work closely together for the rest of the war. Holden had been invalided out of the RNAS after being severely wounded in an armoured car attack at Gallipoli, where he was twice mentioned in despatches. His arrival coincided with Stern's decision to dispense with the Tank Supply Committee through which he was having to run the Supply Department. He viewed the committee as a brake on his powers of decision and he was unused to, and disliked, the consultative process. Matters came to a head at the end of the month.

Bertie Stern and Walter Wilson were assertive characters, highly competent in their totally different fields and frequently at odds with each other. Wilson reported a steering tail at Lincoln which was fouling the track frame. Having previously alerted Stern to what he considered to be consistently poor work by Foster's on these assemblies, he gave notice that he would take no further responsibility for them. Stern refused to accept the disclaimer, reminding Wilson that the tanks were rush orders for warfare, to be assessed as agricultural machines rather than precision motor cars. Continuing tail failures led Wilson to decide to replace the lot with a sturdier version, to be built by Metropolitan without reference to Stern. When Stern got wind of the order it was cancelled from his office by phone next day, 26 July. Stern rightly anticipated that Wilson would appeal to the Tank Supply Committee to reinstate the order, so he called a meeting on 1 August and wound up the committee. Its members were re-formed as an advisory body lacking all executive authority.

Wilson put in a written request for a decision from the new body on a full tail redesign or a simpler reinforcement. Summoned to Stern's office, he refused an order to redirect the request to Stern as Chairman. Christopher Addison, the Ministry's Parliamentary Secretary, was called in and Wilson was ordered to leave the room. The incident typified Wilson's resentment at finding himself subordinate to Stern's decisions on matters of design and engineering. Stern for his part insisted with good reason on his right to exercise final control if targets were to be met. He then decreed that design and policy issues would be decided by a sub-committee comprising himself, d'Eyncourt and Bussell. Wilson was confirmed as Design Engineer and promptly sidelined. D'Eyncourt was not the man to adjudicate on the detail of tank design. Dale Bussell was a level-headed organiser and Admiralty contracts man, but no engineer. Stern freely admitted his modest mechanical knowledge in an interview in 1942:

I was very interested in all mechanical motors. I was one of the early motorists in this country. I had many different types of motors and I perfected the auto-wheel, a third wheel to a bicycle. I had it manufactured by Percy Martin of BSA, in Germany by the Deutsche-Waffenfabrik, in Belgium, in France and in America.

q. How did you acquire your mechanical knowledge?

a. I have been a banker and always employed experts. I was the entrepreneur. I have no mechanical training except I have been deeply interested in the development of the internal combustion engine from the start.[22]

A.W. Wall designed and produced the original Auto-Wheel, a motorised aid for cyclists, in 1909. Stern and Sir Arthur Conan Doyle were associated with a company which took over Wall's machine and improved it in 1912 with considerable success.

Wilson was given a summary of his duties and responsibilities under the new arrangements. He was answerable to Stern who told him: 'As regards your being kept informed of the results and behaviour of the tanks, I will arrange for all useful information on this subject to be passed to you.'[23] The Chief Design Engineer was to be denied direct access to data on the very machines he had introduced. Stern would decide what constituted 'useful information'. Wilson wrote at the foot of the memorandum, '4th Sept. 4 p.m. I saw Major Stern with reference to this and explained that the paragraph re information was not satisfactory. I wished facilities to see things myself and he promised me all facilities both as to seeing machines in this country and abroad.'[24] Stern's formal confirmation of their discussion left him with sole discretion as to which visits Wilson would be permitted to make.

Among other departmental changes, Tritton was engaged as Consulting Engineer on a monthly retainer of 40 guineas (£42.00). Tulloch's association with tank development came to an end. He continued to serve the Ministry on numerous technical committees and was promoted Major.

*   *   *

Stern dropped a bombshell on 3 August. He told Montagu that there were effectively no spares to accompany the tanks to France. Production was geared to continuous assembly in the belief that no machines would take the field until all 150 had been built. No spares were scheduled for supply until the last Mk I tank was completed. He continued:

. . . the machines cannot be equipped to my satisfaction before 1st September. I have therefore made arrangements that 100 machines shall be completed in every detail, together with the necessary spares, by 1st September. This is from the designer's and manufacturer's point of view, which I represent. I may add that in my opinion the sending out of partially equipped machines, as now suggested, is courting disaster.[25]

The supply of spares had been given little consideration in the race to produce finished tanks. Only the Daimler engines came with spare parts. Swinton used his considerable powers of persuasion to try to get Stern to produce parts for two companies of tanks, withholding the news that he had failed for five days before telling Bird. The spares shortage persisted in varying degrees for many months. The tank was viewed by most as a means of crossing a few hundred yards of disputed ground after which it had no purpose. Stern considered it a missile, valueless after first use.

*   *   *

An advance party led by Lt Col John Brough of the Royal Marine Artillery, a very able Staff College graduate, was despatched to France to prepare for the reception and onward movement of the tanks. Operation 'Alpaca' began on the night of 13/14 August when the first half of Maj A. Holford-Walker's C Company entrained thirteen male tanks at Elveden for the journey to Avonmouth docks, Southampton. They embarked for Havre on the 20th. The rest of C Company with twelve female tanks sailed on the 24th.[26]

Swinton was summoned to Haig's advanced headquarters to review shipments with the C-in-C and Butler. Haig pointed out on the map the sector where the tanks were to be committed, emphasising the supreme importance of getting as many machines as possible across to France by 10 September latest. Swinton said he could deliver fifty and, providing the Channel remained free of enemy submarines which had been disrupting sailings, he thought the last half company might be got to Havre as early as the 4th.[27] No sooner had Swinton reported the meeting to Bird on his return, quoting Haig's deadline of 10 September, than a telegram arrived from GHQ which put it at 1 September. Faced with a ten-day discrepancy the DSD sought explanation. Butler confirmed that they had taken Swinton's 'best case' forecast of the 4th and had further advanced it in hope of its fulfilment. The fact that Swinton had attached conditions was not mentioned. Although blameless, he was instructed that in future he must bring back a written note of important decisions agreed with him, initialled by Butler or Kiggell. A hint of unreliability now attached to Swinton.

He returned to GHQ at the end of August to find the atmosphere unhelpful. Reaction to the tanks was a mix of amused tolerance and scepticism. A few were relying overmuch on the handful of machines to bring success to the offensive. The tanks were seen by many as a bit of comic relief. Crews near to exhaustion from unremitting preparation and maintenance were constantly badgered to make the machines perform 'stunts'. The Staff were critical of Swinton's management of tank supply and of the organisation of the Heavy Section in general. Brig Gen Burnett-Stuart had remarked in a scribbled note to Butler earlier in August: 'The whole organisation of this show at home has been on fancy rather than on practical lines.'[28] Swinton was told that Brough was persona non grata and his replacement was requested only three weeks after his arrival at GHQ. He was considered 'difficult', probably with good reason. He had warned against committing tanks in penny packets, had objected to interruptions in training to stage party tricks, and cautioned that the powers of the tanks were still largely unknown. Swinton replaced Brough with Lt Col Bradley, his commander at Elveden, who lasted a further three weeks before his departure was demanded.

Sixteen Zeppelins raided England on the night of 2/3 September. The last of D Company's tanks had entrained and left Elveden the previous night. ASC personnel were now loading sponsons, spare guns, ammunition and stores. Just before midnight the shouts and engine noise on the brightly lit siding were silenced by alarm whistles and sudden darkness as the acetylene flares were extinguished. Zeppelin L32 had dropped incendiaries near Thetford and was blindly searching for an aerodrome near Barnham. It overflew the siding, its commander, Oberleutnant Werner Petersen, and his crew quite unaware of the prize below. L16 followed at a distance, dropping a bomb on the edge of the Elveden estate. Thereafter, Swinton loaded tanks by day and had the site screened from public view. Of the 150 Mk I ordered, 110 had reached Elveden by the end of August. A three-week production interval followed during which a supply of spare parts was accumulated.

Maj Frank Summers' D Company with twenty-five tanks and two spares arrived at the assembly area on 6 September, bringing to fifty-two the number of machines reaching France in time for the coming offensive. The twenty-five tanks of Maj C.M. Tippetts' A Company plus eight spares and a mobile workshop followed mid-month. All tanks were sent on to Yvrench near Abbeville for tuning up and training with the infantry. Haig expected much of them.

Nine

FIRST BLOOD

The tail in France is trying to wag a very distant and headless dog in England.[1]

Col Hugh Elles, Commander of the Tanks, to GHQ, 31 December 1916

C and D Companies moved up on rail to Lt Gen Henry Rawlinson's Fourth Army area between 7 and 10 September. The forty-eight 'Alpacas' plus four spares detrained at Méricourt, north of Arras. Knothe and a team of fitters worked continuously on them for the next five days and nights, snatching the odd hour's sleep while awaiting a part or completion of a test. Sir Douglas Haig's Somme offensive had advanced the 30-mile front by up to 4 miles at unimaginable cost in lives, mutilation and suffering. The enemy regularly and determinedly counter-attacked. The terrain had become a naked waste of pulverised farms and villages marked only by the stain of their brick dust. The wrack of recent fighting lay everywhere: smashed supply wagons and horse teams, abandoned equipment and the unburied dead. For the tankmen it was a horrifying foretaste of what lay ahead.

The coming assault was part of a simultaneous offensive with the French in a renewed attempt to destroy the German Army, which had also sustained heavy losses. Haig was gambling on breaking through to Bapaume with no reserves save tired troops. His attack would pivot on Gen Sir Hubert Gough's Reserve Army on the left wing. The main thrust would be delivered by the Fourth Army between Morval and Le Sars, with a supporting push by the French to the south. The few tanks to be committed assumed an importance greater than their numbers or untried performance warranted, but the surprise element remained, for what it was worth on this scale.

Rawlinson had initially submitted a scheme which called for a night assault under a full moon to protect his tanks from artillery and to prevent the enemy from getting a good sighting of them. The machines would be withdrawn before dawn. The shock and uncertainty as to what had hit them and what its powers were would thus cause maximum alarm and despondency among the Germans. However, the C-in-C rejected the plan as impracticable and lacking boldness.

The daylight attack was confirmed for dawn on Friday 15 September. Rawlinson's primary objectives were the villages of Morval, Les Boeufs, Gueudecourt and Flers. The forty-two tanks assigned to him would work in threes to destroy strongpoints while accompanying infantry rushed the intervening sections of trench. As soon as a breakthrough was achieved the cavalry would race through with other arms along the line Morval–Bapaume. Gough's army with eight tanks would cooperate and take Courcelette, among other objectives.

Lt Cols Bradley and Elles attended the planning conferences on 10 and 13 September with Rawlinson and his Corps commanders. Bradley was handicapped by his junior rank, the restricted scope of his command, his ignorance of the conduct of operations and unfamiliarity with the terrain. He said little. His responsibilities were administrative, in liaison with the units to which his force was attached. Theoretically it fell to Maj Allen Holford-Walker and Maj Frank Summers, his Company commanders, to agree tactics with their opposite numbers in the infantry. In practice, because the tanks were to operate in small battle groups of three, that liaison was more often between individual tank commanders and the infantry units they were to support.

Possibly for security reasons, Swinton's detailed paper *Notes on the Employment of Tanks* was not circulated below Senior Staff level at GHQ. It is remarkable that no exception was made for Elles who was now its tank specialist and was shortly to be appointed to command the Heavy Section in France. He claimed he first saw the *Notes* late in 1918.

Fourth Army issued its *Instructions for the Employment of 'Tanks'* on the 11th. All approach movements would be by night. Aeroplanes were to overfly the area to blanket the sound of engines on the three nights preceding the attack. The machines would assemble on X/Y night 1 mile behind the start line, moving on to it on Y/Z night. At 06.00 hrs on Z day they would move off to reach first objectives five minutes ahead of the infantry, who would follow under a creeping barrage leaving a fire-free lane 100yd wide for each column of tanks. The stationary barrage of heavy and field artillery would lift off the first objectives several minutes ahead of the arrival of the tanks. After clearing up there the tanks were to move on to prearranged positions to act as strongpoints against counter-attack while the infantry regrouped before repeating the sequence under a covering barrage for the second objective. For subsequent advances without artillery support the tanks were to precede the infantry by half an hour – a very dangerous proposition in the light of later experience. The machines needed close infantry support at all times for spotting artillery positions, target opportunities, gathering prisoners and holding newly taken ground.

At 5 p.m. on YZ day the written orders were cancelled and tank commanders were rebriefed verbally. They and their crews were already near exhaustion from days of intensive preparation and lack of sleep, aggravated by their close proximity to the artillery which was delivering a three-day bombardment. Each man was issued with a hard leather helmet shaped like half a Rugby football, a pair of goggles, a revolver, two gas masks, field-dressing kit, haversack, water bottle and iron rations for two days. The tanks' already narrow gangways became choked with more drums of engine oil and grease, a spare machine gun and four barrels, 33,000 rounds of SAA in the female types, thirty tins of food, sixteen loaves, and for some, a basket of carrier pigeons. There was little rest and less sleep again that night as the bombardment increased in intensity. The tanks moved out at zero hour on the 15th beneath a crescendo of covering fire into a thin ground mist and the promise of a fine day. Of the forty-nine machines employed, thirty-two had reached their starting points and eighteen saw action. Nine of these kept ahead of the infantry and caused the enemy much damage. The other nine got away after overcoming various problems – although they never caught up with the infantry they did valuable work mopping up strongpoints. The remainder suffered mechanical failures or became ditched in the expanse of interlocking shell holes and lines of crumbling trenches.

Battle conditions were hellish for the tank crews. When the early machines were fully closed up, vision was limited to the commander's periscope and narrow double glass prisms. These soon shattered as the Maxims raked them with fire. The prisms were replaced on Mk IV tanks by steel plates pricked with small holes. The driver kept his flap ajar as long as possible to see the ground beneath and just ahead of the machine's front horns. The crew suffered unremitting noise from the exposed and unsilenced engine, the gears shrieking and grinding through their straight-cut teeth, the explosive fire of the tank's guns and the 'harsh tapping' of MG bullets striking the armour. All communication was by signs. The air, already fouling with petrol and exhaust fumes, thickened with cordite smoke. Light from four small festoon lamps dimmed in the haze. The wrenching violence of sudden lurches was another hazard, especially for the gunners whose backs were inches from the hot engine, their boots skidding on spent cartridge cases rolling across the heaving floor. Cartridge-case deflectors and bags were installed a year later. The gunlayers on the 6-pdrs worked their guns without elevating and traversing wheels. Instead they gripped a stanchion with their left hand to steady themselves while swinging the gun via a crutch in their right armpit, and their free hand on a pistol grip. They became expert shots on the move.

Bullet splash was a hazard peculiar to the tanks. When standard issue rifle and machine-gun bullets hit armour their lead cores flattened and became molten, the resultant 'splash' entering the hull through the slightest crack as a super-hot spray of atomised shrapnel. Entry points included the knife-thin gaps surrounding loophole and vision slit covers, and the junction of sponson with hull where severe stresses tended to open the felt-packed joint to a crack of daylight. Concentrated Maxim fire could so hammer a section of plate as to cause its internal face to spall, throwing off hot steel fragments and leaving a characteristic rank smell of burned paint. Splash lodged under the skin of face and hands as black pinpricks, emerging weeks later, and commanders and gunners were particularly at risk of being blinded. Various forms of face shield were issued later – principally steel goggles with inadequate vision slits and a square of chain mail beneath to protect nose, mouth and throat – but most men soon discarded them. Hull exteriors could quite literally become shot-blasted, as Lt Henry Williamson, an infantry supplies officer, confirmed to his father in spring 1917: 'My experience of the Hindenburg line is that it is bloody awful. One of our tanks that did come back shined like hell from bullets but the bloke inside was mad.'[2] Yet in spite of all, if any crewman had a fleeting moment to consider his position he thanked God he was not outside with the infantry.

The most notable tank exploit of the day involved D17 'Dinnaken' of Summers' D Company. The male tank commanded by Lt Stuart Hastie was to accompany D9 and D14, advancing some 1.5 miles to Flers village in support of 41st Division before moving on to attack Gueudecourt. The three had barely moved off at 06.20 when 2/Lt G.F. Court's D14 tail-dived irretrievably into a crumbling support trench. In manoeuvring to get ahead to secure a tow cable, D9 with 2/Lt Victor Huffam slid against the ditched machine and they locked sponsons. Hastie's driver, Pte Wescombe, got across and they pressed on alone beneath a heavy barrage. When the tail wheels were damaged crossing no-man's-land they were lifted clear on the hydraulics, steering then becoming a matter of individual track braking. D17 reached Flers accompanied by men of the 122nd and 124th Infantry Brigades, much reduced from enemy fire and now sustaining losses on the heavily wired outskirts of the village. The tank flattened a path through the entanglement and stopped astride the trench behind, enfilading it with MG before rolling on into the village with a badly knocking engine. Some 300 infantry accompanied the tank, moving house to house under continuing friendly and hostile shelling while D17 attempted to get enough elevation for its guns to dislodge snipers in the upper windows. Stick bombs had no effect on the hull. After further destruction of enemy MG positions the tank withdrew under heavy shelling. The engine failed soon afterwards and D17 took a direct hit on a track. The crew bailed out and eventually got back to base.

The other two tanks of Hastie's half-section, D9 and D14, were recovered overnight and were the only ones to fight the next day. They were to support troops of the New Zealand regiment attacking in the direction of Gueudecourt. Huffam's D9 shot up numbers of Germans in shell holes before to their horror the crew saw Court's D14 engulfed in exploding shells. As D9 continued its advance the prismatics and telescopes were shattered, the splinters blinding L/Cpl Archer, the driver. Both port-side gunners were killed as a shell or armour-piercing bullets penetrated the hull. Huffam lost consciousness when another shell hit. When he came round he found L/Cpl Harry Sanders, the relief driver, very badly wounded in the legs. The other four surviving crew, all injured or in shock, had crawled out. Two were sent back for help. Huffam followed after dressing Sanders' wounds, dragging him by the belt from hole to hole across several hundred yards of fire-swept ground. All in D14 were dead or dying.[3] The courage and achievements of this and the other small battle groups won respect for the Heavy Section and its machines.

An RFC observer had watched overhead as D17 rolled through Flers. He scribbled a report and dropped it above the British lines. 'Tank followed by cheering multitude marching through Flers.'[4] It was an exaggeration but the sense was clear. GHQ released the message together with guarded information on the tanks. The story electrified the press and raced around the world. 'A tank is walking up the High Street of Flers with the British Army cheering behind' was typical of the accounts. Other headlines at home read:

Battle Cars That Charge Trenches. Britain's Wonderful New 'Landship' Weapon.
How Our New Forts On Wheels Made Huns Run Like Rabbits.
Our New Weapons That Eat Up Houses – 'The Tanks'.
Tanks Cause 'Indescribable Demoralisation'.
Tanks Take Ditches Like Kangaroos.
Huns Cry 'Unfair Butchery'.
Like Toads of Vast Size.
His Majesty's Land Navy.

A few weeks later the Amsterdam correspondent of *The Times* forwarded a German despatch from the Western Front correspondent of the *Düsseldorfer Generalanzeiger* headed 'The Devil's Chariots'. It graphically described the shock effect of the first tanks on the German defenders:

[As they] looked towards the English the blood froze in their veins as two mysterious monsters came creeping over the crater fields. . . . They have learned not to fear man, but there was something approaching which the human brain, with tremendous mechanical powers, had fitted out for a devil's trick, a mystery which oppressed and shackled the powers because one could not comprehend it with understanding – a fatality against which one seemed helpless. One stared and stared as if paralysed.

The monster approached slowly, hobbling, moving from side to side, rocking and pitching, but it came nearer. Nothing obstructed it; a supernatural force seemed to drive it onwards. Someone in the trenches cried 'the devil comes', and that word ran down the line like lightning. Suddenly tongues of fire leapt out of the armoured skins of the iron caterpillar, shells whistled over our heads, and a terrible concert [from] a machine gun orchestra filled the air. The mysterious creature had surrendered its secret, and sense returned with it, and toughness and defiance, and the English waves of infantry surged up behind the devil's chariot.[5]

Lacking photographs, the press ran shots of armoured cars and Holt crawlers, while art departments had a field day creating visual impressions of the machines. None approached reality, illustrations tending either to be comic or wildly juggernaut. The first photograph to appear in any British newspaper cost £5,000 – coincidentally the price of a Mk I tank. It filled the front page of the *Daily Mirror* on 22 November 1916 under the banner headline: 'HUSH, HUSH' – A TANK GOES 'GALUMPHANT' INTO ACTION ON THE WESTERN FRONT.

* * *

Swinton arrived at Haig's headquarters late on Z day, 15 September. The C-in-C received him cordially and thanked him, saying that although the tanks had not achieved all that was hoped, many lives had been saved by them and he wanted five times as many. Stern joined Swinton next day, later recalling Haig's words to them both: 'We have had the greatest victory since the battle of the Marne. We have taken more prisoners and more territory, with comparatively few casualties. This is due to the tanks. Wherever the tanks advanced we took our objectives, and where they did not advance we failed. . . . Go back and make as many more tanks as you can. We thank you.'[6]

The reaction from his Staff was more subdued. The initial prejudices of many, including senior commanders, hardened after 15 September. Gen Gough's views were particularly damning. A 'cavalry' mentality prevailed which derided the comic appearance and obvious practical shortcomings of the still primitive machines. Adm Bacon happened to be at GHQ on other business when Haig asked him as an informed outsider to inspect the machines and report his opinion. Bacon found the tanks virtually unsteerable, dangerously badly ventilated and excessively noisy. He told Haig they were practically useless in their present state, advising that all should be sent home for alteration while spreading a report that they were a failure. When an improved fleet was ready, 500 should be thrown into a single concerted offensive. Bacon said he was convinced they would walk clean through the German defences. He thought Haig agreed.[7]

Whigham convened a policy conference at the War Office on 19 and 20 September. He was joined by Bird, Swinton, Brough, and Butler from GHQ. Butler led with proposals for expanding the Heavy Section as ordered by Haig. It would be organised into five brigades of 216 tanks each; a brigade to comprise three wings, each of three companies, twenty-four tanks per company. An officer would be appointed to command the tanks in France, and a separate officer was to command the training units at home and the overall administration. Stern's organisation would not only build the machines but test them as well. (The Army regretted this later, realising the dangers of letting a supply department approve its own work.) In noting that the French were building 800 light tanks, the conference agreed that:

> . . . the existing order for tanks to be completed without diminution of output, and a supplementary order for 1,000 tanks *of same type* to be placed. Certain improvements in design to be introduced as and when possible so as not to delay the present rate of output. . . . A meeting has been arranged in Paris . . . to effect complete collaboration between French and British designers with a view to a new type of tank embodying the best points of both British and French designs and all other practicable improvements. The deliberations of this [Anglo-French] Committee are not intended, however, to influence in any way the continuance of the present output of British tanks, including the additional order referred to. [*Author's emphasis*][8]

The subsequent passage of the notorious '1,000-tank order' was accompanied by misunderstanding, mistrust and lack of direction. It was first confirmed, then cancelled, and the cancellation was itself overridden by the Secretary of State for War. The episode was glossed over at the time and was seriously misrepresented later in the official history of the MoM, presumably to avoid embarrassment all round. How and precisely why it unfolded has puzzled historians ever since, including Capt Basil Liddell Hart in the preparation of his masterly history, *The Tanks*. The author has seen contemporary military and Ministry papers which were not open to inspection then; they reveal the distrust of the new weapon at GHQ and Stern's growing isolation from the High Commands in London and France.

The hiatus began with disagreement between GHQ and the War Office as to what they had just decided. This was compounded by a wall of silence surrounding Stern's actions. Two days after the conference Butler told Elles that a joint meeting of English and French engineers would design a 'super-tank' embodying the best of the machines of both nations. He added, incorrectly, 'An order has already been placed for 1,000 of these when the design is approved.'[9] When Butler received draft minutes of the conference he disputed them, writing to Whigham in London on 25 September that the request from GHQ for 1,000 tanks was not for the 'same type' but for an entirely new Anglo-French design which would start production in four or five months' time. Until then, he said, a continuation order 'not necessarily for 1,000' was to be given to maintain current production.[10]

Whigham did not wait on Butler's reply before authorising a production order which was sent to the Ministry on the 26th.

I am commanded by the Army Council to inform you that they concur in a further order for 1,000 additional 'Tanks' being placed in continuation of existing orders. I am to ask whether these additional 'Tanks' could be produced with the existing resources for manufacture by the 1st March 1917.[11]

Butler's letter then arrived and was considered by the Army Council next day. It was decided that the order for 1,000 tanks should be cancelled. The original programme was required to continue unchanged pending investigation of the effectiveness of the machines and possibilities for their improvement. As a face-saver the record of the meeting downgraded the big order to a 'proposal'.[12] Whigham sent Butler a hurried note that night asking for Haig to clarify and formally state his tank requirements. The Ministry was informed that the 'request' of the 26th was cancelled. Of the 250 tanks ordered to date, 40 Mk I remained to be built and Stern was asked to make minor improvements to the balance awaited of 100 (50 each of Mks II and III). A continuation order was promised if no new design was ready on final completion.[13]

Stern was aghast. Weeks before, without reference to the Army, he and Bussell had negotiated with Metro for an additional 1,000 tanks. His charter from the 'Welsh Wizard' gave him licence to place work direct with suppliers and the contract had been issued on 21 August.[14] He had set in train an ambitious tank programme requiring 30,000 tons of high-grade steels, some 2,000 6-pdr guns and 10,000 machine guns. Skilled labour and production capacity was being scheduled. Montagu, his Minister, must have been aware of this commitment and was to give Stern much personal support, but Stern's greatest strength lay in the confidence and even friendship which Lloyd George showed him. The Secretary of State for War and his confidential secretary and mistress Frances Stevenson had weekended as Stern's house guests only four weeks earlier at Highdown, the Worthing home of his brother who was abroad on military service. They periodically joined Stern there when time allowed. (An entry in Frances Stevenson's diary indicates that in 1919 she briefly contemplated marriage to the dashing and charismatic Bertie Stern, though no proposal was made.)[15]

With the cancellation notice of 30 September in hand, Stern shot across to the War Office. Lloyd George was 'staggered'. Stern told him he could sack him if he pleased, but he would never persuade him to cancel the orders he had placed. Gen Robertson was summoned and was asked by the Secretary of State why, as President of the Army Council, he had not been informed. Stern tactfully withdrew but from then on he was a marked man. On 14 October the War Office cancelled the cancellation, finally acknowledging that the original 1,000 tank order was indeed an order. They went on blithely to enquire how many more skilled men would be needed if it were decided to build an additional 1,000 tanks for the Allies – who were now pressing for them. The pendulum had swung from zero to 2,000 machines in the space of a fortnight.

The Ministry confirmed that 1,000 tanks had been ordered but gave notice that it needed 3,000 more workers to build them. Montagu warned the War Office that unless the Adjutant-General released skilled men from the Army and protected existing tank labour from recruitment he had no hope of meeting the programme. If labour was forthcoming he forecast completion of Mks II and III by year's end, and the start of Mk IV production at forty per week from 1 January. The first 600 would incorporate modest improvements pending the transfer to an entirely new design for the remaining 400. A further 1,000 could be built for the Allies with moderate additional labour if the two construction starts were staggered by two or three months. In the event, the needs of the British Army had to come first and no tanks could be spared for France and the other Allies until well into 1918.

The truth behind this episode has been further obscured for over eighty years by a brief and wholly inaccurate account in the official but unpublished history of the Ministry of Munitions. It records an Army Council 'enquiry' as to whether 1,000 tanks could be built by 1 March 1917, and its subsequent cancellation because 'it was entirely beyond the capacity of the [Ministry] to produce the number required within the time named'.[16] In fact, no such issue arose at any point in the exchanges.

Meanwhile, Haig had qualified his exhortations to Swinton and Stern to go home and build many tanks. On 2 October he sent the War Office a personal statement on the weapon which was almost worthless to the supply side. Time was pressing if a tank fleet was to be built for the 1917 fighting season, but the C-in-C went no further than a declaration of intent with a promise of later performance requirements and, crucially, no time frame:

> This new engine [of war] has proved itself to possess qualities which warrant further provision on a large scale. I will submit in due course certain proposals, based on the experience already gained, regarding . . . improvements in design. Meanwhile, I have the honour to recommend that the principle of the expansion of the existing Heavy Section of the Machine Gun Corps be accepted with a view to the eventual provision of approximately 1,000 tanks, together with the necessary personnel.[17]

Promotions had followed at the end of September: Stern and Elles to Colonel, Wilson and Norman Holden to Major, Symes to Captain. Elles took command of the Heavy Section in the field on the 25th. He was Haig's choice and Swinton's nominee, but the appointment of so junior an officer caused considerable annoyance in the upper echelons. His responsibilities included the unit's tactical employment under the C-in-C and its advanced training, maintenance and repair in France. Its HQ establishment – and some inspired appointments made by Elles – comprised a Brigade Major (Capt G. Le Q. Martel); DAA and QMG (Capt T.J. Uzielli); Staff Captain (Capt J.H. Tapper); and Intelligence Officer (Capt F.E. 'Boots' Hotblack). Martel, an Army boxing champion, commanded a field company of the RE in France and had undertaken the 'landscaping' at Elveden. 'Theo' Uzielli was to prove a fine organiser who could open otherwise locked doors and minds at GHQ. The tall and inscrutable Hotblack would become a legend, utterly fearless, much wounded and decorated. They were joined in December by Maj J.F.C. 'Boney' Fuller; his intellectual contribution to tactical planning, strategic issues and the long battles to overcome military hostility was immense. Haig proposed the renaming of the new arm as the Tank Corps with appropriate insignia and a distinctive uniform. The War Office raised administrative objections, announcing on 20 October an imperceptible elevation from Heavy Section to the Heavy Branch of the Machine Gun Corps.

Popular acclaim for the still mysterious tanks led to calls in the press for their inventors to be named. Lloyd George was questioned in the Commons on 12 October but his reply was hardly enlightening. He credited d'Eyncourt with contributing the greatest share in the tank's design, naming also Hankey for first suggesting 'that something of this kind should be tried';

Churchill for initiating the committee and backing it throughout; Swinton for 'having a good deal to do with the experiment from the start'; and Stern for his zeal and business ability. He ended: 'That is all I can usefully say on that question.'[18] Wilson and Tritton were justifiably dismayed. Tritton sent the DNC a telegram next day giving notice that in view of 'the persistent refusal to give any credit to those who have designed and built the tanks, I shall now make all facts known in my own way'.[19] D'Eyncourt replied with an assurance that: 'I have always put your name forward as deserving full recognition for all you have done.' This hardly squares with his six-page 'Report on Design and Construction of First Land Ship' which he had submitted to Balfour and the Sea Lords on 18 September. It makes a fleeting and ungenerous reference to Wilson and Tritton:

The design work still continued under my directions. A little later we obtained caterpillar tractors from America. . . . In the meantime I had been going into a design with Mr Tritton of Messrs Fosters, and at this time Lt Wilson of the Armoured Car Division, an experienced motor and civil engineer, was also brought in and consulted, and a design was evolved generally on the lines of the tanks at present in use.[20]

In a short addendum d'Eyncourt added 'some further remarks as to the officers who have rendered me special assistance', including Tritton 'who very ably assisted me in preparing details of the design', and Wilson who 'also assisted in design and constructional details'. D'Eyncourt's report caused Dr Macnamara, the Admiralty spokesman in the Commons, to tell the House on 18 October that 'the principal credit for the design of the tanks . . . rests with Mr d'Eyncourt [who] has mentioned the following gentlemen as rendering him valuable assistance'. Macnamara listed six names with ranks and Service or civil occupations: Tritton, Wilson, Bussell, Stern, Symes, and Mr Skeens from the DNC's department.

* * *

The Heavy Branch was outgrowing the Elveden site and Swinton had been scouting for a new headquarters and training area. The complicating factor was the need for good rail links with the tank factories and Southampton docks. The options narrowed to Corhampton between Winchester and

Portsmouth, and a hutted camp at Bovington near Wool in Dorset, 6 miles from the coast. GHQ favoured the latter, Butler observing that its proximity to the sea offered possibilities for shipping tanks direct from Wool. Haig agreed.[21] Elveden was closed down and the training centre moved to Bovington (invariably identified as Wool) on 27 October. It was to be Swinton's last service to the tanks for two years.

Having disposed of two senior commanders of Heavy Branch, GHQ now directed its guns on Swinton. A movement to replace him was led by Butler and Burnett-Stuart. Swinton's familiarity with the Army Council cannot have helped him. He was viewed as an engineer officer with unwarranted pretensions to higher command and a weak disciplinarian. The intensive training at Elveden was certainly more concerned with operational competence than orthodox military discipline. Capt H.P.G. Steedman who took command of 711 MT Company on Knothe's departure considered that 'the MGC as a unit was over-officered and under-disciplined'.[22] Butler suggested Swinton's replacement by Brig Gen W. Thwaites, a Royal Horse Artillery Brigade Commander and therefore 'one of us'. Thwaites knew nothing of tanks. Whigham had cautioned Butler at the end of September: 'The disposal of Swinton is rather a thorny problem and must be handled carefully. Personally I think Thwaites would be an excellent man.'[23] Others disagreed and the appointment went to an infantry brigade commander, Brig Gen F. Gore Anley, who took over on 10 November. He declared to nobody's great surprise that his priority lay less in the tanks than in restoring discipline.

Swinton returned to Hankey's secretariat. His removal was greatly resented by all ranks, who respected him for his professionalism and disarming lack of aloofness. He had successfully established and put in the field a revolutionary new arm – inevitably drawing envy and suspicion in high places.

*   *   *

Stern began to receive requests from France for design improvements arising from battle experience. Within a week of taking up his command Elles was calling for more powerful engines, stronger armour, anti-splash measures, non-shattering prisms, better bomb protection of roofs, modified guns and mountings, means of avoiding 'bellying', provision for track adjustment from inside the tank under fire, and a redesign of the sponsons which tended to wedge into the ground when tanks heeled over, leaving them ditched and highly vulnerable to artillery. Knothe's requests centred on track troubles – a tendency to mount the teeth of idler sprockets after becoming jammed with compacted mud, track breakages and better lubrication. He also advocated a third, centre track as a means of overcoming bellying. Other concerns included better security against attacking infantry – one tank gunner was bayoneted in the leg through the door flap used for ejecting spent shell cases by hand – and internal locking for escape doors, shutters and loopholes; excessive stretching of the track links; a lack of spare periscopes which quickly shattered under fire; inadequate depression of MG and 6-pdr guns; and the susceptibility of tail wheel assemblies to fail in use or from gunfire.

Wilson was primarily concerned with these requests, billeting himself and Maj Harry Buddicum, his co-designer, near the Metro factory at Oldbury. Metro's Technical Director John Greg provided draughting services and by March 1917 the entire drawing office at the company's Saltley factory was working for Wilson. Buddicum, fifty-five years of age and 6ft 2in tall, was a striking character whose talents led him to a successful civilian engineering career after another as a cavalryman.

The Tank Supply Department acquired fields at Mill Farm, Broadwell Road, behind the Oldbury works, for the first tank testing station. It opened on 28 September for pre-acceptance inspection of all Metro's output from Oldbury and Saltley, manned by a detachment of twenty-six men from 20 Squadron. The main tank stores opened there under their control in November. Squadron strength at Oldbury peaked at 425 all ranks in April–June 1918. Their loading speed record was twenty-two tanks washed, oiled and entrained off a single ramp in 4 hours.

Attempts were made to clip the wings of Stern's semi-autonomous and sometimes anarchic department. The Army Council accepted in October that all tanks, equipment and spares should continue to be manufactured and tested by the Tank Supply Department, but they quite reasonably insisted on setting the test procedures. They repeatedly demanded that responsibility for despatch to France should lie with the Army rather than 20 Squadron. They also required to be consulted on the specification of new tanks before designs were begun, and on any later changes. The Ministry of Munitions accepted the tests request but opposed changes to design and transport procedures. It cited the Tank Supply Department's independent status under its charter and, so far as design control was concerned, an earlier undertaking by the War Office to accept the transfer of responsibility for munitions design to the

Ministry. The War Office was left with responsibility for deciding the general nature and amount of its weapons and equipment needs, and for distribution of munitions to the troops. These inter-departmental trials of strength flared at intervals for the rest of the war but the Ministry refused to give up design and transport control.

D'Eyncourt, whose standing and calm authority were respected in the War Office, told Lloyd George and Gen Robertson that analysis of the Flers action suggested that each tank and eight-man crew equated in fighting potential to a battalion of infantry, while their morale-boosting effect on British troops was incalculable. He warned that the Germans would respond with more powerful tanks of their own, and 'if we do not keep ahead in numbers and power they will beat us at what is at present our game. . . . From every point of view it is of the utmost importance to develop this arm to the utmost of our capabilities.'[24] Stern for his part was chasing the War Office for confirmation of its proposals for a second batch of 1,000 tanks. Montagu told Lloyd George: 'Stern wants an order for a second thousand tanks. He convinces me he ought to have them. They are far better than infantry. He wants to assure manufacturers of orders. They will, of course, be of new and improved design.'[25]

Kiggell and Butler at GHQ were taking a noticeably more negative view of the tank weapon than the Chief, concluding that 'the tank in its present form is of no value as a fighting unit'. Kiggell considered that 'in the present stage of their development they must be regarded as entirely accessory to the ordinary methods of attack, i.e. to the advance of infantry in close cooperation with artillery'.[26] Assurances of better tanks to come failed to persuade the military to increase their order.

The Army would have to await Mk IV for modest improvements. Stern and d'Eyncourt were determined to avoid interrupting production and losing output for the sake of piecemeal modifications. Most of those planned for Mks II and III were held over to Mk IV, though a few were slipped through including a narrowed conning tower over the driver to allow for wider tracks; the flat roof hatch further aft was replaced with a wedge-shaped manhole giving protected vision; angle-iron surrounds were fitted to loopholes to deflect bullet splash, and inner fastenings were added to secure loophole covers; provision was made for extra track adjustment; better brake linings were fitted; more depression was provided for the guns. Symes' secondary plating for the Mk II hulls was withdrawn in November. Mk III was to have thicker (12mm) plate on vulnerable areas. The trailed steering was abandoned as inefficient and unnecessary.

Stern's rapidly growing Tank Supply Department was renamed the Mechanical Warfare Supply Department (MWSD) in October when it became a separate branch of the Ministry of Munitions and moved to offices at 17 Cockspur Street. Stern's deputy directors-general were to be Dale Bussell and Norman Holden, with d'Eyncourt as chief technical adviser, Sir Charles Parsons, technical adviser, Tritton, director of construction and Wilson, director of engineering. The wide powers of the department and its hard-nosed drive under Stern remained painfully evident to the contracts, labour, materials and other branches of the Ministry. He provoked uproar over his insistent demands for labour and materials priorities; refused to submit progress reports until finally ordered to do so by the Minister; and bypassed him in corresponding directly with the War Office – for which Montagu reprimanded him with exquisite finesse ('My Dear Stern, You have been kind enough to send me a copy of your letter of November 4th to the War Office . . .'). The internal organisation of the MWSD remained mildly chaotic. It still lacked a dedicated supply section, but it met all its problems head-on and usually won through.

Communication between Stern's organisation, the War Office and France deteriorated. The general uncertainty at GHQ on the state of tank supply was visible in a very civil letter from Kiggell to Stern on 7 November. From his list of production queries it was clear that the CGS still awaited a forecast of delivery and completion dates covering Mks II, III, IV and V (the last Mk I was delivered at the end of October). Kiggell wanted more information on a possible second batch of 1,000 tanks for the British Army before placing an order with the War Office. He asked Stern to come over and explain the situation personally, with special reference to future improvements and deliveries 'on which so much of our programme for next year depends'.

At the same time Gen Anley was trying to rationalise the many-stranded lines of communication and decision on tank affairs. He set up a Heavy Section Central Office in Whitehall and installed Lt Col Brough as his Staff Officer of Tanks. Brough would provide the communications channel between Wool, Stern's people, the War Office and Heavy Section (France). Stern, however, enjoyed a direct line to the Secretary of State at the War Office and used it unhesitatingly when thwarted by the military. Anley tried and failed to have it removed.

Kiggell's call for information was accompanied by an Army Council initiative to search for 'the best means of ensuring that the design of tanks is developed in conformity with the tactical employment of those engines'. A flurry of conferences followed in London in late November. The council proposed to set up a design committee comprising officers with recent battle experience as well as technical experts. Its membership was weighted 5:3 in favour of the military, the senior officer to preside. It was intended that all tank transportation to France would be handled by the Army. Stern would carry out the decisions of the committee save only when/if these threatened output. He would also produce spares to the requirements of GHQ and the WO (the spares shortage was becoming serious). Demands for tanks and spares would be routed directly from the WO to Stern. The committee was to meet monthly.[27] As Tulloch had so forcefully pointed out, any such body should have been in almost continuous session daily. Design by committee was dangerous; design of a rapidly evolving and complex weapon by a committee which would meet a dozen times a year was madness.

Stern headed off the proposal, at least for the time being, at an important meeting in his office on the 23rd with Gen Davidson from GHQ, Gen Anley and Col Elles. Stern persuaded them to accept that a joint Army and MWSD conference should be held in London whenever important matters of design, output or delivery arose, to be chaired by himself. This kept design firmly under his control but did nothing to improve communication. Stern urged Davidson to secure the appointment of a military counterpart to himself – preferably a member of the Army Council who could coordinate the tangle of War Office directorates and speak with authority for the Army.

Stern went on to report that production of Mks II and III was expected to complete by 7 February 1917, after which Mk IV would start at twenty per week – half the rate originally forecast. Mk IV was Wilson's design, as were Mks II and III. New features included thicker armour overall, wider track shoes, removal of the petrol tank from the fighting compartment to a less hazardous external position at the rear with a pressurised feed, and sponsons which folded inboard for rail movement when unbolted, the heavier male version being nudged inside by another tank. Sponsons would also be reprofiled to lessen their tendency to become ploughs when the tank heeled over. The long barrels of the 6-pdr guns, which too often fouled obstructions or became jammed with compacted soil, were to be shortened from 40 to 23 calibres. (This had little effect on performance, but the short gun produced a dangerous backblast until rectified. It was necessary to keep the gun closed for half a minute after firing to avoid the risk of igniting the petrol.)[28]

Gen Davidson shook Stern with the news that the Hotchkiss and Vickers machine guns were to be replaced by the Lewis gun. It was certainly necessary to standardise on one MG, and the Vickers had to go anyway because it would not fit in the new female sponsons, but a change from Hotchkiss to Lewis guns entailed larger loopholes, redesigned mountings and a renewed search for several thousand replacement weapons. The change was instigated by Maj Baker-Carr who had established the Machine Gun School at St Omer in 1914 from which, to his great credit, had sprung the MGC. He had just transferred to the Heavy Branch as a battalion commander and would later lead the First Tank Brigade. His friend Swinton and others advised against the switch to the bulkier Lewis gun. Its rate of fire was superior to the Hotchkiss by reason of its 47- or 96-round magazine, but its barrel casing was unarmoured and highly vulnerable, while its high rate of fire could result in overheating, carbonisation and stoppages after 300–400 rounds. The mechanically more reliable Hotchkiss normally used a 30-round metal strip feed, which for tanks was shortened to only 14 rounds to improve traverse in the cramped sponsons. Tank machine-gunners generally dispensed with sights and instead applied fire on to the target solely by observation of the strike. Consequently, by the time Hotchkiss fire was worked on to the target the 14-round strip was nearly exhausted and the process had to be repeated without further gain. Hotchkiss at Coventry had recently introduced a successful belt feed but this was impracticable in the confined space of a tank. Stern and the MoM guns department were also against change to Lewis MGs but were overruled. The new armament was introduced part way through the Mk III production run. When Hotchkiss produced a flexible 50-round strip the following May the War Office readopted the gun, ordering 13,000. By then it was too late to modify loopholes and mountings on current types, and Hotchkiss ammunition had to be stowed awkwardly in racks and boxes sized for Lewis gun magazines.

At a meeting that same afternoon, 23 November, Haig summarised his requirements and promised Stern supportive action:

1. Tanks were required in as large numbers as possible.
2. It was important to get as many as possible to France before May.
3. It was very important to improve tanks periodically.
4. 'Almost any design now is likely to be better than no tank.'

*   *   *

Several new tanks and tracked vehicles were on the drawing board. The ink had barely dried on Stern's charter when Swinton told Gen Bird at the War Office that the Tank Supply Committee planned to build a superior machine, proof against high-explosive shell. The Army called for a top speed of 6mph, no change in armament, and improved trench-crossing ability. Size, and especially height, were to be kept as low as possible. Tritton began design of the 'HT' (heavy tank), later renamed 'Foster's Battletank' and finally the 'Flying Elephant'. Foster's preliminary drawing of 13 July 1916 detailed a box-like hull set on conventionally low-slung tracks, and trailing Tritton's steering tail. At 32ft 6in without the tail, it was 7ft longer than Mk I. The fighting compartment was right up front in a bulbous nose faced with 2in armour. A huge swinging plate of armour hung down from the overhang of the nose as a full-width (13ft) shell burster. The compartment contained all the armament, two 6-pdrs and five machine guns, their combined arc of forward fire running back to just abaft the beam. A double skin of 0.5in flank armour was carried well down over the tracks. Twin Daimler 105hp engines were coupled in V-type form with a common crankcase. A pair of short pivoting secondary tracks were set at the rear between the main tracks. These could be driven if extra traction was needed to get out of trouble on soft ground. Tritton called it a 'Live Belly' system and patented it later that year, though it was never fitted to tanks.[29] The very ambitious Flying Elephant weighed around 100 tons, about twice the weight that chaintrack technology could handle at that time.

Revisions followed in August. Frontal armour was increased to 3in and flank to 2in. To offset weight Tritton reduced its length to 27ft and the width to just under 10ft. The tail and frontal burster plate were scrapped and the two auxiliary tracks were lengthened. The fighting compartment was extended right back and heightened. Two machine guns were mounted on each flank and at the rear, and a single 3in gun in front replaced the twin 6-pdrs. In its revised form the tank looked much like Little Willie. Speed was 2mph. Weight remained at 100 tons. At this point the Elephant's tactical purpose changed from a vague 'attack' role to tank killing. It was feared that the Germans were building their own armoured fighting vehicles. Tritton cut weight to 50–60 tons by reducing armour to 1.5in, and construction of the first machine began in November 1916. Stern reported on 31 January 1917 that it would be completed early in March. He planned to build twenty, but the project was cancelled soon afterwards following unenthusiastic reactions from Kiggell and Butler, and the part-built machine was scrapped. The Elephant offered twice the weight, half the speed and less main armament than the Mk IV. Thinking had moved on and mobility was now felt to be a surer defence than heavy armour. It was a questionable conclusion which would influence British tank design until the Second World War.

* * *

Tritton had begun design of his twin-engined 14-ton 'Whippet' in October 1916. As the Medium A, it was a faster, lighter tank which could range with the cavalry ahead of the 28-ton heavies to break up troop concentrations preparing to counter-attack when enemy lines were penetrated. The idea had crystallised during Tritton's recent information-gathering visit to the 'Loop' near Albert. The Foster Daimler transmission was too bulky for the machine, hence its independently driven tracks, set low and steered on the throttles alone. The Tylor 40hp engines gave a top speed of over 8mph.

Fowler's of Leeds were also commissioned to design a chaser tank. They were instructed in November 1916, perhaps as a fall back, and were to incorporate one of the Rolls-Royce engines originally purchased for Crompton's Pedrails. Their proposals were not taken up. In May 1917 Butler and Elles called for a 'Supply Vehicle (Medium)' on tracks or wheels, with shrapnel protection for driver and engine. Fowler's then got to work on an experimental supply tank based on their chaser. They also collaborated with the Associated Equipment Company to build a machine in mild steel based on an AEC 5-ton lorry. That September Stern reported that an attempt had been made to graft a lorry body on to a 'Medium A tank' but the result was top-heavy.[30]

* * *

Maj Knothe was appointed in November as Technical Liaison Officer between Anley at Wool, Stern in London and Elles in France. It was a sound decision; Knothe and Wilson worked well together. Knothe had just designed a central 'third track' scheme not unlike Tritton's 'Live Belly' system. Metro was ordered to make an experimental set in November but the work was later cancelled. Knothe was also designing a Mk VII heavy tank based on Mk I but lengthened a few feet in the tail and with Williams Janney hydraulic transmission. It went through many revisions before an experimental machine emerged in October 1917; fitted with a Ricardo 250hp engine it performed well in trials. Seventy-four machines were ordered the following January, but only one was delivered before the war ended.

*   *   *

John Greg at Oldbury and Walter Wilson had been working since March 1916 on a tracked gun carrier for a 6in howitzer or a 5in 60-pdr which could be brought up quickly to advanced positions in support of attacking infantry. It was said to have been Greg's idea.[31] The gun could quickly be mounted or dismounted, or fired from the vehicle. Alternatively it could carry 10 tons of supplies or 160 rounds of 6in ammunition.

In May the War Office formally requested 'a motor gun carriage which could keep closer to infantry than a horse-drawn field gun. . . . The object of such a weapon would be the destruction of buildings and emplacements.'[32] Gen Louis Jackson at Trench Warfare also threw his hat into the ring, proposing rather unconvincingly to put a gun on the Pedrail tracks which he had inherited from Crompton's experiments. The commissioning authority, the Ordnance Board, refused to give Stern design approval for the Greg/Wilson unit. He went over their heads the next day, 16 June, and appealed to Lloyd George who immediately authorised production of fifty machines. An experimental carrier was built by Metropolitan and successfully test fired its 60-pdr the following January.[33] Construction of the remainder went to loco builders Kitson's of Leeds.

*   *   *

The fall of Asquith's government in December 1916 and the formation of an all-party coalition under Lloyd George left Edwin Montagu, a staunch Asquith supporter, with no alternative but to resign as Minister of Munitions. Since his appointment in July he had freely given Stern and the tanks programme the support they needed to maintain production. He was succeeded on 11 December by Christopher Addison, who as Parliamentary Secretary had been Lloyd George's right-hand man in setting up the

Ministry. The new government was committed to a more vigorous prosecution of the war. Lloyd George quickly reorganised the system of supreme control. A small War Cabinet was founded under his chairmanship which never exceeded seven members. He avoided the weakness of previous War Councils and Committees which were overlarge and inflexible, their members too burdened with departmental responsibilities to devote time to strategic direction. For Bertie Stern the change brought the welcome assurance of Prime Ministerial backing.

*   *   *

Elles had established his headquarters at the end of November in a château at Bermicourt, west of St Pol. Unhappy with the bureaucratic maze of military and civil agencies on which the Heavy Branch depended, he had the last word for 1916. With heavy irony Hugh Elles informed GHQ on 31 December:

The general organisation of the Heavy Branch in England and France is faulty. In France, the fighting organisation is under a junior officer who, *faute de mieux*, has become responsible for initiating all important questions of policy, organisation, design and personnel through GHQ France, and thence through five different branches at the War Office. In England, the administrative and training organisations are under a senior officer, located 130 miles from the War Office, with a junior officer (Staff Captain) in London to deal with the five branches above mentioned. The system is working now because headquarters in France have been free from the questions of operations for most of the last six weeks, and have therefore been in a position to deal imperfectly and at a distance with the larger aspects of the whole matter. In effect the tail in France is trying to wag a very distant and headless dog in England. [34]

Ten

DIVISIONS

So far as tanks are concerned, this summer's offensive is going to see one of the worst failures and scandals of the war unless certain spares in sufficient quantities are forthcoming and/or certain modifications in design are put in hand immediately.[1]

Col Frank Searle, Heavy Branch technical adviser, to
Brig Gen Hugh Elles, 24 March 1917

A fter breaking with the Landships Committee, Crompton returned to his private battle to persuade the Army to adopt a self-propelled heavy gun. He was joined by the admirable Legros. The Colonel pressed his ideas on the cautiously receptive Munitions Inventions Department. Stern was happy to let Moir's people handle all such submissions. Crompton proposed a technically ambitious 15-ton gunship mounting not one but two 4.5in howitzers. They would fire from the vehicle, their arcs restricted to avoid overturning the machine from the formidable recoil. A number of innovations reflected Strait's and Field's views on pivoting and profiled tracks. To overcome the sagging of long tracks which bedevilled the Bullock machines, Crompton cut his in half and fitted the two assemblies in line on either side of the 16ft hull. A single smaller track was set centrally in front, Killen Strait style, with a matching one aft. These were also driven and were pivoted to aid climbing and add stability when firing. Powered by twin 50hp engines, and at only 6ft 3in high, the outfit had a claimed gap-crossing ability identical to Foster's Little Willie.

Maj Gen Scott-Moncrieff inspected the drawings and a model at Thriplands in March 1916. Crompton had suspended a three-sixteenths-inch steel plate in front of the machine as a shell 'burster screen'. An alternative version was made up like a Venetian blind. The idea had originated with Tom Tulloch the previous summer. Extended arms held the screen 7ft ahead of the hull's frontal armour, putting the viewer in mind of an iron matador with cape at the ready. Scott-Moncrieff stalled; the first tank production orders had just been placed. Crompton was surprised to be told that it would be necessary to refer to the Army Council for a decision concerning motorised artillery following up an infantry advance. In the interval he and Legros refined the design to produce 'Emplacement Destroyer No. 1' (E.D. 1). The second howitzer was omitted, as were the fore and aft tracks and the burster screen.

They were no further forward in June when Moir's successor, Col H.E. Goold-Adams, proposed a redesign to a simple gun carrier or haulage tractor. Legros left in disgust to join the MoM. Crompton dug in, replying to Goold-Adams:

> I have interviewed many engineer officers of standing who have been in charge of sections at the Front, and they all tell me that there is an urgent demand for the vehicle as originally designed by me which can follow up the first waves of infantry advance and take up a new position to open fire without delay. . . . This is the French system which has been so successful. . . . All the evidence agrees on one point, and that is that guns moved by motive power can be advanced over rough ground at a greater rate, present a smaller target and be brought into any position in a manner impossible with guns drawn by [unprotected] animal teams and drivers. . . . I appeal to you as a soldier who wishes to save men's lives that this matter is far too urgent to be put off day after day.[2]

Crompton had one good shot left in his locker – Maj Daw RE, newly arrived from the front. The two met Goold-Adams two days later. Daw told them that in almost every case the ground gained at great cost was lost through delay in bringing artillery up into new positions. He contrasted this with the French whose 75s were hauled from one position to another 'every few minutes'. Goold-Adams immediately commissioned the Colonel to design and build an E.D. 2 machine with further detailed improvements. A general drawing was submitted and reached Tritton for comment in September. It was characteristically strong on sizes of angle iron and details of rivet pitch but lacked much basic information. Tritton's report sank it; he thought the design 'entirely unpracticable'. The assignment was cancelled on the 19th. Crompton sought Churchill's backing for £2,000 to build and test the machine, with no success. He soldiered on alone, producing an E.D. 3 on a single pair of tracks, but the Ministry closed his file in February 1917 before the design was completed. Crompton never recovered £400 of out-of-pocket expenses, a substantial sum. His battle tactics were sound, and he refused to give up until the doors in Whitehall were finally closed against him. The German Army put a flatbed on powered tracks in 1918 as a transporter (*Uberlandwagen*). Several were converted to carry twin field guns as self-propelled artillery.

*   *   *

Anley was so short of tanks by the close of 1916 that instruction at Wool continued round the clock in three shifts. He needed fifty machines to cover the five battalions under training. By January he was down to fifteen very tired Mk Is with five under repair at any one time. Mks II and III were considered valueless for fighting and all 100 were assigned for training only; Anley was promised seventy-five and Elles twenty-five. Many, possibly all, were accordingly plated in mild steel.[3] To avoid delay the fifty Mk II were fitted with Mk I pattern sponsons rather than awaiting conversion to Lewis mountings. So far so good, but it soon emerged that Haig was unlikely to get the new Mk IV in time for the opening of his spring offensive. Elles combed the workshops and training areas for machines. Stern saw a disaster in the making, knowing that a mass failure of worn-out or inadequately protected tanks on the battlefield would probably kill the weapon for good. He cautioned Anley against releasing his twenty-five newly arrived Mk II tanks, warning that they were not bullet-proof. Anley disbelieved him, writing to the D of A on 24 February 1917:

The information that only 15 tanks at Wool had bullet-proof front plates [i.e. Anley's Mk I machines] was based on a minute from the MWS Department. I proceeded to Wool to verify by testing plates with a chisel, and the minute from the MWS Department was found to be incorrect; this was confirmed by a further minute from the MWS Department. The actual position is that 25 Mk II tanks can be sent to France from Wool, of which the majority will be in fair running order suitable perhaps for a short action.[4]

Stern told Addison on 12 March:

As Director General of the Department which has been responsible for the design and which has produced every tank, I have persistently opposed the premature employment of tanks this year. At the War Office meeting last Sunday General Butler assured me that 60 machines of Mark I, II and III which are being kept in France ready for action only as a temporary measure, and which are really practise machines, will be returned for training purposes as soon as they can be replaced by the delivery of Mark IV machines.

I consider it more than unwise to use practise tanks in action under <u>any</u> [sic] circumstances. They have all the faults that necessitated the design of last year being altered to the present design of Mark IV. In addition the training of the men is being delayed by this action. Their failure will undoubtedly ruin the confidence of the troops in the future of Mechanical Warfare. For the sake of 60 machines, the whole future of thousands of tanks will be most unjustifiably prejudiced.[5]

The first Mk IV machines reached Wool on 2 April, almost three months later than planned. The offensive opened the following week. By then the original programme would have given Haig some 400 Mk IV fighting tanks plus training machines. The first nineteen arrived at Havre on the 17th/18th, nine days after Gen Allenby's Third Army moved out from Arras supported by the sixty obsolescent and patched-up tanks scraped together by Elles. They included Anley's twenty-five suspect Mk II machines. Half the force had been knocked out by the time the first of the new types arrived. The great gallantry of the crews, especially of those in the soft-skinned tanks, secured some local successes, but for the new arm it was a bad start to the season.

The Army Council had virtually ignored the provisos on labour provision and protection which Montagu attached to his tank delivery forecasts. Stern had requested 2,000 more workpeople. He got 275 and later claimed he had been let down by the Ministry's Labour Department and the Army. The Adjutant-General's department continued to trawl the tank factories for recruits in spite of the weapon's Priority 1 status for labour and materials. Labour protection for tanks only came at the end of April on Haig's orders. It appears, however, that Stern's appeal for labour was greatly inflated by Metropolitan which put in a request for over 1,000 men in October 1916 when it was contracted to build 600 Mk IV tanks. The company was placed on a special priority list, but Ministry checks revealed that consistently from that date it had almost no vacancies registered with the labour exchanges serving its Saltley and Oldbury tank plants.[6]

The War Office had sought ministerial confirmation in December that tank orders could be met from existing resources. Montagu, on the point of resignation from the Ministry, supported Stern in refusing to give any such assurance. On 6 February 1917 Stern forecast completion of Mks II and III by mid-month, followed by the first 120 Mk IV in March. He expected output to rise to 280 monthly by September, subject to continuation of the current Priority 1 which attached only to tanks and optical munitions. Stern's forecast was torpedoed five days later when Haig was forced to put aeroplanes and gun repair above tank production. The priority on supply of engines fell further, to P4, after the demands of aeroplanes, petrol tractors and light railway engines. Construction of 200 tanks in Glasgow was simultaneously threatened by an Admiralty order for 70 ships at 10 a month which monopolised Scottish capacity for large stampings. By the end of February the MWSD faced a 200-tank shortfall in deliveries over the period March–May.

Labour shortages actually worsened in March as the Army withdrew men from tank work without notice. Others were 'debadged', leading them to expect imminent conscription and resulting in some slackening of effort in the factories. Tritton asked the MoM for 250 skilled men – he was sent one fitter. Gore Anley sent two workshop companies – 110 officers and 368 other ranks – to Metropolitan at the end of the month, and a third followed in April. Fears of trade union hostility proved groundless and the effect on tank output as well as on mechanical training was impressive. Anley wanted to draw 600 men from training battalions for further schooling as workshop personnel; this would prime the pump to maintain a regular pool of that number of trainees passing through Metro's tank factories. Whigham approved, providing their overall training period was not extended. The system was maintained despite attempts by the War Office to drain the pool. It had reduced to 200 men by February 1918.

Addison and Stern were summoned to a meeting of the War Cabinet on 22 March to explain the discrepancy between forecasts and deliveries. Addison reported that a serious miscalculation had been made in the original estimate. After the lessons of Flers, he said, design approval for the Mk IV had been delayed until 23 November. The drawings were completed on 7 January. He hoped the programme would only be a month to six weeks in arrears. Considering their labour difficulties, he thought this a good performance. Addison said he was, however, dissatisfied with the 'tank organisation' and was taking steps to improve it.

Butler was pressing Whigham for more civilian labour for tank production, the CIGS replying that if a large number of men who were potential soldiers were diverted to tank factories, the Army (and the tanks), would have to go that number short. Butler persisted, urging that tanks should have the same manpower priority as guns and ammunition. He reminded Whigham that the Army planned to double the number of battalions from nine to eighteen, and this was reflected in the current supply programme which required deliveries for the new battalions to begin in September–October. For that reason the War Office authorised production to run on after the first 1,000 'at a rate which cannot be fixed at present, but which experience in the Field will determine'.[7] Glad of so imprecise an instruction, Stern ordered Metropolitan to build a further 560 Mk IV, bringing the total to 1,400 machines. Contracts for the remainder had been placed earlier with Foster's, Armstrong's of Elswick and Coventry Ordnance in Glasgow (100 each), and Mirrlees Watson and Wm Beardmore, both of Glasgow (50 each). From Mk IV onwards all Foster's tank plates were riveted to the standard girder pitch adopted by the other suppliers. Tritton's earlier tanks were identifiable by the evenly spaced and closer boilermakers' pitch with which the company was more familiar.[8]

*   *   *

On his visit to France in September 1916 Stern had been much impressed with the petrol electric transmission of the French St Chamond tank which gave much faster speed changes than Tritton's labour-intensive system. Wilson was critical, preferring an epicyclic gearchange for the next generation. With conflicting advice from other quarters, Stern called for a range of transmissions to be evaluated in a field competition. Meantime, a Daimler petrol electric system was installed in 'Mother'. It linked the engine directly to a generator which powered two electric motors, each driving its own track. Stern was so confident of success that he ordered 600 sets on 6 January 1917 before the system had been tested. He planned to upgrade Mk IV after the first 220 machines, putting the petrol electric transmissions into a Mk IVA as a transitional type before a completely new design was introduced. Tests soon afterwards were disappointing – the tank could only pull out of a shell hole in a succession of violent jolts while racing its engine at 1,800 revolutions and suddenly shifting the brushes to deliver

1,000 amps. The order was cancelled. Elles was informed at once, commenting that none of the other types would be of practical value inside six months and that Stern's plans to build 500 Mk IVA by the end of August were unachievable.

Of the other two petrol electric systems selected for the contest, the St Chamond installation was not completed in time after a slow response from the French suppliers; and the British Westinghouse Company submitted a bulky transmission weighing 5 tons. A complex but lightweight multiple clutch assembly by Wilkins was a late cancellation after problems. Walter Wilson had designed a promising light (2 tons) epicyclic arrangement built by Metropolitan. He had realised the speed of steering was critical to the tank's survival under fire and accordingly evolved the epicyclic control in preference to a clutch mechanism as, he explained, 'a brake can stand more punishment than a clutch and is easier to judge in its application'. Wilson's gears ran a virtually trouble-free 300-mile test. The other candidates were hydraulic variable speed systems by Hele-Shaw (5 tons), which also failed to complete in time, and Williams-Janney with an almost equally heavy adaptation of its gear to rotate naval gun turrets. Mk II assembly began at Oldbury in December 1916, and six in mild steel were earmarked for installation of these systems.[9]

Having already established the winners and losers, Stern laid on a demonstration rather than formal trials. He wanted to counter negative attitudes with a show of vigorous progress in British tank development, and to stimulate expansion of the new arm on both sides of the Channel. The 'Oldbury Trials' were staged in great secrecy on 3 March at the 20 Squadron experimental ground, in conjunction with a London conference on the tactical employment of tanks. Over 100 senior representatives of the British and French General Staffs and their tank forces, designers, manufacturers and munitions officials travelled up by special train. The course was a simulated battlefield, the largest craters naturally fronting the viewing stand. Stern added two prototype machines. Tritton's twin-engined chaser had first run four weeks earlier, showing impressive speed and manoeuvrability despite cooling problems. The other vehicle was the sole Metropolitan-built experimental gun carrier, designed by Wilson and Greg. It was first driven on 1 January and mounted a 5in 60-pdr gun which had been successfully fired from the machine. An 'original standard machine' completed the line-up. It has recently been suggested that this was Mk I No. 555, a very much modified (female) machine used solely for experimental work. Alternatively it could have been just about the first Mk IV, the initial nine or ten of which were built that month and delivered 2 April.

Wilson's machine had engine trouble but its epicyclics easily won the day. His transmission provided one-man control at last, releasing the two gearsmen for more destructive work. It was further refined before installation in the Mk V in January 1918 where it was coupled to a purpose-built 150hp engine designed by Harry Ricardo, a brilliant 32-year-old who was forbidden to use aluminium or high-tensile steels in the construction. Stern ordered 700 Ricardo engines for the tank in January 1917 before a single engine had been built and tested. He later refused an instruction from the Engines Priorities Committee to cancel the order. Instead, he doubled it. Ricardo's 150, 225 and 300hp engines became standard tank power plants.

The conference which followed the Oldbury trials sought agreement on tactics. The British General Staff viewed the tank as purely an infantry support weapon and wanted a faster machine to keep up with attacking troops. The designers – Stern and d'Eyncourt – were convinced that this was too limited a role. They wanted tanks to operate on the flanks of an attack, moving over firm unshelled ground far enough from the infantry to avoid drawing enemy fire on to them. They would act as cavalry and attack gun positions in the enemy's rear. D'Eyncourt stressed the value of a surprise attack led by tanks rather than infantry. The general opinion of the Allies was that at present the tanks were too unreliable for such roles, and were of greatest value as infantry support in the later stages of an advance where ground conditions would be good. A surprise mass tank attack was not dismissed, but would have to await larger numbers.

After Oldbury the French Ministry of Inventions rated Britain's tank research and development very highly. Stern proposed that his experimental work should be expanded on a factory site, with French military and engineering representatives permanently attached to his office. He sought Addison's approval for the requisitioning of Foster's works at Lincoln under the Defence of the Realm Act, on terms no less favourable than the company's anticipated returns. Tritton would be freed to devote his whole time to research, backed by the full resources of the Ministry.[10] Stern desperately wanted to keep ahead of the field, Allied and enemy, but Addison was not persuaded. He was never a fervent supporter of the tanks programme and this was not the first time that he had shown undue caution in its affairs.

His relationship with Stern was often bruising, most of the pain, it has to be said, falling on the Minister. The two men were temperamentally poles apart.

Foster's instead became a 'Controlled Establishment' that month under the Munitions of War Act. The customary entitlement to retention of 40 per cent of profits was reduced to 20 per cent, the balance being taken as tax. In return additional capital allowances were given to aid expansion and purchase of equipment. To service its first tanks order Foster's had to build a new erecting shop and enlarge the boiler shop. Other workshops were dismantled and re-equipped. In the ten months to June 1917 Fosters spent £15,600 on land and buildings and over £12,000 on new plant and tools.

*   *   *

A heavy repair workshop, stores and railhead were established under Maj Brockbank's command at Erin-sur-la-Turnoise. Lt Stephen Foot, its resourceful Adjutant, had taken a working party of engineers on to the snow-swept 26-acre site in December 1916. He soon acquired four decrepit local sawmills which he manned with Heavy Branch personnel. The mayors of six villages mobilised their flocks and horses and wagons to fell and haul logs. When Foot's needs were met he bartered timber for other stores, the demand up the line for planks and spars being insatiable. Tank repair sections worked outdoors in bitter conditions, short of engineering equipment and tools, and improvising primitive casting and machining locally.

The Heavy Branch engineers were joined around this time by a number of men from London's bus fleets which completed conversion from horses to motors in 1914. In the process an élite of heavy-transport engineers and designers had formed. They were headed by Frank Searle, chief of Daimler's commercial vehicles division, who had accompanied Stern's party to Flers in September 1916. On Stern's recommendation he was persuaded to join the Heavy Branch, arriving in France as a major in November. Searle was immediately promoted lieutenant-colonel and appointed technical adviser to Elles. He was an entrepreneur and a first-class engineer, rough and tough, an unpolished diamond of a man. After service as Locomotive Superintendent for the Gold Coast Government Railways he had returned to London in 1903 aged twenty-nine to find himself caught up in the omnibus revolution. A failed venture in imported bus chassis led to his engagement by the London General Omnibus Company (LGOC) in February 1907 as Superintendent of their Mortlake garage. He became Chief Engineer four months later with 15,000 horses on the books and a motley fleet of 170 motor buses.

Searle began bus manufacture in-house, his first 'X' Type appearing in 1909. His minimal diplomatic skills resulted in Col Crompton acting for LGOC in lengthy negotiations with the police to secure an operating licence for the new vehicle, the spur-driven gearbox of which had failed strict noise limits. Searle introduced his live axle 'B' Type the following year. By December 1913, 2,500 were in operation. Over 1,000 went to war on the Western Front. The last one ceased service in 1926.

Searle was summarily dismissed from LGOC in 1911 by Capt Dumble (he of the Landships Committee) after a dispute with the board. The two men had joined the company at the same time, Dumble quickly becoming General Manager. Searle was soon the most sought-after bus engineer in the capital and had refused terms to remain unconditionally with LGOC. He moved on to Daimler's of Coventry to establish a successful commercial vehicles operation, and caught up with Dumble and Crompton at the 1914 Daimler–Foster tractor trials. Before joining the tanks, Searle headed a successful British War Mission to the United States to purchase machine tools and other precision equipment for UK munitions plants.

John Brockbank was Searle's loyal assistant at London General, choosing to resign with him in 1911, and rejoining him in France in December 1916. Another from the same stable was George Rackham who had joined LGOC as Chief Draughtsman a month after Searle and Dumble. He helped Searle design the 'B' Type before moving to David Brown & Sons. Rackham's association with tank development began in May 1917 when he was engaged by the MWSD as assistant to Walter Wilson.

*   *   *

Elles had been calling for spares with increasing urgency since January 1917. The situation was now critical. Stern had seen it coming. So had Walter Layton the young Director of Munitions Requirements & Statistics (DMRS), the Minister's right-hand man at the MoM. Layton had drafted a minute to the War Office the previous September on ordering procedure for tank spares. He had said that it was hoped a supply of parts would soon be available. Stern stopped its despatch: 'Please cancel this minute for the present and leave well alone. From my experience I consider this the wisest plan.'[11] He had no intention of prompting the War Office into making what he considered would be a premature switch from tank production to spares. Stern was driven by one imperative – to keep tanks coming out of factories nose to tail. Any break in continuity was anathema to him. What came to be called 'the battle of the spares' began. It would continue for the rest of the year and beyond.

Stern had promised to send a weekly supply in response to Elles' pleas, but nothing followed the first despatch. After three weeks Elles learned that no spares could be sent for a further three weeks. He sent Uzielli over in February 1917 to agree lists of parts for all tank types for assured weekly despatch. Stern maintained that supply had been agreed on a quarterly aggregate basis, not on uniform quantities weekly. The complexities of production made a fixed weekly parts supply impossible. He slipped into the lecturing tones of the banker, admonishing the Heavy Branch for 'failing to cut its coat according to its cloth'. Having agreed a given ratio of spares 'their expenditure on replacement parts must not exceed that ratio or they will always be in difficulties'.[12] Elles was fighting a war not running a garage, and resented such homilies. But his engineer officers had certainly been sending MWSD huge demands for parts, often quite unrelated to the requirements laid down by them in a 'Spares Book' produced by Searle in January.

Rates of wear could be immense. Over 7,000 track shoes were requested in February, on top of 6,000 supplied earlier. Sprocket wheels weighing 200lb were wearing out after 30 or 40 miles because the constant mud was an effective grinding paste. The 'Spares Book' entry for sprockets (20 January) called for supply of 50 per 100 tanks. By 10 March demand was running at 1,500 per 100. Track guide rails and rollers were also in high demand, and mud penetration was wrecking the secondary gears. Lacking replacement rollers, the Erin workshops were filling old ones with cast iron as reinforcement. Stern, Tritton and others attested that the tank had been designed for a 50-mile 'life'. Stern told the MGO that the fighting tank had little need of spares once committed to battle. In other words, training tanks would require spare parts; fighting tanks would require spare fighting tanks.[13] D'Eyncourt (now Sir Eustace) acknowledged that earlier spares estimates had overlooked the fact that training machines frequently covered 100 miles in a week.

Stern was struggling to produce sprocket wheels and other steel castings despite a return to Priority 1. Demand had tripled between January and April. His programme already called for 16,000 tons of castings over the next seven months. The six firms building Mk IV were asked to send in weekly returns of castings ordered and received. Stern undertook to put pressure on the foundries to honour these, despatching his assistant, Lt Cdr P. Barry, to Leeds with instructions to stand over them and force production. Others were sent on similar missions. A new plant was laid down to produce 1,000 tons of castings per month for tank assembly and spares, but no new foundry could produce satisfactory material in less than six months. Steelfounding was still an inexact science with variable batch quality. In the first half of 1917 from 33 to 40 per cent of track link castings were being rejected on account of blowholes, and segregation of sulphur and phosphorous at the points of the link where sound steel was essential. The shortage of track links was a limiting factor in tank production and seriously affected Stern's delivery forecasts. Because of the small size of the 14lb links, only the first part of the ladle of molten steel could be used in casting them. The remaining 60 per cent was fit only for much heavier castings up to 180lb each. Unfortunately there were few foundries which were equipped to produce castings across that range. Stern's department initiated experiments which eventually raised tensile strength by heat treatment from 28 to 40 tons per square inch without reducing output. It was a significant metallurgical advance which eased the link shortage.

The tank builders and the fighting men were separated by much more than 22 miles of salt water. The balance of technical expertise lay firmly with Stern's team which expected its views to prevail. Stern was determined to keep his distance from a War Office bureaucracy which had nothing constructive to offer, while the Heavy Branch in France was demanding more involvement in matters of design and production than he considered sustainable. Stern knew how precarious his manufacturing base was, and saw no reason to increase liaison when all his energies were concentrated on maintaining uninterrupted production. On 24 March Searle's first report exploded in the near silence. His findings were characteristically blunt:

So far as tanks are concerned, this summer's offensive is going to see one of the worst failures and scandals of the war unless certain spares in sufficient quantities are forthcoming and/or certain modifications in design are put in hand immediately. . . . Of spares required, we have only been able to maintain an average of 25 tanks in service out of 125 tanks in France; 60 of this number were certainly left [abandoned] on the Somme, but many of these could have been brought in had spares been available. . . . I feel it would be a crime to manufacture and send to this country machines which there is no possibility of maintaining. With a modification in design the quantity of spares necessary could be halved . . . but I understand the Ministry of Munitions do not agree. . . . You have here in the various Battalions a lot of enthusiastic, capable engineers and I am satisfied the same spirit and talent exists in the engineering department at the MWSD. It is surely criminal to keep them apart in water-tight compartments.[14]

Searle went on to criticise the designers for failing to visit France for the past four months. He deplored the design and ordering of 200 Whippet chaser tanks without prior consultation with the end users. He recommended halving the order pending full field trials in France. He conceded that 'colossal' quantities of spares had now arrived but were unrelated to the parts actually wanted. The 1,000 machines in the pipeline would consume spares at the rate of 400 tons every 50 miles. In a covering letter Elles added that the original policy of 'any tank is better than no tank', agreed in November to maximise output, had failed. Not only that, he saw no reason to believe that future production would be maintained or that the necessary spares would be forthcoming. 'I therefore urge very earnestly that the present situation regarding design, output and maintenance be definitely stated by the Ministry of Munitions.'[15] (An earlier draft read 'extracted from' in place of 'definitely stated by'.) He ended with an appeal for a conference with the Ministry and, if necessary, a new policy based on facts rather than fantasy.

The report precipitated a meeting chaired by the Minister on 3 April. Those present included Maj Gen Furse (the MGO), Anley, Searle, Stern, d'Eyncourt and Wilson. The military men laid down that they required the same number of spares for training as for fighting machines. Stern objected that compared with a training tank, the fighting machine was a projectile and after an action it was effectively expended. This was not accepted, and the future spares requirement was confirmed at the same high level. (Five weeks later, Heavy Branch in France more than halved its spares estimates for fighting tanks.) MWSD officers would visit France 'at least monthly', and a working party would report back on the spares situation.

Stern, Wilson, Symes and others from MWSD crossed the Channel on 13 April for a ten-day series of meetings with Elles and his staff at Bermicourt, and with French tank experts. The tank actions of a few days before in the battle of Arras had again demonstrated the weapon's value, though all machines were confined to supporting roles. Two had been cut off and captured. French tanks fought for the first time on the 16th over a wide front on the hills overlooking the Aisne. Eight companies of Schneider tanks went in. Three of them were cut to pieces by artillery. The remaining eighteen-tank companies crossed the second line of enemy defences but heavy MG fire prevented the infantry from following them. They suffered heavy losses before rallying at nightfall. Of 132 deployed, 76 remained ditched or broken down near the enemy lines. They had greater success on 5 May when Schneider and St Chamond tanks led an attack on Laffaux Mill.

Stern's party reviewed the spares situation and tank supply with Uzielli, Searle and others. Searle took an aggressive line, having earlier challenged Stern's assertion that it was impossible to obtain castings for gear pinions in less than five weeks. He had earlier produced a letter from his company, Daimler's, confirming recent receipt by them of stampings for pinions from the Albion Drop Forging Company in seven days from date of order. It was a contrived comparison. The MWSD required final drive gears in the form of steel castings, these being superior to gears cut from mild steel stampings which were almost always low carbon because of the near impossibility of making acceptable stampings in higher-grade steels.

Searle had next written direct to the Minister, enclosing Daimler's letter and complaining that training tanks had been laid up for want of these parts since they were ordered in mid-January. He now accused MWSD of lacking knowledge and energy. Stern took Searle aside and warned him not to create bad blood between the departments, to which he agreed. Their further discussions were balanced and valuable, many design defects being noted for correction. Stern announced that orders had been placed for the Mk V (actually this was very premature – Metropolitan was on stand-by but the design was unfinished and the first contract was not placed until August).

Stern lunched in Paris with Lloyd George, Hankey and numerous generals, and later met Haig and Butler. His diary records that the C-in-C again told him that he wanted as many tanks as possible and instructed him not to delay while perfecting them. Haig considered them second only to aircraft, and a tremendous lifesaver. He asked who at the War Office did not believe in the tanks. Stern named the Adjutant-General's department which continued to recruit skilled men engaged on tank production. The following day Haig wrote to Gen Robertson in London that tank output to date was 'most disappointing' and asked him to take a personal interest:

The further experience of the recent battle around Arras confirms my view that as large a number of reliable tanks should be put into the Field <u>as soon as possible</u>. Although the present tank is admittedly defective in many respects, the excellent service rendered by a percentage on every occasion on which we have used them has made it quite clear that a force of well organised reliable tanks is a necessity for the modern battle, and is likely to greatly contribute to winning a victory and reaping its fruits.

I also hold that tanks will greatly contribute to economy in men, because not only can a few men accomplish in a tank, without loss, far more than a much greater number of men can do, without a tank; but the employment of tanks has been found to reduce casualties in the attacking infantry. Consequently I am of opinion that the allocation of personnel either to the Heavy Section in the Field, or for the manufacture of tanks in England should not be restricted in such a way as to interfere with the development of tanks to the fullest extent possible.

Hoping that you will personally be able to support my recommendations in this very important matter [Haig's emphasis].[16]

Stern returned to London on the 25th. Elles convened a board next day to inspect the Lewis gun mounting which was giving trouble in the newly arrived Mk IV tanks. It reported that they were arriving in France unfit to fight – the aperture in the ball mountings was too small and Central Workshops could not grind hardened steel. No date could be given for battle readiness. The three-man board, which included Searle, went on to record sixteen other defects. Similar reports were arriving from Wool. The inherent weakness of self-inspection by the producer department was only too apparent. Stern at once repeated his plea that a single representative body be established to give authoritative decisions for the Army on tank matters. He also asked that his department be given its own workshops in France and at Wool. He was absolutely right to do so, but this still begged the question of effective inspection. Haig simultaneously called for a WO Tanks Department. The fight for control of the weapon's design, production and development was reopened.

In response to Haig's letter, Lord Derby, the Secretary of State for War, called a WO/MoM meeting on 1 May at which a War Office Tank Committee was formed to correlate battle experience with design and production. Maj Gen John Capper, a divisional commander, was appointed President. As a pioneer of Army aviation Capper had overseen the formation of its first

Airship Battalion in 1906. He was joined by Lt Col E.B. Mathew-Lannowe (Anley's GSO 1), Lt Col Sir John Keane (War Office), Lt Col Stern and Sir Eustace Tennyson d'Eyncourt. The absence of anyone from the Heavy Branch in France was an extraordinary omission in view of the committee's purpose and Elles' repeated pleas to be given a direct voice on precisely this subject. The committee would produce performance specifications for the designers and would give design approval before any construction was begun. All field trials for tanks of new or approved design would be conducted under the orders of the committee. Addison, who supported Lord Derby's initiative, considered that the tank weapon was now established and its production should be administered exactly as any other munition. He was also tiring of Stern's corner-cutting and constant invoking of his charter in inter-departmental disputes. He readily agreed that the Army should collect its tanks in England and provide all subsequent transportation. This was never implemented because 20 Squadron already operated a highly efficient system and the reorganisation required for an Army version was unjustified, but Heavy Branch officers took charge of acceptance trials before the Squadron shipped the machines across to France.

Addison also agreed to transfer responsibility for inspection from Stern's department to the Ministry's munitions inspectorate. It was a necessary move but Stern stalled the handover for months. His contracts and finance sections similarly lost their independence on Addison's instructions and were placed under the central authority of the Ministry. This unsettled the tank contractors and brought protests from those threatened with renegotiation of previously agreed terms. Much more seriously, Stern's charter became waste paper overnight. Without freedom to control its finances and contracting, his department was now exposed to scrutiny and the inevitable delays and procrastinations of bureaucracy. Stern and d'Eyncourt were also faced with a military majority on the new committee. They would now have to fight their battles on two fronts.

Stern at once condemned the balance and functions of the committee, telling the inaugural meeting that he believed the imposition of the standard War Office organisation would wreck tank development. The connection between the fighting tanks in France and the people responsible for design and construction must be instantaneous and direct, he emphasised, bypassing a WO filter. Stern proposed the appointment of a director general responsible for all aspects save action in the field, nominating Capper and urging his appointment to the Army Council. He said Capper should leave design and supply to MWSD but give final design approval. The duties of the MWSD should widen to embrace not only inspection, transport and research, but also all repair, including the Central Workshops at home and in France. He was heard out in silence.

Promotions and appointments followed. Capper replaced Gore Anley who had been appointed only six weeks before as Administrative Commander of the Heavy Branch and given a London HQ. Brig Gen W. Glasgow took command of the Wool training centre. Hugh Elles was gazetted Brigadier-General, effective 15 February.

Stern repeated his proposals in a long and anguished memorandum on 18 May co-signed by d'Eyncourt. It catalogued eight months of frustrated plans, labour and materials shortages, repeated and disruptive design changes and alleged military misjudgements. The latest concerned the proportions of male and female types. Stern's department had originally set equal numbers of each. This was altered during the winter by the WO to one male for every two females. Subsequently the Army wanted three to two, but there were insufficient 6-pdrs to achieve this. On 13 June a WO weapons requisition confirmed another change to all-male type.

Their joint memorandum shocked the War Office which directed retaliatory fire at Stern; none was ever aimed at Tennyson d'Eyncourt who, despite his undeviating support for Stern, lived a charmed life. Capper called on Stern to tell him that CIGS Sir William Robertson wished him to withdraw the paper, assuring him that his criticisms would be met with alterations. It was a hollow promise. The military members of the committee soon began to impose arbitrary rulings on points of detail in design and production – matters of which they knew next to nothing. They forced a decision on 30 May that experiments should no longer be conducted as and when the MWSD decided. Instead, the committee would decide the main lines of enquiry and would itself initiate experiments involving matters of principle. They wanted free access to Stern's experimental department and called unsuccessfully for Wilson to join the committee.

*   *   *

Haig's pressure brought a dramatic increase in the tank programme. On 5 June he confirmed the adoption of two classes of fighting tank – the current 'heavy' and the lighter and faster 'medium'. He planned to form nine battalions for each. The production programme for the 1918 fighting season was accordingly identical for both types – a first establishment of 540 tanks plus replacements at 108 per month for 12 months, totalling 1,836 heavy tanks and a like number of medium machines. Additionally, 203 infantry supply tanks were required, giving a total of 3,875 machines.[17] It was a near quadrupling of the 1917 programme. Haig nominated Mk V as the preferred replacement for the heavies. As to priorities, aircraft, motor transport, light railway locomotives and gun ammunition would all take precedence over tank production.

The Tank Committee viewed mock-ups of Wilson's Mks V and VI at Saltley on 23 June. Both machines were to take his epicyclics. The military members decided to adopt the more advanced Mk VI in spite of the preference at GHQ for Mk V, and d'Eyncourt's reservations that the Mk VI was under-gunned and too great a technical leap in the dark. In place of sponsons it was to mount a single short-barrel 6-pdr forward between the track horns, with secondary armament of six Hotchkiss MG. There was an overall saving of 5 tons of armour. Other changes included much wider tracks, more interior space due to an offset engine, and a slight increase in speed. The following week the War Office ordered 1,600 Mk VI, the first 700 of which were required for training well before a battle-ready deadline of 1 March 1918.

Four weeks later the military members of the committee were persuaded by Stern and d'Eyncourt to reverse their decision and accept the view that it would be unwise to proceed direct from Mk IV to the radically different Mk VI. They were offered instead an improved Mk IV with the Ricardo/Wilson power train. Stern proposed to install the one-man control system in the last 400 as a transitional Mk IVA series pending the earliest possible switch to Mk V. Capper was delighted to approve.

At this point the War Office cast doubt on the entire 1918 programme. In an extraordinary communication the Army High Command declared on 27 July that tank requirements would in future be governed by the availability of scarce manufacturing resources. In other words tank production would no longer be determined by operational objectives. The news implied an imminent production cutback. Tank procurement was becoming a revolving door of orders and countermands. At the same time Stern and d'Eyncourt refused to attend further meetings of the WO Tank Committee, damning it as a waste of time. Stern had appealed to Lloyd George:

A crisis has arisen in the relations between the War Office and the Ministry of Munitions re the progress and development of Mechanical Warfare, namely design and production. . . . I continually pressed the War Office that they should establish a special department of tanks . . . with whom my department could deal as a link between the fighting and production sides. The War Office has set its face against this most resolutely. I have had to visit nearly every department of the War Office on all sorts of vital questions and, naturally, with most unsatisfactory results. . . . The committee is now interfering in design and production which, if allowed to continue, will result in chaos and disaster. I refuse to allow this.[18]

Stern yet again urged the appointment of a director general of tanks at the War Office. He also asked for more technical officers and for the granting of proper rank to his military staff – Rendle, his Assistant Director, was a Lieutenant; Walter Wilson still a Major. These requests were repeatedly refused by the military. Before sending the letter Stern showed it to the DCIGS, Sir Robert Whigham, who surprised him with the welcome news that a tank department was about to be formed. The War Office Tank Directorate would formulate military requirements for tanks, control their use and supply, and train personnel. It was designated Department SD2 and began work in August under Capper.

The axe fell on 24 August. The War Office informed the Ministry that it had reviewed its requirements following word from Sir Douglas Haig. The total of fighting machines for 1918 was cut by almost 25 per cent. The programme now comprised:

Type	(WO order, 5 June)	revised 24 August	of which, required by 1 March 1918
Heavy	(1,836)	1,600	700
Medium	(1,836)	1,200	600
Supply	(203)	800	450
Gun carriers	(–)	100	48
Totals	(3,875)	3,700	1,798

GHQ was employing its tanks piecemeal and had allowed itself to become further disillusioned by their sometimes inconclusive performance. Haig had been persuaded to reduce future fighting strength and greatly increase infantry supply capability. Lines of communication were shelled into oblivion and only tracked and splinter-proof machines would serve. For the heavies a decision as to type was avoided, the War Office leaving it at 'Mk V, Mk VI or any improved type'. The armament requirement of 13 June was changed again from all-male to equal numbers of male and female tanks. Production of the 1,200 medium machines would commence with Tritton's Whippets and run on until a replacement materialised. Stern seriously doubted the ability of drivers to control the twin-engined machines in action, and was critical of the Army for committing to so many medium tanks before any had been delivered and battle-tested. Elles shared his misgivings.

In short, the Army wanted over 42,000 tons of tanks of all types for the start of the 1918 fighting season. On Priority 5, Stern would be allocated only a proportion of the strategic materials he needed. Track link castings and ball bearings were his greatest supply problem, together with a serious shortage of draughtsmen whose trade was unprotected from recruitment. He was in no position to deliver. Nevertheless, that evening he gave Metropolitan a provisional order for 800 Mk V. The contract was awarded in September. The military knowingly ignored or failed to understand the consequences of these monthly changes of direction.

Lucien Legros held strong views on the inability of the High Command to comprehend and organise for mechanical warfare. As President of the IAE he had told his members:

This is an engineer's war . . . yet the mechanical engineer is not a recognised factor in the Army! There is no Chief Mechanical Engineer corresponding to the Engineer-in-Chief of the Fleet, and it has been necessary to create a Ministry of Munitions to deal with vital questions of production. The same applies right down the scale with the result that men of high mechanical ability and qualifications are officered by men with only ordinary military knowledge or mere administrative capacity.[19]

Having assured the Tank Committee on 25 July that the remaining Mk IV machines would be built with one-man control, Stern transfixed Capper four weeks later with the information that it could not be done, telling him unconvincingly that 'circumstances alter frequently and such changes are inevitable and might occur at any moment'.[20] In fact, Metropolitan had warned Stern earlier that week that if they were instructed to put the Ricardo/Wilson system into the remaining Mk IV machines the assembly process would have to close in preparation for the changeover. Skilled labour and stamping and machining capacity would be transferred to other munitions work. Stern and his team agreed the 'absolute necessity' of maintaining continuity of output and resolved to press on with Mk IV until its completion. Stern told them 'if the Army does not take the last 3–400 they will get nothing else' and in that case he would sell the surplus tanks to the French.[21] The need to break continuity for the upgrade had been entirely predictable, at least to Metro, the only surprise being the delay before Stern became aware of it.

The infuriated Capper refused to accept Stern's word and alerted the Army Council. Stern's retraction destroyed what remained of his credibility with the already hostile military. As early as January 1917 Elles had confided to Brig Gen Wigram at GHQ that he thought Stern's department was badly organised and unreliable: 'We want facts and dates, not hot air. D'Eyncourt is of course very reliable.'[22] From the Army's standpoint Stern had consistently failed to meet his own delivery forecasts on which operational planning relied; he had inflated by 40 per cent the number of Mk IV machines ordered by them; and now he had withdrawn his assurances of the vehicles' convertibility to one-man control. Perhaps understandably, the military were less concerned with the underlying reasons.

Stern's forecasts were proving undeliverable because he was denied materials and skilled labour despite his forceful pleading. The MoM was also experiencing a general tendency for munitions suppliers to give over-optimistic delivery forecasts and tanks were no exception. Tritton, for example, had told the MGO, DCIGS and Elles on 30 April that he 'hoped to have 50 to 100 Medium tanks in France by the end of July'.[23] The first two or three reached Elles late that October. The 100th was not delivered until the end of February 1918.

Stern and the DNC pursued volume at almost any price for the 1917 campaign, knowing they could do so only at the cost of delay in introducing real improvement. Stern repeatedly pointed out that 'Quality without quantity is of small value in this war.'[24] The next generation of tanks was coming off the drawing boards, however. Construction of the superior Mk V was planned to start in October, but the slower than expected rate of Mk IV production pushed this back to January 1918, too late for any spring offensive. There is a passing reference in September 1917 to an experimental Mk IV tank which had been fitted with the Ricardo/Wilson system.[25] Harry Ricardo records in his memoirs that at that time his new 150hp engines were being used to replace the Daimler units in Mk IV tanks.[26] It is unlikely that this amounted to a large-scale conversion.

Stern had other problems closer to home. He had reorganised the MWSD at the beginning of the year after calling in Percy Perry, Managing Director of Ford Motor Company (Europe), who had been sourcing American engines for the tank programme. Perry was asked to set up the department on the lines of a motor manufacturer. He separated its activities into thirteen divisions, but Walter Wilson as Director of Engineering had a nebulous role lacking authority, without a department and with no official design function despite his own pivotal contribution. The Design Department was controlled by Lt F.B. Shaw.

By June Wilson could take no more. Stern had set up a departmental Experiments Committee in late May to which Wilson, Tritton and d'Eyncourt were given honorary membership. Stern emphasised to Wilson that this was an advisory appointment and that he had no executive powers. Wilson addressed his letter of resignation to the Minister. He contrasted the speed with which Mk I was introduced with the continuing delay in starting Mk V production: 'I have nothing but a title "Director of Engineering". I have no authority, no responsibilities, am in a purely consultative capacity, and to give my opinion only when asked. . . . I have twice been dismissed by Col Stern but have refused to go.'[27] Christopher Addison patched things up and Wilson withdrew the letter, but his action exposed weakness at the top.

Throughout the war almost every fighting tank was built to Walter Wilson's design. The transmission system which he introduced from the Mk V onwards transformed the weapon's performance. Yet he was sidelined by Stern, to work on his own initiative up at Metro's Birmingham offices. In a report later that year Sir Arthur Duckham, a member of the Munitions Council, praised the quality of the department's personnel but added 'the designers must be brought under one strong head who thoroughly understands his subject. They must not be allowed, as now, each to work out his own ideas and submit them separately to the Head of the Department [Stern] who, not being an engineer, suffers the disability of not being able to give full weight to technical consideration in making decisions.'[28] Years later Bertie Stern gave his opinion on the proper place for engineers: 'I have always believed that a brilliant engineer should be kept, metaphorically speaking, in a cage, or rather in the drawing office but never near production or in an executive post.'[29]

When Stern's contracting and finance operations came under Ministry control in May 1917, his contracts section under the imperturbable Dale Bussell found itself in the inflexible grip of the Munitions Contracts Department (MCD). Hitherto the MCD had been forced to stand off, leaving Stern free to negotiate and award contracts direct under his original charter. Stern managed to break free for the gun-carrier work when, having obtained Lloyd George's approval in June to build the machine, he was careful to end his formal acknowledgement with the words: 'This work will be carried out under the original charter of the Tank Committee.'

Bussell's files were now combed. The MCD concluded that Metropolitan's profits on the 1,000 Mk IV tanks were excessive, notwithstanding that Stern had negotiated prices down the previous August to £4,300 per male tank and £4,250 per female, against the £5,000 paid for Mk I. Later design changes further reduced these to £3,820 and £3,770.

MCD officials dug in for a protracted battle with Metropolitan. Negotiations were reopened on 1 June, the Ministry securing an offer from Managing Director Lincoln Chandler to cut prices by £500 per machine in return for a further but unquantified order at the same price. The MCD held out for a reduction of £2,500 and no side order. Chandler withdrew the offer 'very much upset' in July, proposing instead a new contract at £3,000 per tank for twelve months' output. Ever more complex negotiations continued in tough bargaining. At a July meeting between MCD officials and Metropolitan Stern made no secret of his view that the company's original offer should have been accepted. This wrecked the Ministry's negotiating position. Metropolitan then refused to deal further with anyone save Stern and his deputy, Norman Holden.

The Director General of Munitions Contracts, Philip Hanson, was wheeled in and was compelled to negotiate through Stern. Having conceded the original terms for the 1,000 Mk IV, his objective shifted to a unit price for the 1,600 Mk V. After consulting Stern on terms acceptable to the Ministry, Hanson asked him to communicate them to Metropolitan with a face-saving request that Metro should appear to have originated them by formally submitting them back to the Ministry. Stern phoned the details to Metropolitan, only to be asked by Hanson next day to withdraw the proposal due to a miscalculation. Stern could take no more, telling Hanson on 16 August:

I wish to point out that this is a matter of vital urgency; it is holding up the production for 1918. The War Office order was dated June; these negotiations were started in June and nothing has yet been settled. I therefore hold you, and the Contracts Department, entirely responsible for at least one month's delay and any further delay that occurs from this date. I wish also to point out that my Department were able to design, manufacture and deliver the first 100 tanks within 7 months . . . and that this was due very largely to the powers given me by the Ministry of Munitions to make my Contracts through my Contract Department with the advice of your Department. . . . Owing to the endless delay . . . I must warn you that unless the matter is settled within the next 48 hours I shall close the contract on my own responsibility and inform the Minister accordingly.[30]

A base price of £2,850 for 1,600 tanks was agreed on 5 September. It would be increased by the costs of retooling from Mk IV to Mk V, to be mutually agreed. The formula was a compromise for both sides, Metropolitan having been promised special confidentiality over book inspection. A contract was signed on the 22nd, three and a half months after the War Office order. Metropolitan confirmed that because of the uncertainties it had not given preparatory work its undivided attention over that period. Five days later, Philip Hanson was replaced by John Mann.

The Contracts Department's obstruction across all munitions procurement led to a move in 1918 for decentralisation. Heads of production insisted on the need for their departments to award contracts immediately on completion of negotiations. Sir John Mann, as he had become, was summoned by the Ministry Warfare Group in July and given a roasting, but he preserved his department's procedures unchanged.[31]

Bertie Stern's correspondence and later memoirs reveal almost nothing of his personal convictions, but in August 1917 he wrote frankly to Hanson (a senior civil servant, late of the Dublin Office of Works) after accusing him and his department of intolerable delay:

My Dear Hanson,

I believe it is from ignorance of each other's point of view that our contentions flow. When a cold penury blasts the abilities of a nation and stunts the growth of its active energies, the ill is beyond all calculation. Mere parsimony is not economy. Expense, and great expense, may be an essential part in true economy. Economy is a distributive virtue and consists, not in saving, but in selection. Parsimony requires no providence, no sagacity, no powers of combination, no comparison, no judgement. Mere instinct, and that not an instinct of the noblest kind, may produce this false economy in perfection.

The other economy has larger views. It demands a discriminating judgement and a firm sagacious mind. It shuts one door to impudent importunity only to open another, and a wider, to unpresuming merit.[32]

*   *   *

Haig's first opportunity to use his Mk IV tanks came in June 1917. Gen Nivelle's Spring Offensive had failed and mutinies were sapping the will of the French Armies. Following Nivelle's replacement by Gen Pétain the French needed time to restore morale. It fell to Haig and his sixty-four well-equipped divisions to take the lead. He decided to carry out an earlier plan to strike the German right flank, forcing it back sufficiently to open a coastal corridor to the Dutch frontier and neutralise enemy submarine bases in the Belgian ports. From there a drive on Lille could clear the road to Antwerp and Brussels. The first phase was an assault on 7 June on the Messines ridge to straighten out the Ypres salient. It was a model attack, preceded by the simultaneous explosion of nineteen huge mines beneath a 10-mile stretch of the German front line. Sixty-two Mk IV tanks met little resistance, silencing numerous Maxims and outrunning the infantry later that day to hold gains while they caught up. The ground was badly broken but dry.

The second phase, which became the third battle of Ypres, was preceded by a record twenty-four days of artillery bombardment from over 3,000 guns along 11 miles of front. It obliterated all watercourses and land drainage, leaving a quagmire which ensured the ultimate failure of the offensive. The assault opened on 31 July in heavy rain which continued intermittently for weeks. It was kept going against all logic until finally it submerged 4 miles further on in the swamp wilderness of Passchendaele in November at a cost of 250,000 casualties. The 28-ton Mk IV was no amphibian. Heroic efforts were made to bring the machines into action and new unditching gear came into its own, but many at GHQ expected the impossible of the new weapon and lost interest in it when miracles were not achieved. Haig remained confident but was recklessly wasting a prime asset. Maj Philip Hamond commanding 18 Company of F Battalion described the conditions in which tanks struggled simply to reach their start lines. He led eight tanks up on the night of 21 August:

All my people worked like blacks to get the tanks ready as we were desperately short of time and a perfectly devilish road to go down. The road from Weiltje Dugout went east to the old front line and thence straight away down to the Steenbeek. All rations etc. had to go down this narrow causeway, as the mud could and did drown anyone who got off the few duckboard tracks. The remains of the *pavé* was just about the same width as the tank tracks and in many places to pass a tank you had to climb along the side of it. There was an abyss of mud and water each side. The position was such that if any tank broke down and was knocked out during the approach march, every one behind it must needs wait on the road until daylight and then be shot like a garden thrush; too easy. There was no such thing as turning round or going back without getting ditched. As this was the one main highway you can guess that the Bosch shot it up the whole night long, and it had such long straight stretches on it that it was under fixed MG fire too. The holes in the *pavé* were filled with broken rifles, kit and corpses, the whole overlaid with stinking slime. It was really a bad place and the further you got on down the slight slope the worse it became.

. . . Well, we started off with just enough time to do it if all went well. We got . . . to a huge crater, and then the trouble began. I was walking in front of the leading tank and each Section Commander was leading his own lot. We had quite a short interval between tanks, I think too short really but they were all in such a funk of losing touch, with the possibilities of a tow from the tank ahead in case of a sideslip, that they came hurrying on behind me. My feet were as cold as ice and the thing I was really afraid of, for myself, was that I should cop one and the leading tank would drive over me without seeing me in the dark.

We could only crawl along and . . . the Bosch kept putting over small shells but all burst in the ditches each side of the tanks except two or three which burst actually on the road between the tanks. When we got about level with Rat Farm which was to be my advanced HQ and report centre, I turned round to speak to Dad Hill in the leading tank, and just as I did so there was a violent explosion and sheet of flame right under his offside track by my legs. It blew me away off the road but I got up and came back to Dad. I told him to come very slowly ahead as there was the horrible probability that his track was broken, and if we could catch up the ends of the track on top of the tank we might still be able to mend it and save the situation. With my heart in my mouth I watched his track coming gently and steadily along and thank God it had suffered no damage. . . . I saw that we had run over a box of rifle grenades and they had all gone up with a bang.

Finally we got as far as the Steenbeek which was supposed to have a bridge over it. We drove over the powdered remains of this, which was simply a harder place in the surrounding sea of swamp. Beyond this there was an immense crater stinking to heaven and full of, and surrounded by, dead of all sorts. I got my tanks all ready to deploy before zero and moved them up towards Spree Farm. . . . It is a never to be forgotten miracle that we ever got them to the jumping off place at all. The slightest slip, or failure in guts or skill of one of those drivers and we were all done in without a chance.[33]

The campaign was a near disaster for the tanks. Many were lost, half-sunk in the morass and then blown to pieces at the enemy's leisure. There were local successes – on 25 September one tank followed by two companies of infantry had cleared 1,500yd of trench in one hour, taking 362 prisoners for five casualties among the attackers – but to continue to commit the tanks to such conditions was a fearful waste of machines and brave men. Their potential was thought by many to be negligible. Lt Gen Gough's Fifth Army HQ reported that they were slow, vulnerable and susceptible to the 'bad going' which, they said, would exist on any battlefield. This last was a disreputable statement – the tanks were never built for artillery-induced swamp.

The Heavy Branch gained its independence as a Corps on 27 July 1917 by Royal Warrant. It became the Tank Corps, but if it was to have a future it needed a chance to fight on the firmer ground for which the machines were designed.

Eleven

CRISIS

Stern . . . is, or was, the most superb organiser and team leader I have
ever met, and it is no exaggeration to say that but for his leadership we
should never have had any tanks in the last war.[1]

Sir Harry Ricardo to Lord Hankey, 13 February 1942

Get rid of Stern.[2]

Brig Gen Hugh Elles to War Office, 7 October 1917

In a surprise move by Lloyd George, Churchill replaced Addison as
Minister of Munitions in July 1917. Winston had returned from France
in March the previous year to rejoin the House of Commons and
prepare for the Dardanelles Commission of Enquiry. Its verdict fell more
heavily on Kitchener and Asquith than on Churchill, but he remained
politically isolated with few influential friends. He desperately wanted to
return to high office with an opportunity to invigorate the direction of the
war. Lloyd George was not unsympathetic but time was needed for Tory
knives to be sheathed. He asked Addison in March 1917 if the Ministry
could discreetly offer Churchill a post without 'special executive
responsibilities'. Addison consulted d'Eyncourt who suggested Churchill
should lead a small mission to the USA to secure steel and other strategic
material for Britain's tank programme and to encourage the Americans to
build their own tank army.[3] The proposal was well timed – America entered
the war against Germany next day, 5 April, but Addison was not persuaded.
The Ministry already had a resident munitions purchasing group over there,
and Foreign Secretary Arthur Balfour's politically sensitive mission to the US
was about to sail. Winston's roving presence as a wild card would have
invited trouble. Addison twice spoke to Churchill, inviting him to consider 'a
small <u>ad hoc</u> committee under his chairmanship which should consider and
discuss the general question of the tank programme . . . and to consider the

use of such weapons in warfare and to advise generally on the subject'. [Addison's emphasis]'[4] It was a lamentably inadequate role which Churchill instantly dismissed.

Addison then spoke of his willingness to let Winston take his place at the Ministry. Despite strong Conservative opposition the Prime Minister acted on the offer and invited Churchill to join his government as Minister of Munitions. Winston's acceptance precipitated an immediate threat of resignation from Lord Derby, Secretary of State for War. He withdrew it, providing Churchill refrained from interfering in the conduct of the war and in the business of departments other than his own. Addison chose a regular meeting of his heads of department on 24 July to introduce his successor. He ended his valedictory address with a caution for Churchill that in time of materials shortages and restrictions the role of the Minister of Munitions was inevitably unpopular. To a coolly unresponsive audience Churchill replied: 'Well, at any rate, I start from scratch in that respect.'[5] He went on to set out his plans for the Ministry and for accelerated munitions production. By the end of a brave and sincere address he had completely won over hearts and minds.

The MoM had grown to over fifty munitions departments by now. They were controlled by captains of industry in line with Lloyd George's founding policy. These men instinctively operated in fierce competition with each other for labour, priorities and materials, routinely pleading their case to the Minister who, as the organisation grew, became overburdened with the task of mediating in turf wars. Churchill slashed and burned. The departments were merged into ten large groups whose controllers were directly answerable to him. Each was a member of a Munitions Council which worked across group boundaries. The Mechanical Warfare Supply Department fell into Group W (Warfare) under Sir Arthur Duckham, its other constituents being Mechanical Transport, Inventions, Trench Warfare, Agricultural Machinery, and Electric Power Supply.

There followed a lightning ministerial interrogation of each department. Churchill reached Mechanical Warfare on 3 August, asking Walter Layton, his Director of Statistics, for a situation report 'on a single sheet of paper':

> How many tanks, and of what patterns, are to be ready month by month
>   for the next twelve months?
> By whom, and to what extent, have these programmes been approved?
> How much steel do they require?

How much do they cost?

How much labour, skilled and unskilled, do they require in these twelve months?

What are the principal limiting factors in material and class of labour?

Apart from the number of tanks, what quantity of spares, and what maintenance plant are required?

Give the money value or weights of materials or proportion of labour required or whichever of the three is most convenient and representative.

Let me know the number of people in the tank department, the principal salaries paid, and the aggregate of salaries paid per annum.

Show particularly any part of tank production which overlaps aeroplane production, i.e. any transferable margin, whether of skilled mechanics or of ball bearings etc. in which these two branches of production are clashing competitors.

Show also the proportion of steel, of money and of skilled and unskilled labour proposed to be absorbed in tank production in these twelve months compared with the general budget of the Ministry.[6]

Stern replied that he needed 8,000 tons of steel each month (1 per cent of national steel output). Monthly production costs based on 200 heavy and 100 medium tanks with spares totalled £1.4m. Tank factories were short of 950 skilled or semi-skilled men. Ball bearings, small castings and nickel for armour plate were the principal factors limiting output. As to quantity of spares required, Stern answered 'impossible to estimate'. MWSD was preparing to supply 300 tanks per month, based on 160 heavies, 100 medium and 40 supply tanks. That was the limit. There was no spare capacity.

The War Office and Stern were now completely at odds. Churchill came under pressure to replace his controller of tank supply. A Munitions Council Sub-committee on Tanks was formed and chaired by Winston himself. It met on 5 September to question Stern and d'Eyncourt. Stern had circulated a secret memorandum the previous day in which he summarised the 1917/18 programme and argued that the estimated 1,000 Mk IV machines available in the coming year should fight alongside the emerging new types. He continued: 'The military authorities suggest schemes such as altering the engine and transmission. The Army should devote themselves to training and fighting.'[7] Stern was under great pressure, but his flat rejection of any collaborative role for the Army in developing its new weapon was ill-considered. Churchill subjected the operations of MWSD to a forensic examination. He was well prepared. Ominously, a secretary was instructed to make a verbatim record. The meeting began badly for Stern, and worsened:

Churchill: What tanks are now in existence?

Stern: You can take 700 of Mk IV. I do not know what they have lost at the Front. There are about 600.

Churchill: Surely you know from day to day or from week to week?

Stern: They will not let me know what are destroyed. I suppose they think it is not my business.

Churchill: Surely we ought to know exactly the number of tanks that are in action?

Gen Headlam: I cannot give you them out of my head but I am going back [to France] tomorrow and I will get them at once.

Churchill: We ought to know what are the tanks at the Front in action and under repair. How many are there? You do not know?

Stern: I know exactly what I have delivered. I have delivered of the first mark 250 . . . and now we have delivered roughly 600, but where they are and what they are doing I do not know.

Stern: They have about 600 in France and in their training camps here.

Churchill: I do not want to know that. I want to know how many there are there and how many there are here.

Stern: They do not let me know that. I deliver them to the Army. If I ask anything I am told to mind my own business.

Churchill: Mr Hutchins, telephone over to the WO and ask them if they would give us their estimate of the number of tanks at the Front in action and under repair and training at home.

Churchill: What have you in your 1918 programme?

Stern: 1,600 heavy tanks.

Churchill: Additional?

Stern: Apparently.

Churchill: What do you mean by that?

Stern: It is very difficult to see from the WO minutes what they want. They wanted us to alter the last 500 of our 1,400 [Mk IV] into Mk V, which we cannot do.

Churchill: Are these 1,600 heavy tanks in addition to the 700 you still have to deliver?

Stern: It is a little doubtful.

Sir A. Duckham: I should read the letter to say they were.

Churchill: What basis are you making on?

Stern: I can only produce 160 tanks a month of this type, the heavies, and therefore I have given a preliminary order for 800 [Mk V] which keep my factories going for 5 months. In the meantime I was going to try and have this elucidated, whether they mean the 500 or not.

Churchill: There is nothing easier in the world than to elucidate it.

Layton: You cannot start on January 1st with 160 a month? Your last minute said you doubted whether you could do that.

Stern: Well, we can do it.

Layton: Not at the full rate.

Stern: No, we start at from between 100 to 160. It is difficult to get materials, but we ought to carry on our production clean through.

Churchill: I want to know what is your programme for 1918?

Stern: I have taken 1,600 heavy, 1,200 light tanks and 800 supplies, and they want some gun carriers. My manufacturing programme is, I can give them 160 a month heavies, 50 a month lights – working up to 100, and the supplies are not yet designed.

Churchill: What about the supply tanks?

Stern: The supply tank is not designed yet. We are getting on with the design.

Churchill: It is an amazing thing you have not got a design by now. It is a most obvious line of development. Anyone could see at least a year ago that it would be needed, and far more useful than that thing lugging a great cannon about. It is extraordinary we have not got on with it.

Stern: The one that lugs the cannon about can be used as a supply tank. That is the point I want to bring up. The real point is this – that we wait for the experience of the fighting season before we start the new design. This is very experimental. We had the greatest difficulty to get any orders at all for this; in fact most of these were made without orders. We only started in September, not a year ago. We waited for the new designs that are required. They want all sorts of changes. We could give them a supply tank with the old design with great ease. It is a question of sprocket wheels. They now want a chain drive [for greater endurance, but entailing a complete redesign of the final drive].

Churchill: But surely you have an experimental establishment, have you not? Which is under the entire control of this department, and you can build any kind of tank you want – one tank?

Stern: Yes.

Churchill: Do you not think it would have been a prudent thing nine months ago to get on with a tender tank?

Stern: We have got a gun carrier which will carry 10 tons of supplies. We have redesigned that. That is ready to be made, and that is what I suggest you should have made.

Churchill: Then you have got a design for the supply tank?

Stern: Absolutely.

Churchill: It is not the kind you are putting up to the War Office?

Stern: No, they want something different again.

Churchill: I think the supply tank is more important than any other class of tank.

D'Eyncourt: There was only a demand from the War Office for a supply tank not more than 6 months ago.

Churchill: You remember it is now nearly a year ago that I talked to you about it. I do think anyone could see there was a development. The one thing is to get the stuff up to the lines after an advance, and here is the only method of getting the stuff over the ground.

D'Eyncourt: The gun carrier type forms an excellent chassis for a supply tank, and even the original heavy tank can be made, though it is not very fast. We have been trying to develop the best design for a supply tank, which we are doing now.

Churchill: With the result that when the fighting begins on the 1st March, there will not be a sufficient number of supply tanks to help the Army. There will be beautiful ones coming on, but they will be too late.

Stern: You do not appreciate the fact that we have never been allowed to do anything; we have never been allowed to have any factories. While I was getting my supply tanks built, five times have the railway people stopped me going on with my order. [Sir E. Moir's Transport Department, MoM, had reluctantly released capacity at loco builders Kitson's of Leeds for assembly of gun carriers and a supply variant.]

Sir E. Moir [member of Munitions Council]: This is all nonsense, and nothing to do with the question. You have got possession of Kitson's absolutely, and have always had it. This is nothing to do with the design of a carrier tank. [In fact, at the urging of Moir's department the Ministry had given notice on 18 June that Kitson's were to build the first eighteen gun carriers only, before reverting to loco work. Four weeks later the War Office overruled this instruction.]

Churchill: I am on the experimental point, because if there is any proper experimental department which can make variants of this and have them ready, I consider it is the duty of the Tank Department of the Ministry of Munitions to be ahead of the military in this matter. As to building a great number of tanks to a particular order, that you do not do until the WO ask for it, but none of these ideas originated with the WO at all, and we ought to have specimens of the best eight or nine different variants which are possible, made and worked out and ready and modelled, so that if at any time the military come and say 'we should like this' we can reply 'well here is a pattern; we are perpetually improving it'. It ought to be entirely on an independent footing from supply. Have not you got anything of that?

Stern: Yes. I have had the greatest trouble to get anything, because we have been an experimental department. I have had practically no assistance to carry on my business at all. We can get neither officers nor engineers. I am not getting anyone. I have had the greatest difficulty getting anything. . . . It is not a year ago since we went into battle, but directly after that battle I put every sort of transmission into an experimental machine. . . . We are carrying out all experiments, and our difficulties have been of construction, design, brake and transmission. Now we have solved that.

Churchill: It is perfectly obvious what the first thing is to be done. Sir Arthur, you will make proposals as soon as possible for meeting the WO demand for 450 supply tanks in the best possible way open to us now, by the 1st March.

Sir A. Duckham: I think the first thing to be done is to get over this trouble with the WO.

Sir J. Stevenson [member of Munitions Council]: It seems to me the Design Department wants straightening out. Frankly, I do not understand how it stands now. One moment you say you are responsible for design and the next moment you say you are not.

Stern: I do not say I am not. I say we are responsible for design. You only want to look at the papers . . . and they [the War Office Tank Committee] have done everything to interfere with us.

Sir J. Stevenson: Then it is not satisfactory.

Stern: I put it up to Dr Addison time after time. As I could get no satisfaction, I put up a minute to the War Cabinet. . . .

Churchill: As I understand the procedure it ought to be this. The Army say 'We want so and so by such and such a date.' The Ministry says 'We submit the following proposals' . . . then they take their choice. . . . I should have thought that it was the most simple thing if you were not so completely at loggerheads.

Stern: We are not at loggerheads. The point is this – that there has been no-one at the War Office (I have been pressing for months and months and months) whose business it was to deal with tanks until quite lately when the Master General of Ordnance took it on. I have been told that there probably would be no tanks [required] at all, that they want other things before. I am restricted in my factories. You know perfectly well, Mr Layton, that they said that they did not want any more gun carriers; they wanted railway material before.

Layton: We have done our best to give decisions on those points.

Stern: Dr Addison did not take the slightest interest in it.

Churchill: I am only pointing out to you how easy it is to get into difficulties. Instead of making heavy weather of it, it is quite easy to make the best plan you can. If that is not accepted, you then make a less good plan. What I am complaining about with regard to these supply tanks is that I do not think that any plan of getting the numbers realised has been made.

Stern: When was the desire first expressed?

Churchill: I heard of supply tanks certainly as soon as I arrived here.

Stern: Nobody could give a decision on anything.

D'Eyncourt: There has been nobody to say 'Yes, go on with supply tanks.'[8]

And so it continued. It was left that Duckham would propose means of meeting the full programme to December 1918; Churchill would consider a draft letter to the War Office setting out the basis for authorising design; d'Eyncourt was to find a way to convert Mk IV tanks for supply and for towing trailers; Stern would urgently submit proposals for meeting Haig's request for 450 supply tanks by 1 March, and would produce basic design alternatives for a medium machine. He was also asked to list the twelve best ideas for immediate experiment, to which he replied: 'I will give them to you but it is a very complicated thing. One affects the other. We are so near the limits of possibility.'

Stern was either tired or badly rattled – perhaps both. Throughout the meeting he had been off balance, truculent and defensive, sometimes dissembling. He conveyed a lack of grip in the conduct of his department which convinced Churchill that he must go. Mindful of the Prime Minister's regard for Stern, Churchill wrote to Lloyd George four days later, marking his letter 'Secret':

There are one or two points on which I want to know your views before acting. Stern has rendered very good service in the past about tanks, but I am sure he is not the man to carry this job further. It is in a very bad condition. The Tank Supply Department and the War Office are at loggerheads and this is particularly true of Stern and the soldiers. You know I do not set undue store by their opinion, but I am sure that the development of tanks is prejudiced at this stage, however it may have gained in the past, by Stern's methods and personality. Personally I like Stern and should be very sorry to hurt his feelings, but I have no doubt whatever that the moment has come for him to go. . . . It would be very difficult for me to find him another suitable job, but he has certainly deserved a KCMG or something of that sort. Have you a strong view against his being superseded, and if not, can I count on giving him the honour?[9]

Lloyd George approved Churchill's proposals. The Minister let the matter lie while a search was made for Stern's successor. Duckham's report to Churchill saluted Stern and his team for their achievement in developing a practical method of mechanical warfare in face of 'much opposition', but he found the design department lacking firm direction and expertise at the top. Designers were working out their own ideas and submitting them to Stern for decision. Duckham pointed to the limited expansion of the Tank Corps and the need to encourage America to build a mighty tank fleet. A dynamic individual should take a small staff and a Mk V over there and promote volume tank production. He nominated Stern.

Churchill chaired a conference at the Ministry on 29 September to review, in his words, the 'very serious and unsatisfactory' state of the 1918 tank programme. Butler, Whigham, Capper, Elles, Duckham, Stern and others attended. The session underlined the lack of communication between Stern's department and the War Office. The Army was largely ignorant of the capabilities of the supply side, and the supply side was uncertain of what was required of it. Butler reminded them that the number of tanks required was dictated by the 18,500 men to be made available for the Tank Corps in 1918. (Corps establishment was then 12,000 to 13,000 officers and men.) The Army wanted 700 heavies and 600 medium types by 1 March. Churchill had to tell the meeting that the Ministry could supply no more than 200 and 250 respectively by that date, and only 200 of the 450 supply tanks, comprising converted Mk IVs. There was no problem with the 48 gun carriers. In other words the Ministry expected to deliver only some 9,000 tons of the 28,000 tons of fighting tanks required. The March deadline was put back to 1 June.

The Army representatives returned to the charge that the Ministry was building 40 per cent more Mk IVs than ordered. They wanted none of the unauthorised 400. Stern wisely avoided citing in his defence the vague War Office continuation order of 21 March – he had acted on it and contracted out the extra 400 before a single Mk IV had been built.

Elles left the meeting deeply dissatisfied with progress. He set out his concerns in a memorandum to the War Office a week later. They centred on the inadequacy of Mk IV, the delay in introducing a Mk V replacement, and on having to decide between continued production of Tritton's three-man Whippet, which had performed disappointingly at its acceptance trials, and its replacement by Wilson's Medium B for which no trials machine or performance guarantee was available to assist him. This was hardly surprising as the drawings had only just been completed. The Medium B reverted to a single engine, a Ricardo 100hp unit with epicyclic transmission, located well back and separated by a bulkhead from the four-man crew in front whose fighting compartment was topped by a large turret. A 2-pdr gun was planned. (Elles chose the Medium B; 650 were ordered on 8 October for delivery by July 1918. Stern had wanted to build 1,200. The 2-pdr was replaced in March 1918 by four Hotchkiss MG.) Elles called for a system of batch manufacture in which large orders would be broken down into small production runs, each of some four months' duration. Urgent design improvements could then be introduced more frequently, between batches. He and Capper appear to have believed that the extra production breaks would remain compatible with high output providing they were systematised in this way. Stern and Metropolitan disagreed.

As to labour shortages and strikes, Elles wanted 'a variety of designs ready proved and tested, so that manufacture can be switched from one pattern to another at the shortest notice'. It was a wildly impracticable idea. Standby production would have to be tooled up and supported by stockpiles of materials and sub-assemblies, all standing idle awaiting possible trouble. Striking labour would almost certainly 'black' these fallback measures wherever they were. Elles continued:

> Relations between the producers and users of the machines are unsatisfactory. . . . The user has no reason for confidence in design. On our proposals to date there has been little or no progress except on paper and very little of that. . . . There has been no trial under battle conditions. The experimental Department has only been formed in the last six weeks and no serious effort on practical experiments has been made until the last fortnight. The ideas and suggestions both of designers at home and of the practical users in France are in the hands of an individual [Stern] who has seen one battlefield for the space of three hours. A very serious lack of confidence exists.[10]

Elles scribbled a telling footnote:

> Desiderata.
> Separate design from supply.
> Put design in France.
> Manufacture by blocks.
> Build experimental types.
> Get rid of Stern.

Realising the gravity of his position, Stern asked to see Churchill. He told him that the three previous Ministers had shown him their confidence and support, and without the same backing from Churchill he could not make a success of the operation. The Minister assured Stern of his personal confidence but said that the War Office wanted him replaced, accusing him of lumbering them up with useless tanks at the front, wasting public money, neglecting experimental work and losing a year's development with a total failure of design and progress. Stern, who was taking notes, emphatically denied the charges and asked Churchill if he had consulted d'Eyncourt and other informed sources before making the allegations. Churchill said he had not, but had been briefed by Duckham as head of department. Stern challenged the Minister to give one instance in which he had prevented progress or a free play of ideas, adding that he had been 'fighting the forces of reaction' since the cancellation of the 1,000 tanks order. As for research, he cited the Oldbury transmission trials and his request in March to turn Tritton's works into an inter-Allied tank development unit. With that the interview ended.[11]

After an anxious weekend Stern confronted Duckham, who assured him that he had said nothing critical of him to the Minister save the objection that too many experiments and designs were in train. This hardly squares with Elles who had just criticised Stern for producing too few of either. Stern exploded: 'What a damned liar he is . . . why does he want to get rid of me?'[12] Duckham told him that Gens Whigham, Butler and Elles considered him a hindrance to the development of tanks; Churchill's mind was made up and Stern was to be sacked. Duckham suggested he took a team to America to foster tank production, but Stern dismissed it as a job his butler could do. Duckham turned to the design department, saying it needed reorganisation and Walter Wilson 'locked up so as not to be allowed to interfere'. Stern made it clear he would go down fighting because he believed his remaining in post was in the national interest. He saw the Prime Minister that evening but Lloyd George had already approved Churchill's decision. All he could offer Stern was the assurance that he had seen the Minister who had promised to arrange matters satisfactorily with Stern.

The end came the next morning, Tuesday 16 October. Stern and d'Eyncourt asked for a joint interview with the Minister, the DNC adding his considerable weight in support. Churchill asked d'Eyncourt to leave before telling Stern there was nothing more to say. He acknowledged Stern's excellent work but said he had taken Duckham's advice, adding: 'I was kicked out too and thought I was right.' Stern refused to resign, forcing Churchill to dismiss him.[13] Years later Stern referred to the meeting, saying he had challenged Churchill to fight for more tanks as his Ministerial predecessors had done. He claimed Churchill replied that:

he had been out of office since 1915, the beginning of 1915, and that he knew his business and his business was to supply the requirements of the War Office and not to tell the War Office what they ought to have, and therefore he could take no action. I told him that he undoubtedly knew that the Army required large numbers of tanks for the campaign of 1919 and that if he did not push it, it might be good personal politics but not honest public policy.[14]

Churchill reminded him: 'that is all right from Bertie to Winston but not from Stern to your Minister'.[15]

Vice Adm Sir Archibald Gordon Moore took over the MWSD two days later, starting with a clean sheet. He had never seen a tank. D'Eyncourt wanted Stern to remain and had strongly objected to his dismissal. Walter Wilson was appointed head of design and given control of all experimental work. The MWSD was renamed the Mechanical Warfare Department.

Given the shifts and conflicting demands of war, tensions between the tank producers and the Army were unavoidable. What had been so very damaging was the descent on both sides into mutual contempt and relative isolation. Bertie Stern had no time for the politics and prejudices of members of the High Command and no career to protect. When they turned on him he flashed his ace – a direct line to Lloyd George, his friend and their Secretary of State. Stern's unshakeable conviction in the value of the tank was shared by a few field commanders. Haig was an early supporter in spite of the efforts of many on his staff. Stern's war was directed as much at military hostility and its plodding organisation as at fighting for the resources to build tanks.

Against the expectations of the Army Council, Stern had forced it to withdraw its 1,000-tank cancellation in September 1916. His profoundly significant victory opened the way to marshalling labour, materials, tooling and armament for volume production. It enabled him to deliver nearly 800 Mk IV machines between April and September the following year, and compelled the Army to expand the Heavy Section to receive them. Had he failed, production would have reverted to a small-scale and open-ended run-on of Mk III construction which was all the War Office was willing to sanction while it deliberated on 'the utility of those now employed and the possibility of improvements'. There would have been no time to build sufficient machines and train crews for a mass deployment in 1917, finally establishing the tank as a decisive weapon and galvanising production for 1918.

Stern's sons, John and David, recall his intolerance of anyone holding views opposed to his own, but he inspired intense loyalty among kindred spirits. Harry Ricardo told Hankey years later that 'Stern is a difficult man . . . he is, or was, the most superb organiser and team leader I have ever met, and it is no exaggeration to say that but for his leadership we should never have had any tanks in the last war, but he is very much an individualist.'[16] Others disagreed. Lord Weir was Controller of Aeronautical Supplies at the Ministry in 1917 and his Priority 1 for engine supply was under regular attack from Stern. He recalled: 'I do not think Sir Albert is a good team worker. . . . Quite frankly, Sir Albert Stern is an enthusiast and a driver and works best when he is in full charge and is doing everything his own way.'[17]. Such views typify reaction to Stern's supercharged style. His task was to build tanks. To do so he and d'Eyncourt had to fight every inch of the way.

Five weeks after his departure the first mass attack by tanks at Cambrai brought victory and vindication for the new weapon and transformed war policy. The discredited master builder sent Elles a telegram of congratulation, receiving a generous and well-earned acknowledgement in reply: 'Very many thanks. It was your battle too.'[18]

Twelve

THE PRODUCTION
BATTLEFIELD . . .

The resources are available, the knowledge is available, the time is available, the result is certain; nothing is lacking except the will. . . . We have instead only carried out a series of costly experiments, each of which has shown us the chance we have lost and exposed our thought to the enemy.[1]

Churchill on lost opportunities with the tanks;
paper to War Cabinet, 5 March 1918

The War Office Tank Committee was flawed and had contributed little of value to the tank programme. Sir Arthur Duckham in the Ministry of Munitions brokered a smaller and genuinely representative 'New Tank Committee' which was agreed a week before Stern's dismissal in October 1917. It was chaired again by Gen Capper as Director General of the War Office Tank Department, the other members being Gen Elles, Stern's successor Adm Moore and the dependable d'Eyncourt as chief technical adviser. They were to meet fortnightly, alternating between France and England. The committee would consider tank requirements and formulate delivery programmes, advise on the lines to follow in experiments and where they should be conducted (in recognition of past failure to test jointly with the Corps in France), and establish the cordial relations which were so lacking between producers and users. On design they would only provide a general specification to meet conditions at the front, leaving the detailed work to Moore's MWD. An MWD office was to be set up at Central Workshops in France. Wilson's design team would include a representative from the Corps in France and from the WO. Duckham's initiative was well considered and long overdue.

Churchill offered Stern the new post of Commissioner for Mechanical Warfare (Overseas and Allies Department), Ministry of Munitions. He would have the same status as Moore, reporting direct to Churchill with Duckham as 'adviser'. He was to 'investigate the possibilities of supplies of tanks in France and America and elsewhere and to arrange in what manner the Allies and ourselves can render the greatest assistance to each other and to take charge of all such negotiations'. He was to set up and control a workshop in France for conversion of Mk IV and other obsolescent tanks to improved types. Mention was made of full-scale production at a later date. Stern was also to create a distribution system to channel tank materials and parts from one Allied country to another. He would control matters of design, experiment and supply between Britain and her Allies and would have his own representative on Moore's design committee. Stern was not, however, to be a member of the New Tank Committee, though he would receive the minutes. He accepted the post on 24 October, while remaining profoundly disturbed by events. Stern warned Churchill bluntly a few days later:

> The demands and preparations of the Military Authorities with regard to Mechanical Warfare for the fighting season of 1918 are entirely inadequate, and the changes which you have made in this Department at this critical time (and which involve reconsideration of design and consequent loss of production) will most seriously affect even the efficiency of this programme for next season's fighting. This is also the considered opinion of my technical and commercial advisers.[2]

Stern got to work at once, contacting Maj James A. Draine and Maj Herbert W. Alden of the American Army. They were in London, detailed by the Chief of Ordnance in Washington to report on tank developments in Britain and France. There was no question for Bertie Stern of 'eventual' production. He rapidly secured agreement for an Allied programme of tank design and assembly. D'Eyncourt joined them in a follow-up meeting in Paris to confer first with M. Munich, a spokesman for M. Loucheur, the French Minister of Munitions, before reporting to Gen John J. Pershing, commander of the American Expeditionary Force in Europe. M. Munich emphasised that France had no interest in heavy tanks and could give no assistance to a joint programme, though there was no objection to an assembly plant in France. The party then proposed to Gen Pershing that the USA and Great Britain should urgently co-design and produce 1,500 heavy 'Liberty' tanks. Of the main components, Britain would contribute the guns, ammunition, armour and track assemblies; America the power train, track links and chains. Pershing gave his approval on 15 November and appointed Draine American Commissioner. Draine had been a General in the National Guard at home, and as fellow businessmen he and Stern would work well together.

D'Eyncourt went one further, calling for a 'United Allied Board of Mechanical Warfare' to unify control of design, production, strategy, tactics and development, with Stern as chairman and representation from the Army, MWD, the USA, France and Italy. It was an unattainable proposal which the War Office would certainly refuse, but d'Eyncourt made some telling points. He deplored the scattergun approach to tank development, the multiplicity of types, the penny-packet numbers ordered and the loss of output resulting from design changes imposed during production. He wanted Britain and the Allies to adopt and build a single heavy type and to drive production forward without interruption, regardless of demands for refinements. He urged the immediate cancellation of the Mk IX infantry supply tank (Rackham had begun its design in September), and of Mk V and Medium B production after August 1918. No new design of tank or engine should be considered. MWD should concentrate all its efforts on building the 800 Mk V and the 650 Medium B to schedule, without distractions. On their completion d'Eyncourt wanted Britain and the Allies to standardise on a Liberty heavy tank with infantry supply and other variants as necessary. Not the least of the benefits of a common battle tank was the opportunity to pool production of parts and assemblies, assigning specialist work to individual countries. If this was agreed with the Allies, he believed there was a sporting chance of putting tanks in decisive numbers into the field in July 1918. He pressed for the formation of three tank armies, perhaps one each from Britain, America and France, each of 100,000 men with 500 machines as their primary weapon, and with infantry and artillery as auxiliary arms. Their very presence along an extended front would pin down enemy forces fearful of attack, preventing them massing elsewhere for an offensive. Their strategic potential was self-evident.[3]

It took another war for that concept to become reality. The DNC's paper brought a considered response from the General Staff in London which disputed his assertion that one tank equated to some 400 infantry in attack, but conceded that the machines brought 'economy in personnel'. This was mere hair-splitting. The War Office saw no strategic role for the Tank Corps, nor any reason to increase its manpower until tank strength rose in August

1918, ignoring the fact that such delay meant the fighting season would be over by the time a new intake had been trained.[4]

Churchill attended a conference with M. Loucheur in Paris on 3 December at which Loucheur was given the details of the joint project and asked if his government approved. He affirmed that it did, providing some of the resultant tanks were allocated to France. An outline specification for the Liberty tank was agreed next day at a joint British/American conference chaired by Churchill at GHQ. The first 600 of the Mk VIII, as it was later designated, would go to the American Army. The machine superficially resembled the current heavy tanks with all-round track and sponsons, but there were to be many improvements including a 14ft trench-crossing capability as against the 11ft of the Mk IV. For the American Army the power unit would be a suitably modified 300hp US Liberty aero engine, with a similarly rated and as yet unbuilt Ricardo engine for British use. The large fighting compartment with a crew of eight (eleven in the US version) could accommodate a further twenty men, and was separated from the engine by a bulkhead. A short 6-pdr gun in each sponson would be supplemented by five machine guns mounted in an elongated roof turret above track height to give all-round fire. Overall length was just over 34ft, against the 26ft 5in of Mk IV.

A design committee was appointed, to be led jointly by commissioners Stern and Draine, with Capt G.A. Green and Maj Alden representing the British and US Tank Corps respectively and d'Eyncourt as technical adviser. When Gen Capper was informed he lodged a formal objection, telling Duckham it would sideline his committee and leave the MWD and the fighting side of the Tank Corps in France without a voice. He considered Green a competent engineer but out of his depth on the wider issues. Stern's department would effectively determine the design of the British Army's next main battle tank. The argument was patched up with an undertaking that while detailed design would be decided by the Anglo-American team, matters of general design would require the approval of Capper's committee. Capper remained hostile to the introduction of an Allied voice in design, and implacably so to Stern's role.

*   *   *

Gen Capper's Tank Committee did not meet until the end of November 1917 – the battle of Cambrai intervened. It opened on the 20th when for the first time the tanks attacked *en masse* as their pioneers intended, and over almost unshelled ground. A total of 476 machines were deployed, of which 378 were fighting tanks supported by gun carriers, supply Mk IVs, 3 wireless tanks and 32 special wire clearance tanks. The action was originally conceived in August by Col Fuller, by then Tank Corps GSO 1, as a great one-day tank raid to restore British prestige and strike 'a theatrical blow' after the disaster of Third Ypres. His objective was to penetrate the allegedly impregnable 'Hindenburg Line' just south of Cambrai in the area of Gen Sir Julian Byng's Third Army, destroy the enemy's guns, demoralise and disorganise the defenders, and demonstrate that the tanks could break the line at any time and at any point. Byng was receptive and saw possibilities in extending the raid to take and hold Cambrai. Haig agreed, but Kiggell, his Chief of Staff, strongly opposed the scheme, saying troops could not be spared from the Ypres front. Fuller's plan was accordingly shelved until mid-October. Haig then approved a modest tank action limited to forty-eight hours. Byng inflated it to an offensive to push cavalry through the break and take Cambrai before moving on towards Valenciennes. He had six divisions of tired infantry and four of cavalry, three tank brigades and some 1,000 guns. After Ypres there were no reserves save his cavalry to exploit success, or even to secure the long flanks resulting from a deep penetration.

Elles and Fuller had barely five weeks to prepare. Success relied on surprise, on getting the tanks across the exceptionally wide German trenches, and on effective cooperation between tanks and infantry. Surprise was to be achieved through Byng's insistence on avoiding all preparatory bombardment, which also ensured good going for the tanks. Instead of registering the guns on their targets and so forewarning the enemy, all gun-laying was plotted by survey.

Trench crossing was left to Col Frank Searle and Maj John Brockbank, his number two. The Hindenburg Line's forward trenches had been considerably enlarged and deepened to serve as tank traps. Central Workshops at Erin worked eight-hour shifts round the clock to produce 400 tightly bound large bundles of brushwood and release gear, each tank carrying one on its nose for tipping into a trench before passing over it. As the tanks fought in sections of three they could sequence the drops to get the section across all three trench lines, the crews marking the crossing points with a red/yellow flag for the following tanks. Each drum-like 1.75-ton bundle was made up of between 90 and 100 smaller bundles or 'fascines' cut to 10ft lengths and laid in an open cradle over a pair of wire ropes. The rope ends were thrown across the top of the heap and shackled to a tank at either end before the machines drew the 'super fascine' very tight to a diameter of 4ft 6in. Two securing chains were fitted before the cables were relaxed. A soldier scrounging for firewood was filing through a chain when it snapped under tension, killing him. Rumour had it that the chain's whiplash cut him in half. The fascine release gear was operated from inside the tank.

In the event most machines were able to cross the trenches without help from the fascines; the German firestep was cut so wide that it supported the rear of the machine and stopped it tail-diving. Erin also made up 110 timber tank sledges for bringing supplies to forward rallying points ('tankodromes'). Their tow tanks were fitted with roof-mounted hitching gear, the protruding rear track horns preventing any lower coupling.

Fuller evolved an attack drill with infantry. The lead tank of each section would keep about 100yd ahead of the other two, raking German parapets and drawing fire away from the following tanks, behind which the infantry advanced in single file over the flattened wire. The troops would mop up trenches and, importantly, support the machines by spotting for enemy guns. When guns were sighted, tank commanders were alerted via an external bell pull at the rear, or the banging of a shovel or crowbar left hanging beside a sponson door. Signalling was primitive; a shovel waved through the tank's roof indicated 'Tank broken down. Don't wait'. The infantry could call for assistance from tanks by raising a rifle topped by a helmet. Conversely, a red/yellow flag was waved from the tank. A wireless tank was attached to each brigade and was usually run up to a 'sheltered' position where messages could be relayed by company commanders to brigade HQ. The system was little used, tank commanders having two carrier pigeons as preferred options providing the birds were not asphyxiated by then, or their feathers oiled.

The wire-pulling detachment was led by Stuart Hastie, now a captain, whose progress through Flers had so electrified the press in 1916. His thirty-two tanks were to clear three 60yd-wide lanes for the cavalry and following troops and guns immediately the first line of trenches had been taken. They would continue until every succeeding belt had been dealt with. The tanks each pulled a heavy four-fluke grapnel on a 30ft wire cable secured to a short roof-mast. A machine could peel the ground bare of 20 tons of wire and iron pickets, so engulfing it that sometimes the sponson doors could not be opened.

On YZ day Elles issued an inspiring Special Order to his men:

1. Tomorrow the Tank Corps will have the chance for which it has been waiting for many months – to operate in the van of the battle.
2. All that hard work and ingenuity can achieve has been done in the way of preparation.
3. It remains for unit commanders and for tank crews to complete the work by judgement and pluck in the battle itself.
4. In the light of past experience I leave the good name of the Corps with great confidence in their hands.
5. I propose leading the attack of the centre division.

Fuller tried to persuade Elles not to enter the battle, fearing the consequences to the Corps if he were badly wounded or killed, but he was adamant. Fuller later admitted he was wrong: 'To lead his command was to give life and soul to all our preparations – it was spiritually the making of the Tank Corps, and in value it transcended all our work.'[5]

On 20 November after heavy overnight rain, the tanks moved off in thick mist at 6.10 a.m., the infantry following. Byng threw in every machine, keeping no reserve. Ten minutes later at zero hour his 1,000 guns opened fire for the first time, laying down a creeping barrage on a predicted shoot. The absence of a preliminary bombardment had avoided alerting the enemy and precipitating a counter-shelling to cut up infantry and tanks in their jumping-off positions. It was a stunningly successful action. The advance had penetrated over 5 miles when it was broken off for the day as winter's early dusk set in. Four immensely strong defence lines had been overcome and only an unfinished stop line lay between the tanks and open country. Some forty-eight tanks had been disabled or destroyed. Over 100 guns and 8,000 prisoners had been taken. Most of the German wire was sited on reverse slopes where artillery was unlikely to cut it, but Hastie's detachment had cleared lanes in a few hours. Casualties in killed, wounded and missing among the tank crews were very heavy, totalling 118 officers and 530 other ranks. Casualties among the six attacking infantry divisions were estimated to total 76 officers and 2,508 other ranks. Thereafter, exhaustion among the crews and the infantry, and the absence of reserves of either, greatly reduced the scale of further combined actions. The enemy were overwhelmed and put up little resistance that first day, but their later reinforcement soon halted further advance and the cavalry served only to choke lines of communication. A well-prepared German counter-attack on 30 November wiped out almost all the gains, but the devastating effectiveness of the tanks had rung the church bells at home and shown the way forward for 1918. They had penetrated up to 10,000yd in 12 hours from a base of 13,000yd. At the Third Battle of Ypres the base was 25,000yd and it took three months to achieve a similar gain, with the loss of hundreds of thousands of men and millions of shells.

Cambrai was the world's first great tank battle. It was a personal triumph for Fuller whose meticulous planning of tank tactics and organisation became a Staff training study for many years. Above all, it was a most gallant victory for the crews and their machines, regardless of the wider outcome of the offensive. They had begun to win the confidence of the Army, but Elles considered it was well into mid-1918 before the void between the pro- and anti-tank factions among the staffs was bridged with those willing to assess the weapon dispassionately. Gen Capper observed after Cambrai, 'I do not [sic] think that the battle confirms the view of those who hold that Cavalry are out of date. They should be invaluable to obtain speedy and decisive results.'[6] He was, nevertheless, convinced of the tank's growing role, writing to Elles: 'Gen Furse [Master General of Ordnance] is a strong supporter, and cannot understand the attitude that is taken up by many still as to the purely accessory nature of the new arm, which I think will more and more develop into a main feature of the battle.'[7]

Stern was able to remind Churchill of the charge that he had lumbered up the front with useless tanks and wasted a year of development – Cambrai told a different story. He warned the Minister that the MWD under Moore would never produce tanks in sufficient quantity or speedily enough to win the war in 1918. Stern also criticised the creation of his own parallel O&A department alongside the MWD, and his exclusion from the New Tank Committee. Churchill spoke of difficulties but promised to get him into membership. (He tried and failed; the committee agreed to invite Stern to 'relevant' meetings but not to participate as a member.) The interview brought a private rebuke from Duckham who warned Stern that he could not continue to ignore his negative attitude.

*   *   *

The New Tank Committee (henceforth 'the Tank Committee') heard Adm Moore's first situation report as Controller on 26 November. His delivery forecasts were based on current materials and labour priorities.

Type	Initial order	Completion in 1918: forecast (actual)
Mk IV fighter	950	January (late April)
Mk IV converted to tank supply tenders	205	End of January (July)
Medium A (Whippet)	200	April (October)
New types Mk V	600	June (400th delivered June. Production then ceased)
Medium B	380	175 by June (Priority reduced. 26th tank delivered Armistice week, 11 November 1918)
Mk IX infantry supply	200	Contract about to be placed. Completion expected May (23 delivered by Armistice)
Mk II Gun carriers, etc. Gun carriers	120	Just contracted, no forecast possible (None built)
Salvage	30	As for GC above (None built)

The War Office had earlier given notice that it was prepared to accept 216 of Stern's 400 unauthorised Mk IV overproduction if they were converted to tank tenders, but it refused to take delivery of the remaining machines. It was also clear that the heavy tanks would have to cross much wider trenches. Mk V production was accordingly halved in December to 400 machines as the type was unable to cross gaps greater than 10ft. Deliveries began in February 1918.

At the same time the WO ordered 300 of a male variant, the Mk V Star. It had been lengthened by 6ft, increasing trench crossing performance to 13ft. The order was raised early in 1918 to a total of 500 male and 200 female machines. Delivery began in June and by the Armistice 579 had been built.

Instead of the box-like rear turret with two revolver ports as on the Mk V, the fore and aft plates of the Star's turret were each fitted with a ball mounting for a machine gun and sloped to give them greater elevation. David Fletcher of the Tank Museum believes this modification was made to aid street fighting – the Germans knew that armament on tanks could not be elevated to sweep Maxim and bombing positions on the upper floors of adjacent buildings.[8] It was intended that the Star should have Ricardo's new 225hp engine to compensate for a 4-ton weight penalty but these fine motors were not available in time. With the Ricardo 150hp engine of the Mk V the Star was under-powered, and a pig to steer by virtue of the longer run of track in ground contact. A Two Star version with the 300hp engine was ordered in January; the 300 machines were to be delivered by 15 November. The length of track in ground contact on a hard surface was cut to only 6ft to improve steerability, and the fighting compartment was moved from the waist to the front of the tank. Shortage of steel delayed production. The first Two Star machine was completed in December 1918, and a total of twenty-five were built.

Central Workshops at Erin had been the first to improve trench-crossing performance by cutting a Mk IV in two and inserting panels to stretch it by 6ft. Metropolitan was instructed by MWD on 3 October 1917 to do the same, working to Rackham's drawings, but the order was cancelled two days later. Instead, Foster's was asked to stretch three Mk IVs by 3, 6 and 9ft respectively, and to fit Ricardo 150hp engines. Tritton tackled the job differently. Instead of Erin's cut-and-shut infill, he extended the track frames rearwards by butt-strapping a pair of mild steel horns to them. The first Mk IV conversion was completed in December. The 9ft 'tadpole tail' extension was adopted for Mks IV and V, the kit being interchangeable and easy to fit. (A set was tested the following May on an experimental Mk V Star, boosting its length to an almost unsteerable 41ft.) When Frank Searle said he could convert ten Mk IV per week, 300 sets were ordered. The first reached Erin in May 1918, where rows of extensions soon cluttered up the rail loading ramp area. There is no record of stretched Mk IV tanks or tadpole tails seeing action.

Churchill remained infatuated with the idea of a supertank. Anticipating a need for fighting machines capable of crossing the canal systems which lay ahead in a general advance, he told a doubtlessly shuddering d'Eyncourt that he wanted twelve 250–300-ton 'Reservoirs'. With characteristic wit his cover name reflected their giant size relative to the 'Tanks'. He envisaged machines up to 90ft long to carry four 18-pdr guns and twelve machine guns, with a

100-mile radius of action. They could be built near the coast in England
before crossing over on special barges and driving cross-country to the front.
Elles and Capper favoured the idea; Butler disagreed. D'Eyncourt passed the
assignment to Moore who reported in December that every draughtsman was
needed to prepare working drawings for Mk V and the Medium B. All
attempts to date to produce tanks over 50ft long had failed because of the
great weight of machinery necessary to deliver power, which in turn raised
transmission and track problems. He was accordingly preparing sketches for a
50ft machine with a breadth of 13ft and weighing 80 tons for cross-Channel
shipment in sections and then movement by canal. Power from two of Harry
Ricardo's 225hp engines, soon to be built, would drive 'four parallel tracks
each side, having a heavy short and a light long track'. It would mount two
12-pdr guns in sponsons, and at least ten Hotchkiss MG.[9] The Tank
Committee discreetly shelved the scheme.

*   *   *

1918 opened with a reorganisation of the Tank Corps in January in the light
of experience at Cambrai. The current establishment was for
18 battalions, 9 heavy and 9 light, each with 60 tanks. The balance was now
adjusted to increase the number of heavy tank battalions to 12, each with 48
tanks, and reduce the medium-equipped to 6, each with 65 machines. At three
battalions to a brigade the establishment allowed for growth to six brigades.
Tanks were additionally demanded to equip two further brigades with heavy
and one with medium machines. In all, the requirement for fighting tanks for
1918 to early 1919, including replacements at 20 per cent per month, totalled
1,654 heavies (increase of 406), and 1,120 medium machines (increase of
92). Other requirements comprised 325 tank tenders (216 of which were the
converted Mk IV), 18 wireless-equipped tanks (principally Mk IV), 9 cable-
laying tanks of infantry-carrier type, and 312 infantry carriers. It amounted
to a small increase in fighting tanks, from 2,276 in October pre-Cambrai, to
2,774 – a token endorsement of the weapon's staggering performance.

Churchill received this information coolly. He was pushing the tank
programme hard regardless of military calculations. He told Moore and Stern
that he wanted them to gear up to achieve 10,000 tanks per year, 4,500
from Britain and the rest from a new Anglo-American factory in France. It
was a tall order for Moore, involving vastly more steel and a monthly

allocation of 1,400 6-pdr guns and 5,000 machine guns, against current supply of 320 and 1,600 respectively. All the 6-pdrs would have to come from Armstrong's, the sole suppliers. America's vast industrial resources could not be turned around to volume war production of armour plate and ordnance for many months, perhaps a year. In addition, Stern had taken with him some key members of the MWD headquarters team including the production director; the MoM establishments branch blocked Moore's repeated requests for more management staff; the War Office persisted in ordering in small batches followed by non-productive delays before reordering; and Moore's design and drawing office departments were heavily overladen. Working drawings for the Mk IV conversion engaged almost the entire staff, delaying a start on Medium B. Rackham's Mk VIII involved hundreds of drawings and caused draughting work on Mks V, V Star and Medium B to be transferred to Metropolitan in Birmingham. Manufacturers were unable to maintain delivery schedules for supply of gearboxes and epicyclics. By the time Mk V production started in February it was clear that output would be over 100 tanks below estimate by the end of March. Churchill intervened, securing Dudley Docker's undertaking to build 660 Mk V and V Star by 30 June – in the event Metropolitan managed a respectable 518.

Moore put in a demand to the Labour Department in February for a further 1,040 men and 260 women for assignment to Metro. If approved, he expected production of the Mk V series to reach forty per week in April. Churchill directed that labour should be diverted from gun manufacture and that tanks were to have the highest priority for all resources controlled by the Ministry. Later that month he formed 'Council Committee 57 – Tanks' to accelerate delivery of the 1918 programme and to plan production for 1919. Duckham and fellow Council members controlling ordnance and materials collaborated intensively for three weeks to organise reinforcement of Moore's operations. Churchill set them a national production target of 100 tanks per week. He also made a point of advising them to invite Stern's proposals. Production improved considerably for a few months but could not be sustained in face of competing demands for resources, not least for steel for the Admiralty. Moore's hand was greatly strengthened, however, by the appointment of the energetic and vastly experienced Percival Perry as his Deputy Controller on 21 March.

Many production difficulties were quickly overcome with resourceful management and the excellent relations which existed between manufacturers and their local MWD supply officers. Other problems were less straightforward.

Medium A production was slowed by a severe shortage of ball bearings for the track rollers, an outsize having been specified in the mistaken belief that the country held large supplies. Production of engines and gearboxes fell sharply from late July through September after the Ministry took over direct control of forging facilities in May. Only 60 per cent of the stampings required for tanks, aircraft and motor transport were met. The drop stampers assigned by the Ministry to Moore's MWD were unfamiliar with the class of work required by the engine-builders, and both sectors refused the orders. After daily conferences with the Department of Forgings and Castings the MWD undertook to place orders for the stamping of gearboxes, blanks and engine parts directly with stampers in a series of unsatisfactory compromises, and output was not fully restored until control was lifted in September.

Moore was caught in the crossfire between the supply side led by the Prime Minister, Churchill, Stern and d'Eyncourt who saw the tank as a decisive weapon to be built in large numbers to an acceptable but not ambitious performance standard for use *en masse*, and the Army – including especially Capper and Elles – which wanted fewer machines with regular performance upgrades for limited tactical objectives. The Army was unconcerned that high output was attainable only with long unbroken production runs. It could point out that the Ministry had consistently failed to meet its own production forecasts and any call for higher volumes of a given type would simply lock in obsolescence over an even longer period. The obvious case in point was the interminable production of the 1,015 Mk IV fighting tanks, the largest and longest run of any British tank in the First World War. Deliveries began in April 1917 and Armstrong's despatched the last machines in October 1918. By then the design was so obsolete that seventy or eighty ex-works machines were dumped in a park on Newbury racecourse where they were embarrassingly visible to passing trains at a time when every tank was known to be wanted at the front. Capper rated long runs of a given type as 'a distinct evil. . . . Too much standardisation cripples advance in design and must always leave us with numbers of out of date machines.'[10]

In pursuance of its policy the Army had halved production of Tritton's Medium A the previous October and instead ordered Wilson's Medium B, 650 of which were contracted out to builders. In January 1918 the 'B' Type in turn was considered inadequate and Elles called for its cancellation in favour of a much superior Medium C for which Tritton had just built a mock-up. It was 1.5 tons heavier than the 'B' Type, offering male and female versions and nearly twice the radius of action at 120 miles. Moore told him that the Medium B was too far advanced to stop and the first 120 would be built in May; this was purely a blocking move – the first machine was rolled out in September. D'Eyncourt pointed out that it would be a very serious matter if word got out that the Ministry was throwing labour and scarce materials at an unwanted tank. Moore asked Metropolitan to try to phase out the 'B' Type, switching labour instead to boost Mk V output pending a start on the Medium C. Six weeks later, on 24 February, Elles condemned the Medium C in turn as being too slow at 6.5mph, too heavy at 19.5 tons to load two per tank rail wagon, and inadequately armed with the proposed 2-pdr gun which would be useless as a tank destroyer.[11] A redesign to provide the 6-pdr and increase speed to over 8mph was followed by an order for 200 in March and a further 400 on 31 May. Faced with these changes of direction it was hard for Moore to plan and place work coherently, or to avoid drops in output while responding to new orders, revisions, cutbacks and cancellations. Whereas Stern the banker had periodically ignored or exceeded War Office demands, Moore the Admiral tried reason. He had been Director of Naval Ordnance until 1914 and was more at home than Stern with production processes and disciplines. (It was Moore who gave Tulloch his 'Tri-nitro Tom' nickname.)

The progress of the gun carriers was another object lesson, not least to Churchill. In August 1917 the War Office had doubled its requirement to 100 machines. The fifty-two in the new batch were to be built as gun transporters rather than firing platforms. The order for these Mk II carriers brought renewed objections from the Ministry's transport department which demanded the removal of all gun-carrier work from Kitson's in Leeds to free capacity there for priority locomotive construction. Stern asked Metropolitan to take the work. The War Office then cancelled the order in September, asking if the balance of unbuilt Mk I carriers could nevertheless be constructed as Mk II. It was wholly unrealistic to retool for what amounted to some thirty-four machines of substantially new design. Instead, and without reference to the WO, Churchill authorised construction of 150 Mk II GC chassis, 100 of which would be built as supply tanks, 10 as tank salvage (recovery) vehicles, and the remaining 40 as gun transporters. Five days later on 15 October, the War Office withdrew its cancellation and ordered 50 Mk II gun carriers plus 20 salvage tanks.

The saga continued on Stern's departure that month, the War Office objecting that it had not ordered the remaining 80 supply tanks on GC chassis, preferring to await the purpose-built Mk IX. Churchill again changed the order – to

120 gun carriers and 30 salvage machines. When the War Office later repeated its refusal to accept any GC types in excess of its order for 70, it was given the customary blocking reply that production was too far advanced to halt – a large exaggeration since no Mk II was ever built. A further revision followed in January 1918 when the WO trimmed its order for salvage machines to seventeen. Designs for the gun carriers and salvage tanks were still not signed off as approved when in March the War Office ordered all work on GC types to cease. The surviving Mk I carriers were fitted with cranes at Central Workshops for salvage duty. Churchill had experienced the same vacillation from the Army High Command which had so enraged Stern. Their reactions were identical, but overriding and second-guessing military requirements was no solution.

Adm Moore favoured a 'divide and rule' policy concerning his main tank contractors. He told Duckham:

> We desire to register the strongest possible protest against relying too implicitly upon the resources of the Metropolitan Company or any other one firm. Past experience indicates that this Department must control the situation and such control is impossible when too much reliance is placed upon one contractor. There seems to be a desire on the part of the Metropolitan Company particularly, to achieve a position of monopoly in Tank Production. If this ambition is fostered then the Department will be subservient to the Contractor.[12]

Moore's policy meant further fragmentation of final assembly, already shared by twelve firms in a chain of plants between Birmingham and the Clyde. They all relied in varying degrees on a network of 4,000 specialist suppliers and services. Metropolitan and its subsidiary Patent Shaft dominated with a total capacity of 210 tanks per month, dwarfing Marshall's of Gainsborough which was the next highest at 30 (Mk IX supply tank). Coventry Ordnance of Glasgow (Medium B) and Foster's (Medium A) were geared to build 22 and 20 per month respectively. The remaining assemblers fell below these levels. Total monthly productive capacity was 350 heavy tanks or equivalent tonnage. Moore may also have feared the crippling effect of industrial disputes on such a concentration of output at Metro. The 1915 Munitions of War Act outlawed strikes and lockouts, but strike action persisted intermittently throughout the war. The Darlaston area was almost shut down by strikes in February 1918, cutting all supply of bolts and rivets to Metro and delaying Mk V assembly. Strikes that month on 'Red Clydeside' hit Coventry Ordnance, preventing use of new machinery for tank stampings, Beardmore's, where riveters working on tank assemblies were out for over four weeks, and Foster's in Lincoln, which consequently ran short of track shoes. The printed letterhead of Crossley Brothers of Openshaw, Manchester, a major supplier of Ricardo tank engines, is indicative of the general state of industrial relations. It cautioned: 'We do not accept any responsibility for delay in execution of orders due to Strikes, Lock outs etc. etc.' This was no idle disclaimer. Production of 2,100 150hp units was crippled for several weeks later that year by the refusal of Crossley's fitters to accept 200 female operatives.

Moore established a new production centre in the vast workshops of Glasgow's North British Locomotive Company (NBL). By 1914 the company had built over 20,000 steam engines in Europe's largest railway engineering complex. Churchill ensured that much of its capacity was turned over to tank production despite the higher priority attaching to locomotives. NBL was appointed lead contractor for British Mk VIII tanks, undertaking in April to build 1,040 machines. It was hoped monthly output there would reach 90 tanks by October. Another Glasgow tank plant was initiated at the same time at the suggestion of Sir William Beardmore whose company managed one of sixteen National Projectile Factories for the Ministry. The Cardonald works was producing heavy shell in ten of its thirteen bays; he proposed conversion of the remainder for tank assembly. Proximity to Beardmore's Parkhead steel mills which rolled much of Moore's plate was an added advantage. Additional tank bays were to be constructed and an order was placed for 335 Mk VIII machines for delivery at ten per week, doubling to twenty on completion of the extension in July/August. In the event no tanks were built there, the order was cancelled in September and the extension remained uncompleted – hope had outrun the reality of machine tools and other shortages at that late stage of the war. Moore also signed up a South Lancashire consortium led by West's Gas Improvement Co. Ltd of Manchester. The group of some twenty-five engineering firms became the Manchester Tank Group which was contracted on 7 March to produce all 1,500 Liberty Mk VIII hulls for shipment to France for fitting out there. It was also to build the Ricardo 300hp engines at 320 per month.

*   *   *

A site for the Anglo-American tank factory had quickly been found 150 miles south of Paris at Chateauroux with good rail links to the capital and the

Channel supply ports. A nine-bay plant was to be built. It would assemble 300 tanks per month and be capable of extension to 1,200 monthly. Despite numerous appeals the French authorities did not grant permission to start work on site until the end of February 1918. Meantime, production of armour and other components in Britain and America awaited working drawings from Rackham's Mk VIII design team in London. Rackham found himself working on two types – a Mk VIII to be built in Britain for Sir Douglas Haig's forces, and a Chateauroux-built version which varied from the British in numbers of gears and other details. Design was proceeding in parallel with preparation of working drawings, a situation always to be avoided. Additional draughtsmen were engaged and funded by America, and Moore's offer to turn his entire drawing office over to Mk VIII work was gratefully accepted. The Allied design was approved on 7 March by Gen Sir John Capper, Gen Elles and Col Samuel D. Rockenbach, Chief of the American Tank Corps. It was hoped to assemble 100 tanks in France in July and to reach 300 monthly by September. To ensure full interchangeability of parts, all jigs for British and American use were made by a single firm, the Leeds Forge Company. It was discovered in March that the limits specified on the jig drawings were incorrect, leading to further delay.

Stern's relations were further deteriorating inside the Ministry and with the Army. He continued to criticise Moore's operations, driving Duckham to recommend his replacement. Duckham told Churchill in late February that he regretted ever suggesting Stern's appointment as Commissioner. At the same time the War Office contemplated urging Churchill to place Chateauroux under American control as 'any joint control must depend for smooth working on the personality of the Controllers, and is more liable to lead to friction and loss of efficiency than a single control'.[13] Counsel's opinion was sought on the risk of breaching the Anglo-American Agreement if Stern was dismissed. He confirmed there was no problem. Lord Derby chaired a meeting at the War Office on 8 March attended by Capper, Duckham and others at which it was decided 'to give Colonel Stern another chance – if he again interferes the Ministry of Munitions will remove him'. Meantime, Stern was to be stripped of his rank and uniform through demobilisation 'if possible', and Capper and Duckham were to find means to limit his powers.[14] The ensuing series of minutes on a War Office file would be hilarious if the matter were not so serious. Loss of uniform would unsettle Stern's Allied partners and undermine his authority. Most of his senior staff were commissioned officers – as a civilian Stern would have no authority over them and his position would at once become untenable.

MS (through AG [Adjutant General])
Will you take up the question of disposing of this officer . . .
for DCIGS [Gen Whigham]

AG
The normal procedure would be to transfer him to the General List. Will this meet the case?
12.3.18 [signature indecipherable]

MS
What we want is to get him out of uniform – will your proposal do this?
14.3.18. [Gen Whigham]

DCIGS [Deputy Chief of the Imperial General Staff]
No it will not. People at the Ministry of Munitions who hold commissions of any sort are allowed to wear uniform.
18.3.18. [indecipherable]

S. of S. [Secretary of State]
Do you agree to Col Stern being transferred to the General List?
20.3.18. [Gen Whigham]

If we can't take him out of uniform there is not much object in making any change. The matter had better remain in abeyance for present.
21.3. 18 [Lord Derby].[15]

*   *   *

Stern called for the War Cabinet to appoint a special Council immediately to get a grip on the tank supply situation. He had warned in February that:

Unless a decision [on the 1918/19 programme] is taken in the very near future, say within two months at the latest, the chances of an overwhelming Allied Mechanical Army for 1919 will be frittered away and our superiority over the enemy in this arm lost for this war. Unless factories for the necessary guns and machine guns are immediately provided, a

1919 programme on a large scale will be outside the bounds of possibility.[16]

Lloyd George promised Stern that he would call a meeting of the War Cabinet if any group of ministers supported it and let him submit his views. Stern used political contacts to invite the Labour ministers of the coalition to see and hear about the tanks. They were duly impressed, promising to secure a War Cabinet meeting and to urge the building of tanks to the full capacity of the country. The meeting took place on 8 March. Churchill shrewdly circulated a paper two days before which quoted intelligence reports from prisoner interrogations suggesting that Germany was building tanks in quantity. He included Moore's estimate that if the enemy had begun preparation of drawings on 1 January, they could have completed construction of 400 tanks by 1 August. Stern and d'Eyncourt attended the meeting, at which Churchill presented his vision for 1919 of 200,000 fighting men sweeping forward 10 miles in a day in an armoured armada of fighting tanks, personnel carriers, chasers, wire crushers, etc. He went on:

The resources are available, the knowledge is available, the time is available, the result is certain: nothing is lacking except the will. . . . We have instead only carried out a series of costly experiments, each of which has shown us the chance we have lost and exposed our thought to the enemy. It surely lies with those who shake their heads to say on what alternative method of attack or on what alternative form of superiority they can rely to win a military victory in 1919. . . . If there is an alternative plan let us have it. If not, let this one have its fair chance.[17]

Churchill carried the meeting with him, winning approval to jump-start an extended tank programme by drawing 1,500 tons of steel per week from the 80,000 tons held as Admiralty reserve. He was authorised to increase production from 3,400 tanks to 4,559 machines between February 1918 and March 1919, precisely as he had planned. The civilian pioneers and politicians were now imposing tank numbers on the Army. It was a significant victory for Churchill and Stern, but the knives were out. When the meeting broke up Lord Derby, Gen Sir Henry Wilson (the new CIGS), Capper and Duckham met to plot Stern's removal from uniform.

*   *   *

Within days of the decision to gear up production, GHQ exploded a demolition charge. Haig ordered a reduction of the Tank Corps from six to four brigades and the transfer to the infantry of some 2,600 trained tank personnel already in France. As the Corps was not yet up to establishment the effect of this severe reduction was all the greater. Elles threw up a series of quibbling points of order and successfully stalled its implementation. One might conclude that the C-in-C was bringing pressure to bear on a reluctant War Cabinet to release more men for the killing fields. Either that or he was losing his reason.

Elles and his senior officers were already fuming at the inadequacies of tank supply and the *laissez faire* attitude at GHQ. Fuller, the thinking soldier's soldier, had sent Churchill a very frank confidential memorandum shortly before the War Council meeting of 8 March. He spoke for all at Bermicourt:

The three main difficulties which confront us are:

1. GHQ is inert and will lay down no policy.
2. No efficient higher organisation exists in the Tank Corps.
3. Design and production are not assured.

As regards '1' I am of opinion that it is sheer waste of time to continue attempting to convince the Inconvincibles. It is like trying to teach a Kaffir the integral calculus. Let us cease this folly. The firing line appreciates our value, so do the higher civilians at home, but these two are separated by a missing link – GHQ. If no suitable link can be found to fill the gap, then we must shorten up the chain by welding the civilian to the firing line. This means that the Cabinet must decide on the 1919 Tank policy, whether GHQ likes it or not.

As regards '2' the present tank organisation is monstrous. It has three heads but no single controlling brain. . . .

(a) General Capper works under the War Office.
(b) General Elles works under GHQ.
(c) Admiral Moore works under the Ministry of Munitions.

We want a Director General, one head, for preference a civilian unshackled by 1870 tactics, who has direct access to the War Office, GHQ and the

Ministry of Munitions. . . . The Headquarters Tank Corps in London to be done away with, and replaced by a General Staff Officer and an Administrative Officer at the War Office.

As regards '3' we are now faced by a race for tank supremacy. . . . This problem is a twofold one – design and production. Design requires a man who <u>knows</u> [*sic*] what we in France want. Production requires a man who <u>is</u> [*sic*] an expert in production.[18]

Fuller nominated Col Frank Searle as the only possible man to control design and production, which he said was the pivotal and most immediate requirement. He emphasised that he wrote for Elles as much as for himself – Elles would be in a more difficult position had the letter come from him. Churchill replied with an assurance that 'production will carry all before it', but that he could not make the personnel changes requested. Churchill was powerless to help on the first two points. He was not a member of the War Cabinet and his views outside munitions production were not welcomed by the Army Council.

The continuing failure of the staff at GHQ to formulate a policy for tanks was unforgivable. As late as 10 June 1918 Haig's CGS told Capper that the General Staff could not lay down its performance requirements for future tanks because 'the role of the tank is not yet definitely fixed'.[19] So far as the tank weapon was concerned, another year was drifting by with no firm hand on the tiller in France. Meanwhile, the Armies bled.

*   *   *

The German offensive opened on 21 March 1918 in the British sector along a frontage of 43 miles. Ludendorff's sixty-three divisions were supported by some 4,000 guns which had been brought up under concealment to shoot a pre-dawn hurricane of fire without prior registration. The onslaught struck the fourteen divisions of Byng's Third Army and fourteen more of Gough's Fifth Army. In the first few days Haig lost over 30 per cent of his infantry in France. The Tank Corps had grown from three to five brigades with twelve battle-ready battalions and others in formation. Knowing what was coming, Haig had earlier decided to treat his tanks as armoured keeps which could be dug into pits from which to emerge to provide defensive fire, a task for which they were never designed. Elles' advice was ignored and his tanks were thinly spread along a frontage of some 60 miles from Roisel to Bethune. They fought most gallantly, driving back or deflecting the onslaught in many limited actions with heavy loss in crews and tanks. The Germans were fighting to unfamiliar tactics; instead of advancing and digging in to consolidate gains, pockets of resistance were simply bypassed by highly trained storm troops who led the attack, leaving strongpoints to following troops to clear. The dispersal of the tanks made a concerted armoured counterpunch impossible to organise. GHQ had deployed the machines essentially to stiffen local defences rather than concentrating them in two or three powerful response groups. Byng's Army held the shorter frontage and resisted so effectively that no very serious penetration was made for the first 36 hours. Elements of the much more extended Fifth Army held on until widening breaches forced Gough to fall back behind the Somme on the 23rd, leaving many tanks abandoned for want of petrol or spares. Next day their crews – and the instructional staff of the Tank Driving School at Aveluy – formed Lewis gun teams and fought on. Tanks of the 8th Battalion held off the enemy long enough to enable one of Byng's divisions to withdraw. Their action was repeated by other tank units that day and the next.

The Medium A Whippets first saw combat on 26 March when twelve machines of the 3rd Battalion were sent from Bray to plug a 4-mile gap in Byng's front. They met about 300 of the enemy advancing on the village of Colincamps, but the Germans fled in disorder on seeing the strange machines. The Whippets moved on to disperse numerous enemy patrols before withdrawing without loss. They had done well in checking an enveloping movement at the break in the line.

Ludendorff's wedge had attempted to split the British from the French before rolling them up to the coast and driving them into the sea. Having penetrated over 40 miles across the old Somme battlefields, his offensive outran its supplies. Ludendorff was driven back at Arras and before Amiens. By 4 April it was clear he had failed, but at terrible cost to Haig's armies. The enemy had taken 80,000 prisoners and captured 975 guns.

The German High Command had accepted the value of armoured fighting tracklayers in November 1916 when a design group was appointed, in the *Allegemeine Kriegsdepartement 7, Abteilung Verkehrswesen* (General War Department 7, Traffic Section). It had put a Holt tractor through trials and, unlike Scott-Moncrieff's committee, pressed on to adapt Holt's system and produce the A7V tank, its name being a contraction of the department's title. The 45-ton machine was powered by twin Daimler 100hp engines. It had the appearance of an armoured turtle, its high carapace being carried down over the underslung tracks almost to ground level, topped by a small observation turret. A single 5.7cm gun was mounted frontally with six Maxim machine guns distributed about its flanks and rear. One hundred were ordered, though only twenty were built, the first emerging in October 1917. Though it had a higher power/weight ratio than the British tanks and sprung tracks for greater speed, it proved a failure. Its high centre of gravity, fore and aft overhangs and short tracks made the *Schwerer Kampfwagen* A7V a poor cross-country performer and incapable of crossing trenches. Four A7V tanks and five captured Mk IV machines were employed in the opening phase of the offensive.

The historic first tank *vs* tank action took place on 24 April at Villers–Brettoneux during a small-scale German attack on a 4-mile front. It was led by thirteen A7V tanks which had much the same effect on the defenders as when British tanks appeared at Flers in 1916. The village was taken and the German machines moved on, three of them running into an advancing section of the 1st Battalion, Tank Corps. The single male and two female Mk IV tanks had just been subjected to heavy gas shelling and some crewmen had been helped out and left behind. Capt John Brown MC, the Section Commander, rode in the male machine which was reduced to a crew of five. He dismounted to alert his other tanks and to direct the section on foot for the rest of the action despite the heavy fire, a regular and often lethal procedure for unit leaders.

Moments after engaging the German machines the two lightly armed females were badly damaged by return fire, withdrawing with large holes in their sides. The remaining Mk IV commanded by Lt Frank Mitchell manoeuvred to present the nearest A7V to his left side gunner, Sgt J.R. McKenzie, who was working the 6-pdr single handed owing to the gas casualties. He himself was half blinded by gas in his right eye and was laying his gun from his left. At this point the tank was raked continuously with machine-gun fire from the A7Vs. An armour-piercing bullet wounded the rear Lewis gunner in both legs. McKenzie, cut about the face by bullet fragments, was firing repeatedly from a heaving platform at a moving target. Mitchell took a chance and halted the tank momentarily. McKenzie got in three direct hits, the German machine running forward out of control down a slight slope and overturning. Its crew baled out to become targets for Mitchell's machine guns. The two remaining A7Vs turned towards the Mk IV and could have wrecked it with ease, but both were forced to retire under a hail of 6-pdr shell, the crew of one leaving their tank, possibly having stalled it, and fleeing. The victorious Mk IV was crippled later that morning when a shell blew off a track. Mitchell and his crew and John Brown all got back safely to the British trenches. Brown was awarded a bar to his Military Cross, Mitchell received the MC, and McKenzie was awarded the Military Medal.

Nearby, Capt Tommy Price's detachment of seven Medium A tanks was alerted that morning by a message dropped from a reconnaissance aircraft that two enemy battalions were grouping in a hollow near Cachy. Mitchell saw the Whippets go in at full throttle, their machine guns flaying through some 1,200 panicking storm troops. The machines turned about and continued the attack, three Whippets finally emerging. Only 21 men had killed an estimated 400 of the enemy at the cost of 3 killed, 1 wounded and the loss of 4 tanks.

* * *

Two pillars of the War Office hierarchy fell in those closing days of April. Lloyd George sacked Lord Derby for failing to promote the aims of the War Cabinet, appointing Lord Milner in his place as Secretary of State for War. Gen Whigham followed, to be replaced as Deputy Chief of the Imperial General Staff by Gen Charles Harington. Lloyd George had already dismissed Gen Willy Robertson in February, appointing Gen Wilson CIGS. The changes opened a new era of progress at the War Office for mechanical warfare. Milner supported Stern's activities. 'Tim' Harington, former Chief of Staff of Second Army, quickly became a firm believer, telling Churchill: 'We want a definite General Staff policy as to what nature of tanks we require and how we want to employ them and I intend to get this laid down at once.' In Capper's view 'GHQ Staff will need a lot of conversion still.' He was right. At the end of May the reinvigorated War Office snubbed GHQ by increasing its demands to 6,940 tanks, of which there were to be 900 Mk V Two-Star, 2,400 Mk VIII (including the 1,500 at Chateauroux), 1,750 Medium C or D and 1,400 infantry carriers, all for completion by 1 June 1919. GHQ capitulated on 18 June and withdrew its cut in tank manpower.

The Prime Minister's 'house clearance' at the War Office brought immediate results. The question was no longer whether the Army would accept a great tank fleet, but whether one could still be built.

Thirteen

...AND A BODY COUNT

I have had more difficulty in getting the hang of the tank question since
I arrived [at the War Office] than all other questions put together.[1]

*Maj Gen Charles 'Tim' Harington, Deputy Chief of the Imperial General
Staff, to Maj Gen The Hon. C.J. Sackville-West, British Military
Representative, The Supreme War Council, 21 May 1918*

T he 'High Speed Destroyer Tank', otherwise known as Medium D, was
the work of Maj Philip Henry Johnson, a gifted design engineer in the
same mould as Walter Wilson. His interest in heavy traction stemmed
from service in the South African War with the 45th Steam Road Transport
Company RE, which coincidentally he and Col Crompton joined in the same
month in 1900. Johnson had later worked for John Fowler of Leeds before
rejoining the Army and transferring to the Heavy Section in July 1916 as an
Army Service Corps officer. He helped set up Central Workshops with Searle
before promotion to Major and command of D Battalion Workshops. Since
December 1917 he had controlled the experimental work at No. 3 Advanced
Workshops, Searle's newly created experimental establishment at Erin.
Johnson's particular interest lay in developing a tank suspension and track
system which would permit much greater speeds than the present unsprung
assemblies. The 'D' Type was to have the range, speed and firepower to
replace the cavalry and penetrate deep into enemy territory following a
breakthrough. It was thought that speed would also reduce vulnerability to
anti-tank fire. German field guns were increasingly positioned in forward
areas in concealed gunpits, from which they were quickly pulled to fire over
open sights at approaching tanks. Tank losses from these tactics were to
reach 50 per cent.

Attempts had already been made at Central Workshops to speed up the
Medium A Whippet. Early in 1918 Johnson and Searle fitted a leaf-spring

suspension between the track frames of an experimental machine. They replaced its twin 45hp Tylor engines with a single 175hp Rolls-Royce Eagle aero engine, and fitted a modified epicyclic transmission salvaged from a Mk V. At 8mph the standard Whippet was the fastest tank available, but the test machine exceeded 20mph in trials. It was a sensational advance. Tank HQ produced a performance specification and packed Johnson off to London in May to develop the new tank. His brief was to produce a machine not exceeding 20 tons with an operational range of 200 miles at speeds of up to 20mph, and with potential for amphibious use. He was promoted Lieutenant-Colonel and for the rest of that year he shuttled between Bermicourt and the MWD Experimental Station at Dollis Hill in north London. It conveniently adjoined the McCurd lorry factory, now dilapidated but still standing near Staples Corner. McGrath's 20 Squadron had moved there from Wembley Park in July the previous year.

Johnson had been working on a radically new approach to the problem of track inflexibility. Higher speeds over uneven ground would increase the damaging shock loads, and because steering would entail heavily braked skid turns, the stresses of higher turning speeds on the track plates would be unsustainable. In June Johnson's old employers, Fowler's, made up and fitted his flexible track to Mk V experimental tank No. 9425. The standard rigidly linked track plates were replaced by narrow wooden shoes which were free to pivot laterally on swivel links, strung together on an endless tensioned wire cable and hanging at all angles like a shark's-teeth necklace. Because the 'free' shoes pitched randomly in all directions the machine looked like a heap of scrap, but once in ground contact they were responsive to braking turns and surface irregularities. The testbed Mk V also incorporated Johnson's suspension system. It was brilliantly simple. A steel cable was secured to a powerful spring anchored inside the front of the track frame, and then led rearwards threaded over and under the track rollers before securing to a similar rear-mounted spring. In this way the tensioned cable itself became an elongated spring so that the rise or fall of alternate rollers over rough ground was damped by the opposing cable pressures on the adjoining rollers. Fowler's was instructed in August to make four experimental Medium D tanks in mild steel, all to be capable of flotation for river crossing. Four more were ordered from Vickers in September, plus a 'Star' and a 'Two Star' variant with progressively wider hulls to compare stability in the water. By December the experimental Mk V with a Ricardo 150hp engine had covered 530 miles with little track or suspension wear at speeds on the level of 10–12mph, reaching 25mph on slight downgrades.

Fired by the possibilities of Johnson's system, Fuller had submitted an imaginative and radical paper on 24 May, 'The Tactics of the Attack as affected by the Speed and Circuit of the Medium D Tank'. It became 'Plan 1919'. In his refreshingly crisp style uncluttered by military jargon he set out a scheme for paralysing the enemy's brain before smashing his main body of troops. The German command structure behind the front was to be disrupted *before* the main assault. A large 'Disorganising' force of Medium Ds would punch straight through along a 90-mile front and drive on regardless, to reach and scatter the German divisional, corps and army headquarters up to 20 miles beyond. The 'Breaking Force' of tanks, infantry and artillery would strike next, and when the defences were fully penetrated a 'Pursuing Force' of Medium Ds and Cs with lorried infantry was to sweep ahead. Fuller proposed a British contribution of 27 heavy and 9 medium tank battalions, requiring 2,998 tanks and a further 37,000 of all ranks.

It was obvious to some that without a tank policy from GHQ the Army was having to devise tactics around Ministry designs instead of the reverse. Harington in London confessed that: 'Re tanks . . . I am trying hard to get a General Staff policy laid down . . . I have had more difficulty in getting the hang of the tank question since I arrived than all other questions put together.'[2] Gen Sackville-West, the British Military Representative at the Supreme War Council, agreed: 'For some unknown reason anyone to do with tanks seems to be seized with a spirit of opposition to everybody else who has to do with tanks. The result is it is quite impossible to get any sort of collective view on the subject.'[3] Even Gen Guy Dawnay on Haig's Staff was confused, telling Sackville-West that though he well knew the views of Fuller, Elles and Capper on tanks, 'I do not know the views of the General Staff. The fact is that [their views] have not solidified on the subject. I could not explain to you my own views at all convincingly and, as you say, no two tankists agree.'[4] Harington cut through this intellectual sloth and wrote a General Staff policy at the end of May with Gen Henry Wilson's approval. It centred on an offensive timed for 1 June 1919 and employed tanks on a large scale to penetrate on a broad front of 40,000 to 100,000yd. Fuller's 'Plan 1919' had arrived only days before and had not been digested. Harington's tactics were less unorthodox, involving a series of frontal attacks with tanks supported by infantry in tracked carriers, the rapid pile-driver blows giving the enemy no time to regroup and counter-attack. The size of the force and number and type of fighting tanks was not stated, it being left to the Supreme War Council in Versailles to quantify and agree national contributions.

The barely concealed contempt in which the tank was held at GHQ is revealed in its response to the paper. In a hitherto unremarked 'Note on Proposals for the use of Tanks in 1919' written in June, it quoted Harington's proposition that 'a definite break-through on a broad front can only be made successfully by the employment of a very large number of tanks', before commenting:

> If the time and the opportunity were available to train sufficient divisions to the standard of the original Expeditionary Force it would be another matter, but as matters stand at present the above [proposition] can be accepted in principle. In any case it is agreed that tanks are a necessity.

The implications of the statement and its disregard for the terrible lessons of the past three and a half years need no further comment. Haig sent the notes to London with a personal covering letter, a draft of which survives, confirming that they represented his views.[5] A modified 'Plan 1919' was the basis of the policy finally adopted in late July in a 'Memorandum on the Requirements for an Armoured Striking Force for an Offensive in 1919'. Fuller's pre-emptive first strike at the enemy's 'brain' was put back to follow closely behind the main assault. It called for a total of 10,500 tanks from Britain, France and America, and a British quota of 7,296 cross-country supply tractors.

In June the Tank Committee agreed the outline specification for another fast tank to be called the Medium E. At Elles' suggestion a design competition between selected firms was agreed, but Johnson kept ahead of the field and the 'E' Type investigation lapsed.

*   *   *

When the Americans asked Stern to build a camp at Chateauroux for instruction of members of the AEF, he told Lord Milner, the Secretary of State for War, that he saw great advantages in expanding this to a Central Military School and training ground for an 'Inter-Allied Heavy Tank Army' serving the British, French and American forces. Standardised tactical training would allow the pooling of reserves of manpower and machines, and economy in rail transport. Stern believed reason would triumph if he was authorised to negotiate on these lines. Though the subject was entirely outside his remit, Stern put the idea to Loucheur and the two dined with Gen Petain on 24 April. Stern lunched with Gen Foch next day, both commanders agreeing the inter-Allied training proposal and the absolute necessity of pushing tank production to the utmost. Still uncaring of the proprieties, Stern contacted Gen Sir Henry Wilson who told him he would inform Haig that evening – he never got around to it. Stern then asked Churchill for full powers to develop the scheme. They were not granted, and the French later opened an identical school near Fontainebleau.

Stern, a mere colonel, had dined with the French High Command, opened discussion with them on sensitive matters entirely without authority, and spoken directly to the CIGS, all career-breaking military crimes. Capper in particular was incensed. He had never forgiven Stern for withdrawing his assurances on the convertibility of Mk IV. He told Harington he considered Stern to be unfit for his post and called again for him to be parted from his uniform.[6] Capper's shrill objections failed to impress the New Order and Stern got off with a caution.

Bertie Stern had other reasons to feel isolated. Since becoming premier Lloyd George had worked to establish a unified system of Allied command in place of *ad hoc* conferences. He succeeded in November 1917 in setting up the Supreme War Council, based in Versailles with inter-Allied permanent military representatives and a planning staff. The British section was attached to the War Cabinet Office rather than the War Office. The Council formed an Inter-Allied Tank Committee to coordinate national tank programmes and formulate tactics. It first met at Versailles on 6/7 May 1918. Gen Harington appointed Fuller to represent Britain. GHQ blocked the assignment saying, rightly, that Fuller would present his own views rather than those of the High Command. Capper took his place. Gen Estienne spoke for France, Col Gargiulo for Italy and Col Rockenbach for the USA. Stern cabled Duckham on 6 May: 'Does this cancel my charter of last November and will [Capper] be responsible for all tank matters as I am unaware of what action he is taking or what policy he is following.'[7] Stern and Draine attended none of the four meetings of the committee, but Capper succeeded in persuading it to agree that 'a large increase in our tank force will give the best prospects of success in 1919'. They set a British contribution of 3,300 tanks and 45,000 men.

The committee produced much paper of negligible value and was wound up in October.

Stern was unable to persuade Churchill to back him officially in his attempts to unseat Capper and take his place on the Versailles Committee. He told all who would listen that he would fight everyone until he was satisfied with tank organisation, and he threatened to put the whole situation to the press. Gen Harington had reached his own conclusions and was able to persuade Stern to put the pin back in his hand grenade by assuring him on 30 May that the War Office intended to assimilate the Tank Corps as an integral part of the Army. The tactical side was to be removed from GHQ and placed directly under the General Staff in London. This was confirmed by the War Office in late July and Capper's Tank Directorate was accordingly closed down. The WO proposed to reform and retain the Tank Committee under the Master General of Ordnance, Gen Furse, its military members to outnumber the Ministry men 2:1. Three weeks of proposals and counter-proposals followed during which Churchill appointed an old friend, the energetic and ebullient Maj Gen Jack Seely, as Deputy Minister. Seely had been Secretary of State for War until March 1914, and had commanded the Canadian Cavalry Brigade until some criticism of his command and a recent gassing brought him home. He and d'Eyncourt emerged as pivotal figures in the reshaping of the Tank Committee. Like Stern, the DNC was weary of partisan and ill-informed bodies. He wrote a near ultimatum to Lloyd George on 30 July.

> Dear Prime Minister
> The whole question of tanks is again in the 'cauldron'; only bubbles and hissings come forth, otherwise I might have used the term 'melting pot' from which <u>something</u> [sic] might emerge. Committees are proposed and turned down. The War Office and Munitions are not at one, and individuals in each are grinding axes. Unless a really representative council or board with a good head with the necessary authority is appointed, the output and whole use of tanks as far as this country is concerned will further decline. We shall become a laughing stock to the Americans and other allies, and shall not contribute as we should, to providing the best material necessary to beat the Boche.
>
> I have just seen Lord Milner, and informed him that I can do no good by joining an invertebrate committee on the old lines and therefore propose to retire altogether from 'Tanks' unless a council or board as suggested [by me]

is formed. I have always as you know been most keen to do all I can for 'Tanks' but as there is continual obstruction I must now retire beaten.

I am, [etc.].[8]

Following a dispute over the accuracy of Moore's production forecasts which had been pitched far above actual monthly outputs, Churchill relieved him of his post as Controller, MWD on 4 August. Moore was appointed Chief Superintendent of the Central Tank Testing & Experimental Station, Newbury, then under construction on the racecourse. He would also be Controller of Experimental Design, Testing and Despatch, but these titles failed to mask the fact of his demotion. James Borrowman Maclean, a highly successful industrial organiser and head of the MoM engineering department, took his place. Churchill told the Prime Minister that the Admiral had not been a success and that his replacement by Stern would have involved endless difficulties with the Army. He reassured him that there were plenty of tanks for the comparatively small numbers of personnel currently provided, but warned that the Corps would need 100,000 men for the tanks arriving by June 1919.

Lloyd George chaired a War Cabinet meeting on 8 August at which d'Eyncourt deplored Stern's earlier dismissal. He quoted tank production for the past four months – 555 machines – which was barely half Moore's original forecast. Backed by Seely, d'Eyncourt recommended the creation of a tank board controlled by the Ministry with Army representation, to determine tank development, design, production and supply and with full powers to coordinate an international tank production programme. He was willing to serve as Vice-President and Controller of Tanks under Seely, with Stern as his deputy. He nominated Fuller to speak for the Army and advocated the retention of Moore to control 'experimental design'. His formula was largely accepted. Seely presided over a Tank Board which first met on 15 August and included d'Eyncourt as Vice-President, Furse, Elles, Fuller (now transferring to the War Office at Gen Harington's request to head the new Tank Department), Maclean, Stern (as Commissioner, O&A), and Swinton, newly returned from America and now a major-general. Churchill's friend Adm Bacon, inventor of the portable 15in howitzers, was now Controller of Munitions Inventions at the MoM, and joined the board in September. One of his first tasks was to investigate the fitting of Medium C tanks with scythes on a revolving disc – they were not adopted. The board coordinated demands and held a watching brief on production issues and

War Office policy. All orders to the Mechanical Warfare Department were transmitted from the board rather than the War Office. Despite the growing scarcity of labour and materials Seely's board proved a great success. New ideas were enthusiastically received and obstructions bulldozed aside.

*   *   *

As the War Cabinet debated on 8 August, the Allied offensive opened east of Amiens to the total surprise of the German Second Army. It was spearheaded by Canadian and Australian units of Rawlinson's Fourth Army. This was Cambrai on a grander and generally superbly planned scale. A total of 604 tanks was employed, the entire available strength of the Corps. Nine battalions of heavy tanks – 324 machines – led the attack along a 13-mile front. Two battalions of Medium A Whippets, ninety-six in all, stood by under cavalry corps orders to follow through. The first day's advance of up to 8 miles brought in 16,000 prisoners and marked a turning point in the war. Ludendorff called it 'the black day of the German Army'. The only disappointment was the decision by GHQ to marry tanks with horses. Instead of the Whippets racing through the 11-mile breach in the German defences to wreak havoc on a fleeing enemy 5 or 6 miles beyond, they were hung up in assisting cavalry units caught by rearguard machine-gun fire. When the two cavalry divisions finally reached their third objective, with blanket orders to press on, they sat tight, awaiting confirmation from their own headquarters. It requires an effort of will to understand the thought processes of the staff officers who so mismatched armour with horseflesh and lightly armed troopers. Fuller confirmed that Haig had not one officer on his Staff with any experience of tanks.[9]

Moore resigned his new appointments on 13 August. Maclean had told him he intended to separate physically the design and working drawings sections to stop designers fine-tuning drawings after they had been issued to factories. A stream of design revisions had seriously delayed jig production for Mk VIII in April/May. Moore argued against change and in any case wanted to hang on to the design team, leaving drawings to Maclean who refused. To his great credit the Admiral had successfully expanded production capacity and it was no fault of his that the programme remained in permanent flux. He had been given little chance to hit moving targets. The Army's increasing removal of skilled men from the factories was now pushing production towards free-fall. The munitions industry had lost 100,000 highly trained men since January, including draughtsmen and gauge and tool makers. Metropolitan's tank factories lost 600 men precisely when the Army wanted maximum output. For the sake of making up a few companies of infantry, the equipping of perhaps four or five battalions with tanks had been lost. Churchill wrote Lloyd George on 22 July:

Questions which the Prime Minister's conscience should be asking him:
1. Am I not one of the original founders of tanks?
2. What am I doing to push them forward now?
3. Am I doing enough?
4. Can I not do more with my great power?
5. Are they going to be frittered away in more incidental fighting next year 1919 – as every other year?
6. Have I not still got time to get a real move on?
W.S.C.[10]

A radically different body was formed at the end of July. The 'Tank Production Committee' was a high-risk attempt by Seely to bypass the bureaucratic control of production from London and place it directly in the hands of the builders. The committee comprised senior representatives of the major contractors and would receive and action all future tank production orders. It would quote for the work, place contracts, allocate materials and ensure delivery to schedule. A bonus arrangement and penalty clause would be applied by the Ministry. The committee met once, then lapsed as Maclean successfully created further regional groups of manufacturers.

Col Kitson Clarke, of Leeds locomotive builders Kitson's, set up and led a local tank construction group in August to build 200 Medium C machines at ten per week. He did so in response to a Ministry embargo on further tank assembly at his factory, rolling stock having the higher priority. The consortium was to form the nucleus of the North of England Group capable of turning out 100 tanks each month. It began production just before the war ended, completing 12 tanks.

The Scottish Group brought together the existing contractors there in October under the Director General of Munitions (Scotland). Production of the British Army Mk VIII and Medium C was to be concentrated with them. North British Loco was preparing to start volume Mk VIII assembly when trials in

September revealed transmission and track-fouling problems. These apart, the formidable-looking but very heavy machine was raising doubts concerning its suitability for the fast strike planned for 1919. Fuller was instrumental in getting the Mk VIII sidelined in favour of a new run of Mk V construction.

West's Construction Group was at the end of the line for armour and skilled labour for the 1,500 Liberty Mk VIII hulls. Stern complained bitterly that the obligation to supply them for the Allied tank was being ignored in favour of the British type. He failed to persuade the Tank Board to let him take control of West's group. Maclean responded by raising its monthly target from 280 to 500 hulls from November and offering the group a performance bonus. It was all fantasy. MWD had recently assessed the group's construction capability for complete tanks at 40 per month. Making every allowance for hulls only, it could not get anywhere near 500. It was acutely short of riveters and fitters, telling Maclean that as none were forthcoming from the regional labour office its tank programme was 'badly compromised'. West's produced some thirty or forty hulls in November before the order was cancelled. Capt Gelder, RAF, Maclean's deputy, told Stern's people that month that there was nobody in the MWD who could produce detailed information on parts or suppliers for Chateauroux.[11]

*   *   *

Sir Douglas Haig noted in his diary that on 10 September he told Gen Seely they should aim to finish the war now and not delay the production of tanks until the perfect design had emerged. He added that he thought it was a waste of time talking to Seely. On the 17th the War Office instructed the Ministry to supply 3,500 fighting tanks, up to 1,800 of which were to be Mk V or V Two Star, and the balance Medium B or C. For supply work a mix of Mk V Star and Mk IX were requested, totalling 400 machines. Two-thirds of the order was wanted in France by 15 March and the balance by 15 June. Maclean forecast that for the March deadline his fighting tank deliveries would be nearly 1,000 machines (40 per cent) short of requirement, though this would be more than made good by the June date.

Fast completion was promised for the new run of Mk V providing there were absolutely no design changes and all the original jigs could be used. Metropolitan was contracted on this understanding. Bermicourt HQ then asked for over sixty modifications, halting production and causing the much-changed machine to be designated Mk X. By the Armistice, none were completed. The Mk V Star had been relegated to supply because its extra track length and added weight reduced power and manoeuvrability. Attempts to carry forward four MG crews per tank were abandoned when the high temperatures and poor ventilation which dogged the V series left the gunners unfit to fight on arrival.

More tanks meant more men. Fuller proposed a doubling of the Tank Corps to thirty-four battalions. When he was 'personally and viciously' obstructed by Gen Lynden-Bell, the Director of Staff Duties, he went straight to Sir Henry Wilson, the CIGS, who gave him a signed authority. Maclean believed he could boost production from 4,250 to 6,300 tanks over the twelve months to September 1919 if the Army released a further 3,500 skilled men. They were not forthcoming. Meantime, deliveries were still falling behind forecast. No tanks came out of Scotland between August and mid-October 1918 when three were received. The acute labour shortage drove Vickers to seek permission to employ boys of fourteen to sixteen years of age on nightwork, shaping and drilling track links at their Earlstown factory in Lancashire. The boys worked unsupervised because no men or women could be spared. Other firms were similarly stretched. Production of all types was averaging only 135 machines per month, whereas in April/May Mk V alone had run at 150 each month. (Monthly production had peaked at 200 in 1917 during Stern's tenure.) If MWD was to meet the Army's March delivery deadline, output had to triple.

Attempts have since been made to put a figure on the number of tanks which would have been available to Haig the following year if the war had continued. Walter Layton, the Director of Statistics and member of Council at the Ministry of Munitions, was exceptionally well placed to make the calculations. His assessment of 14 November 1918, using all the data at his disposal, was that on 1 June 1919, the date set for the great push, the Army would have had some 2,450 heavy and medium fighting tanks as against an estimated WO requirement for 2,176 after allowance for currently serviceable machines and later wastage. Layton had thrown in the remaining and by then very obsolete Mk IV types before concluding that demand could be met by June. He also forecast delivery by then of 800 supply types (100 Mk IX and the redundant Mk V Star) against a WO requirement for 400. He did not comment on fighting tank completions for the period to March 1919 which were still expected to fall far below requirement.

Almost a year to the day after the first build order for Walter Wilson's 'B' Type was placed, the Tank Board decided on 24 October to accept it 'as an alternative to no machine at all' and relegated it to training only. The army had just received its first machine. The restricted access to the very small engine compartment was quite impracticable in emergencies and there were other shortcomings. Of the 550 on order, 80 in all were built. Tritton's Medium C narrowly avoided a gearbox redesign after tests, but was then further delayed awaiting vacuum pumps for the Ricardo 150hp engines. First orders had gone to Foster's, Patent Shaft and Coventry Ordnance as long ago as February, but none were delivered until January 1919. It was by far the most efficient tank to date. Although Johnson's Medium D was still at the experimental stage, Maclean had plans in place for Vickers of London to build 2,000, starting in May 1919. Fuller accordingly secured adoption of the 'C' Type for the 1919 season. Orders were issued to North British Locomotive and Beardmore's National Projectile Factory respectively for 1,440 and 1,190 Medium Cs, bringing the total on order to 3,230.

The Tank Production Committee was the last of its kind to emerge before the Armistice. Control of the weapon's design, production and development had variously passed through no fewer than nine specially constituted committees and boards in its brief wartime existence. The terms of reference and composition of most of those groups mirrored the power struggle between the supply side and the end user. The victorious tanks had left a trail of assorted bodies in their wake at home.

*   *   *

The Allied tank programme was also moving slowly. Draine had reported in May 1918 that conversion of America's Liberty engine for tank work was beset with problems. Deliveries from the only supplier, Trego Motors of Newhaven, Connecticut, were put back from August to November. In its place the Ricardo 300hp unit had to be got into production at speed. First deliveries were not made until October. The completion of other tank engines was disrupted by the changeover and output briefly fell to 184 per month. West's Construction Group (the Manchester Tank Committee) was last on the list for jigs supply, and when they arrived the group could not get armour plate released through MWD. The American programme of parts production was equally behind schedule, none being expected to reach

France until December. North British Locomotive built two prototype Mk VIIIs in mild steel. No. 1 was fitted with a 180hp Rolls-Royce engine pending receipt of a Ricardo unit and was first tested on 12 August at NBL's Queens Park Works in Glasgow. Two cast-iron gearbox casings 'blew' and there were clutch problems, but nothing out of the usual at this early stage, save that it was found necessary to remove the engine to replace the clutch. No. 2 with the first Ricardo engine arrived at the Newbury testing station on 18 October. It broke down completely with engine bearing trouble shortly after starting a 1,000-mile trial.

Stern's greatest problem lay in getting the French plant built. It was to be geared to production of 720 tanks per month, the first 600 to go to the American Army and an undecided proportion of the next 900 to France, the balance to be split between Britain and the US. The MoM Department of Factory Construction failed to secure the necessary local labour and materials, the French government having contributed 1,000 very inefficient workers, a few huts and four lorries, one at least being a ruinous 1903 Thorneycroft steamer. Only one steam crane was available to erect the several thousand tons of structural steel which had arrived. A proposal from M. Loucheur in July that his Ministry should take over the construction was politely declined for fear that a French foot in the door now would lead to a later bid for production control. Instead, site management was split three ways between the commissioners, the Factory Construction Department and the main contractors, no one person having overall control of the work and the 1,300 men employed. It was a hopeless formula which was quickly corrected. Construction went forward only after Mr Hopkinson of Messrs S. Pearson & Company was secured in August as sole site manager.

Stern set up a Mechanical Warfare Branch of the British War Mission in the United States that month. Norman Holden went out in October as deputy commissioner to run it. The branch would progress orders from MWD and secure materials and components for tank assembly in Britain and Chateauroux. Duckham's deputy, Sir Percival Perry of Henry Ford, visited the US and felt compelled to cable London on 1 October:

> . . . my opinion Anglo-American programme in hopeless condition here. Neither engine gears nor other components in production. Armour plate supplies chaotic. . . . If possible Stern should come to review whole

situation and condition. Unless drastic action taken forthwith am convinced that neither Allied Mark Eight nor American Renaults available for spring.[12]

Perry acknowledged shortly afterwards that he had overstated the position, though American manufacturers were wrestling with red tape and loudly complaining. (Perry headed a programme to build 10,000 light tracked gun tractors for delivery to the Army by 1 April 1919. Based on standard commercial engines and a simplified track already in production, they were to be further developed to replace the costly Mk IX supply tank.) Hopkinson had better news that day from Chateauroux where he confidently predicted the first phase of five bays would be fully operational to assemble tanks by the year end. Draine was able to pull the US operation together and confirm American readiness to ship 200 sets of Mk VIII components in December, rising monthly thereafter. Could the British match this? Maclean said he could, but there has to be doubt that he could deliver. The American Army had selected the French Renault 'chaser' as its light tank and was preparing to build 4,000 in the US. On completion of the Allied programme it also planned to ship parts from America and assemble a further 1,450 heavy tanks at Chateauroux. In October France claimed the first 600 tanks from the factory, though the French government offered no contribution to the costs of the plant and assembly. The Supreme War Council compromised, allocating France the balance of 900 Mk VIII tanks after the first 600 went to America. France and the US had also been pressing the War Office for Mk V tanks for nearly a year, having declined offers of Mk IV. The build-up of British tank battalions and high levels of battle damage left no margin for the Allies save a few token machines.

With the Armistice, all work ceased at Chateauroux. The factory was roofed, a large new power station stood ready and components including track links were about to be shipped from Manchester for riveting there in December. Tank assembly would have followed in January. The complex passed to the French government in 1920.

*   *   *

The accelerating Allied advance after Amiens and much hard fighting for the tanks soaked up spare parts and the slender reserves. Doubts of the tank's effectiveness had shrunk to the point where almost every corps, divisional and brigade commander was pleading for armoured support. The fifteen battalions should have been able to maintain a fighting strength of 720 tanks. They were 391 short in August, falling in September to 420 below establishment. Elles recalled that by 5 November all he could muster was one composite company.[13] The Tank Corps had fought itself to a standstill by the time the Armistice was signed on the 11th. Since its first engagement in 1916 the Corps has lost 212 officers and 1,107 other ranks killed in action or died of wounds. Life expectancy in a tank, particularly in the closing months, was frighteningly low. Their sacrifice and the spirit and courage of all the tank men contributed immeasurably to the final victory. Sir Douglas Haig saluted them in his last despatch:

> Since the opening of our offensive on August 8, tanks have been employed on every battlefield, and the importance of the part played by them in breaking up the resistance of the German infantry can scarcely be exaggerated. The whole scheme of the attack of August 8 was dependent upon tanks, and ever since that date on numberless occasions the success of our infantry has been powerfully assisted or confirmed by their timely arrival. So great has been the effect produced upon the German infantry by the appearance of British tanks that in more than one instance, when for various reasons real tanks were not available in sufficient numbers, valuable results have been obtained by the use of dummy tanks painted on frames of wood and canvas.

Nor should we forget the unsung visionaries and pioneers, military as well as civilian, and the silent army of designers, engineers and men and women in the foundries and factories who fought another kind of war and won another kind of victory. Had they lost their battles, many scores of thousands more would have died.

Fourteen

POWER DOWN

Better to leave the tank where it properly stands, behind the British Museum, and spend our time more profitably adapting the internal combustion engine to the best advantage in other ways.[1]

Maj G. MacLeod Ross MC RE, 1931. Two years later MacLeod Ross was appointed Assistant Superintendent of Design (Tanks).

Almost all tank construction was cancelled within hours of the Armistice. Only Tritton's Medium C 'Hornet' and Col Philip Johnson's experimental 'D' Types were retained, some 500 of the former being sufficiently advanced to justify completion. Three weeks later the War Office financial controllers raised objections on the grounds that the peacetime establishment of the Tank Corps had not yet been determined. The Army Council was under severe constraint from the Treasury as each branch fought for funds. The fledgling Tank Corps with its costly equipment was particularly vulnerable to cutbacks. Fuller realised that if he and Elles insisted on completing all the 'C' Types as previously approved, the chances of securing additional production funding for the promising Medium D would be next to zero. Elles was less impressed with Johnson's untried design, but Fuller recommended abandoning the 'C' tanks to protect the Medium D. The General Staff disagreed, saying Johnson's machine would be too fast for the infantry to keep up with it. Fuller won their approval after countering that it was a 'cavalry tank'. Only thirty-six 'C' Types were built, all by Foster's.

The future of the Tank Corps remained undecided and in limbo for nearly five years after the Armistice. It was finally constituted as a separate arm within the Army system in September 1923. Until then Fuller was its principal champion in the fight not only for funds but for its survival – by January 1920 the Corps faced difficulty in raising even two battalions. He was supported by Churchill who moved from the Ministry in January 1919 to become Secretary of State for War for the next twelve months. Fuller's message was neatly expressed in the title of his essay on the future of mechanical warfare: 'Racehorses Don't Pull Up at the Winning Post'. It won the Gold Medal in 1920 in the first postwar Royal United Service Institution competition. He advocated the phased replacement of horsed transport by tractors, and the formation of a model division with tank-reinforced cavalry and a company of tanks attached to each of its twelve infantry battalions. This was hardly earth-shaking in the light of recent experience, but a storm of protest descended from the cavalry fraternity. Philip Johnson read a paper to the Staff that year on the use of tanks in undeveloped country which caused Gen Lynden-Bell, the Director of Staff Duties, to tell him publicly that he would never succeed in making the tank replace the horse. Even Maj Gen Sir Louis Jackson (knighted in 1918), who had so strongly supported Swinton and Tulloch against Holden in 1915, now turned his back on tanks. In a lecture at the RUSI in November 1919 on 'The Possibilities of the Next War' he dismissed them in short order: 'The tank proper was a freak. The circumstances which called it into existence were exceptional and are not likely to recur. If they do they can be dealt with by other means.'[2] Jackson was on firmer ground in supporting the need for tracked transport vehicles, but as Director General of Trench Warfare Supply since June 1915 his opinion carried weight. It would not have escaped the notice of Lord Peel, the Under Secretary of State for War, who chaired the meeting.

The War Office had already won its long battle with the Ministry of Munitions for control of tank design and development. It took over the operation from Maclean's MWD in March 1919, though construction remained the Ministry's responsibility for the rest of the year. The General Staff was to decide tank requirements and Gen Furse, the Master General of Ordnance, would arrange design and construction. The two liaised through a Tank Committee chaired by Furse which replaced his Tank Board. Members included Elles, Fuller and d'Eyncourt. Philip Johnson was to create and direct a War Office Department of Tank Design and Experiment (DTDE). It set up shop in a hut in Grosvenor Gardens, SW1. Johnson took over the trial ground at Dollis Hill and recruited senior members of the defunct MWD design team including Lt Frank Shaw – previously Joint Director of Design with Maj Wilson – and Lt George Rackham. The junior rank of these and the other highly experienced military members of the old tank design department reflects the point-blank refusal of the War Office to accept repeated requests for their promotion.

Johnson continued to develop the 20-ton Medium D series. Draughtsmen were set to produce an expected 2,000 working drawings. Of the ten mild-steel machines ordered in August/September 1918, Fowler's was to build four standard amphibious 'D' Types and Vickers a further four at its Wolseley motor works in Birmingham. Vickers was also to build one each of the wide-bodied Star and Two Star versions. The Two Star machine was built by the Variable Speed Gear Co., a Vickers subsidiary, at its Crayford factory near Dartford.[3] No doubt it also constructed the Star.

The first 'D' Type was rolled out by Fowler's in March 1919. It was demonstrated to a gathering of staff officers and others on 29 May at Roundhay Park, Leeds, where it averaged a very satisfactory 23mph. Johnson's flexible track and cable suspension showed their worth in the finale when the tank was driven straight at the assembly at maximum speed before breaking off dramatically in a sharp turn and an involuntary shower of displaced wooden sole plates. Several spectators turned and fled, according to Johnson. The machine went on to the Experimental Bridging Establishment in Christchurch in June for amphibious trials. After a promising start it caught fire and was written off.

The War Office had alerted Maclean in January 1919 that it proposed to order 500 Medium D tanks, subject to Treasury approval. Funding problems cut this to 75 in June, 45 in September, and finally in November to 20 of a modified type, the Medium D (M), incorporating changes requested by the Tank Corps. Elles and Fuller wanted a long-barrel 40-calibre 6-pdr, but Johnson warned that the gun was already located well forward of the amphibious tank's point of balance and the heavy mounting would sink it. A 23-calibre gun was agreed. Sixty Rolls-Royce Eagle aero engines were set aside. The heavy cost of making jigs and gauges for only twenty machines was accepted in the hope that more money would be forthcoming later. Only three 'M' Types were built and they were constructed at the Royal Ordnance Factory, Woolwich. They were broken for scrap in 1925.

Furse was replaced by Gen DuCane, who at Johnson's urging merged control of all tracked military vehicle development into a single department, A5, in March 1920. The DTDE moved that August from its cramped hillside at Dollis Hill to the large park adjoining Charlton House, a Jacobean mansion near the Royal Ordnance Factory. Johnson was demobilised a few weeks later, but continued in post with a reduced design staff and with civilian mechanics in place of Tank Corps men. These changes were ominous. He was currently working on an amphibious Light Infantry Tank of some 7 tons, based on the 'D' series. Its successful trials in September 1921 were followed in December by the news that quite unknown to Fuller and Johnson, A5 had secretly been designing a light tank of its own. Indeed, a prototype for evaluation had been produced by Vickers with the Variable Speed Gear Co. and two more had been on order since 26 August. The first 'Vickers Light Tank No. 1' arrived on 17 December at Pinehurst Barracks, Farnborough, a tank testing station set up by A5 four months earlier 'on a temporary basis'. The slab-sided and sponsonless machine was not unlike the Medium B in appearance but its new features included simple coil-sprung bogies. Three machine guns were carried in a dome turret, the first with a full 360° traverse to be fitted to a British tank. The tracks were independently steered through a Williams Janney variable speed hydraulic gear for each, as in the Mk VII. It competed with Johnson's light tank in trials at Aldershot later that month. Johnson's machine reached 20mph, while the Vickers with an 86hp engine was so underpowered that it was beaten by a Medium C. Vickers produced a male version at almost the same time, mounting a 3-pdr gun plus four MG including one on the roof for anti-aircraft work.

Gen DuCane was fully entitled to commission the Vickers design providing he had General Staff approval, but no mention of it had been made by him to his Tank Committee. The decision not to inform and involve Johnson signalled a terminal loss of confidence in him and his department. He had not perfected a design fit for volume production in more than three years of development work. Fuller thought it would take another two to reach that stage. Fuller's earlier recommendation to abort construction of Medium C in favour of the ambitious and unproven 'D' series had boomeranged. Without the 'C' Types a generation of light tanks had been lost and a black hole had opened in the supply sequence. Fuller was now told, quite correctly, that the funds allocated for tank construction in the Army estimates for that financial year were at risk of forfeiture to the Treasury unless orders were placed immediately. The mediocre performance of the Vickers prototype could be disregarded – the third was never built – as the company was already working on the much superior Medium Mk I. The first entered service in 1923 with the 3-pdr gun, six machine guns and a design speed of 18mph, which proved to be nearer 30mph in practice. It heralded the beginning of Vickers' dominance between the wars in the market for cheap and versatile light tanks. The company's Medium series was convertible to other roles as turretless artillery tractors, bridgelayers, weapons carriers and command vehicles. To the delight of the Treasury the development costs were shared by many foreign buyers.

The DTDE limped on through 1922, reduced to begging for old car chassis in order to test track and rope suspension systems for 'soft' vehicles for reconnaissance and supply use. The experimental 'D' series machines were then the world's fastest tanks but they came at a price. There were compromises in armament, hull design and the track profile to achieve flotation. The sophisticated track and suspension gained a reputation for unreliability, allegedly put about by detractors and hotly denied by Johnson. More seriously, at 30ft their great length (31ft 10in for the Two Star) became an unacceptable weight penalty when the trench-crossing requirement was no longer relevant. Fowler's completed three 'D' Types and Vickers two, plus a Two Star version and, almost certainly, a Star. The remainder were cancelled. Johnson had also produced four small experimental Tropical Tanks, built at the Woolwich Ordnance Factory. The sole Light Infantry Tank was withdrawn from service in June 1922. Simultaneously, much of the work at Charlton Park was shut down. Johnson's department closed the following year. As a civilian, his dismissal presented no problem.

The War Office had inherited a world-beating tank design team in 1919. It was blown away after four and a half years of military vacillation over the future shape of the tank arm, failure to recognise the differing functions and timescales of tank design and pure research, and severe financial constraints imposed by a government and nation wearied by war. In those circumstances the Vickers option seemed irresistible. The resulting series of low-budget machines reflected a need for lightly armed and armoured tanks for 'policing' roles around the world. By 1939 the lack of a credible main battle tank left the Royal Tank Corps grievously ill-prepared for another continental war, despite frantic efforts then and throughout the ensuing conflict to catch up with Germany and Russia. France and America were no better off. The British Army had to await the arrival in 1948 of the Mk III Centurion with its superb gunnery to resume a lead in the field which, with the aid of the pioneers, it had first made its own.

Fifteen

BUT WHO INVENTED THE TANK?

I got £1,000 for winning the war.[1]

Maj Gen Sir Ernest Swinton to Sir Basil Liddell Hart, 24.2.1948

The idea of armoured cross-country fighting machines had been around for years. H.G. Wells entered the field in 1903 when he wrote 'The Land Ironclads' for the *Strand Magazine*, a short and rather chilling story of machine warfare involving vast landships on Diplock's Pedrail wheels. *The Listener* published a feverish letter from Wells in 1941 in which he claimed that he and Diplock had effectively invented the tank in the 1903 piece. Wells accused Swinton of 'lifting' the idea and falsely claiming the invention.[2] For this absurdity he had to make written apology and send Swinton a cheque for £500.

The initial explosion of public interest in the tanks and their origins in September 1916 was accompanied by parliamentary statements naming several of the men associated with the machines though barely mentioning Tritton and Wilson. Intense curiosity as to who really invented the tank later faded as the popular press continued to caricature it in near-pantomime terms. The question flared again in the autumn of 1919, but secret nominations for award had followed the 1916 Hatfield trials.

Bertie Stern had written to Lloyd George recommending 'in the strongest possible terms' that at least £1,000 each should be awarded to Wilson and Tritton. The Minister was not persuaded, but Stern continued to press their case. After the first tank action in September 1916 the Admiralty received claims from 'certain officers of the RNAS' and from Robert Macfie, Albert Nesfield, and the Holt Caterpillar Company, which later withdrew. The Admiralty took out a secret 'blanket' patent covering all relevant features, to head off any private attempt to secure rights to any part of the weapon.

Tritton and Wilson voluntarily withheld application in order to preserve secrecy, putting at risk their prospects of re-establishing rights to the design.

Stern persuaded Christopher Addison to appoint a small committee in June 1917 to consider the two engineers' entitlement to award. Stern and d'Eyncourt were members, and at Stern's suggestion it recommended that both men should receive £10,000 on the basis that while Tritton's contribution was greater than Wilson's, Tritton had already received a knighthood. D'Eyncourt objected, pointing out privately to Churchill (who had just replaced Addison), the disparity between his own salary of £3,000–4,000 and the sum proposed, which, he said, 'is more than I get for the design and responsibility of all His Majesty's ships'.[3]

Churchill considered that no monetary award should be given to anyone in receipt of a public salary. He referred the matter to a committee of his Munitions Council which was joined by the Comptroller-General of the Patents Office. It recommended payment of £11,000 to Tritton and £5,000 to Wilson. Churchill again refused to accept the findings. He asked the Treasury to arbitrate awards for all claimants relating to the tanks, explaining that he did not wish to adjudicate because of his close connection with the subject. The Treasury declined. Churchill was aware of the wider consequences if the Ministry opened its funds to a run of claims across departments. He played for time, setting up a third inquiry in May 1918 which was chaired by Lord Moulton, a leading barrister in patent law. Adm Bacon and Gen Scott-Moncrieff sat with him. They were in no hurry, but their conclusions came as a shock eight months later. The panel recommended payment of £50,000 jointly to Tritton and Wilson, who had agreed to share any award equally. Churchill was saved by the bell – the government set up a Royal Commission on Awards to inventors in 1919 to hear all claims.

The Commission's task was immense. Over the next fifteen years it received 1,834 applications for awards ranging from better bombsights to innovative nosebags for draught-horses. Its terms allowed it to consider claims arising from Crown use of unpatented inventions for which the claimants had no strictly legal entitlement to reward. This covered all the 'tanks' applicants, who would have to rely on the discretion of the Crown as advised by the Commission. In Mr Justice Sargant it had a chairman respected for his common-sense approach to complex issues. 'Looking at the matter broadly' was his favourite opening phrase to a summation. He was supported by five assessors. The tanks hearings took place over six days in October 1919 at London's Lincoln's Inn Hall. The proceedings were formal and judicial. Evidence was taken on oath and open to cross-examination. The Crown was represented by the Attorney-General, the Solicitor-General and two eminent counsel. They mounted a determined exercise in damage limitation on behalf of the Treasury, courteously but remorselessly dismissing claims out of hand or attempting to diminish their worth. Most claimants had felt intimidated before the hearing by the Crown's perfunctory written disclaimer, and had felt obliged to engage counsel at heavy cost. They found themselves and their activities subjected to rigorous and challenging scrutiny. Winston Churchill was first called by the Crown. He was not a claimant, and in taking the Commissioners through the course of events he emphasised his belief that while credit was due to all concerned with the creation of the tank, no single man was its inventor.

The Commission's findings were fair but hardly generous.[4]

MAJ GEN SWINTON'S CLAIM

This officer, acting outside the scope of his general duties, made an important contribution to the invention and adoption of the Tank. This contribution included, first, the conception in October 1914 of a machine gun destroyer of the general character of the Tank. Secondly the persistent, energetic and successful advocacy from then onwards of the value and feasibility of employment of such an instrument of warfare, and thirdly, the specific definition in June 1915 of the necessary characteristics of the weapon, the conditions of its use, and the tests which it must be required to satisfy.

We conceive that the terms of reference to us do not contemplate the recommendation of awards for general services such as those secondly above mentioned, but limit us to those which contributed to the invention and design of the actual weapon of warfare in question; and in respect of these latter services we recommend an award of £1,000. But beyond this we desire expressly to recognise the still greater value of that part of Major-General Swinton's work for which a pecuniary award is not appropriate.

Swinton was the only applicant to present his own case. He claimed a very large share of the credit, and so far as the Army was concerned, the sole credit for the introduction of the tank. His difficulty lay in the fact that while he was certainly associated with its origination, his only claim to invention was the performance schedule to which the designers worked. The Commission had stretched a point in recommending a token award. Ernest Swinton took its modest value as an insult to be added to his dismissal as Britain's first tank force commander. He received a belated but very well-earned knighthood in 1923.

CDRE SUETER'S CLAIM

This officer contributed in a definite degree to the evolution and adoption of the Tanks. He appreciated at an early date and urged on Mr Winston Churchill the importance of caterpillar traction for attack across country. He organised the Diplock trials in February 1915, and he was the main cause of the appointment of the DNC Committee in the same month. We think that his services were of great value. But on the other hand he was acting throughout within the scope of the duties assigned to him, and no specific invention of great merit is attributable to him.

We consider that the case of this distinguished officer falls within the general rule to which we have given effect on previous occasions that (unless in quite exceptional circumstances) no award should be made to a servant of the Crown for the efficient discharge of duties definitely assigned to him.

Murray Sueter had claimed the greater of half the total awarded to all other claimants, or £100,000. His application centred on his Pedrail demonstration to Churchill on Horse Guards Parade and his later activities in support of the Landships Committee, of which he had never been a member. His good work on the armoured cars and lorries had no direct bearing on the tank's invention, but it was Churchill's evidence which sank him. Churchill told the Commission that Sueter 'failed altogether to solve the mechanical difficulties connected with the production of tanks'.[5]

CLAIMS OF LT COL BOOTHBY AND MAJ HETHERINGTON

In each of these cases we consider that valuable services were rendered by the officer in question for which he deserves high credit. But inasmuch as in each case these services were rendered within the scope of the employment of the officer, and there was not any such exceptional invention or discovery as might possibly justify an award even under these circumstances, we are unable to recommend an award to either claimant.

Boothby told the Commission that he had obtained a Killen Strait tractor on about 2 February 1915 and had arranged for its demonstration to Sueter. He said this resulted in the formation of a 'Sueter Committee' which employed Crompton, and which later that month became the Landships Committee. Boothby claimed to have been present at Churchill's bedside meeting when the committee was formed, to have joined it then, and to have remained a member until about the end of June. His account intermittently coincided with reality.

Churchill had made the point that there were two types of claimant – those who vigorously advanced the idea and fought apathy, and those who made specific technical suggestions resulting in the machine itself. Hetherington was firmly in the first category, his problem being his espousal of giant wheels and the perception that he had backed the wrong horse, as Sargant himself observed when he interrupted counsel's opening statement for Hetherington. Hetherington's counsel went on to suggest that his client's continuous and active membership of the Landships Committee was reason enough for award, provoking Sargant to tell him that that was a monstrous proposition. Hetherington's case never recovered from these opening exchanges.

CLAIMS OF MR MACFIE AND MR NESFIELD

These are separate claims but we deal with them together because they are in effect rival claims to the merit attaching to the conception, embodiment and communication of the same set of ideas. These ideas were of considerable value, but on a careful review of the evidence, there is no conclusive proof that they were brought to the notice of or communicated either directly or indirectly to the actual designers of the Tank, so as necessarily to form a link in the chain of causation resulting in the evolution of the Tank. In view, however, of the general similarity of these ideas, as evidenced by Mr Nesfield's provisional specification with those embodied in the Tanks, we have given these claimants the benefit of the doubt and credited them with some share in the evolution of the weapon, and we estimate the value of this share at £1,000. . . . We recommend the award to each of them of a sum of £500.

Nesfield produced a model, the design of which was also claimed by Macfie. Its quite advanced hull and track configuration was not adopted until after the appearance of 'Mother', though the projecting and angled track in front bore similarities. It was confirmed that the model was held in Boothby's office in July 1915 and was seen by Crompton, Hetherington, Sueter and others, but Wilson had no knowledge of it until 'Mother' had been designed. Nesfield had engaged a KC and two supporting counsel to present his claim for 5 per cent of the cost of manufacture of all British tanks to date. He resented both the amount of the award and its apportionment. He refused the money, telling the Commission that as his claim was contradicted by Macfie's and as one or the other must be false, he could not accept 'the benefit of the doubt'. He added that £500 was less than half his costs. Years later he withdrew his objections and unsuccessfully sought payment of the award.

Macfie went further. He claimed to have invented the concept of the tank as a weapon, its use of chaintracks, its tail steering, the angled track contour for climbing, its ability to ford rivers and its tactics at Cambrai. He asked for 7½ per cent of the value of all tanks ordered. At costs averaging £5,750 for each of the 2,704 heavy machines built to date and £4,240 for 316 medium tanks, this would net him over £1.25m – approximately £375m in today's terms.[6]

SIR E. TENNYSON D'EYNCOURT'S CLAIM

This is a claim with regard to which we have found much difficulty. This claimant undoubtedly rendered exceptional services . . . in the selection and elimination of the various forms of design proposed . . . and he was acting outside his duties as Director of Naval Construction. On the other hand he was acting within the general scope of his duties as Chairman of the [Landships] Committee . . . on the whole, we recommend the award of £1,000.

D'Eyncourt had claimed £100,000 in recognition of his responsibility as Chairman of the Landships Committee for the control and approval of all design and construction of the first tank, this being work entirely outside his normal duties. Tritton countered in his statement to the Commission that the DNC contributed nothing to the tank's design and only once gave him instructions when he was asked verbally to build a machine based on the

Bullock tracks. He said that d'Eyncourt never approved his drawings in any meaningful sense, never signed off a drawing as approved, though it was standard naval practice to do so, and gave no expert criticism or assistance when shown drawings. D'Eyncourt cannot have anticipated the rigour of the inquiry and was perhaps unwise to have put in a claim.

Joint claim of Col Crompton and Mr Legros

These claimants were employed for some six months as Consulting Engineers to the DNC Committee at a substantial agreed remuneration. In the discharge of their duties they worked loyally and very hard, and no doubt supplied the Committee with useful data and sound advice. But they did not, in the result, invent or discover the special features subsequently incorporated in the tanks, and we cannot consider their services as of such an exceptional or extraordinary character as could alone justify an award in addition to their agreed salaries.

Crompton and Legros had jointly claimed the greater of £100,000 or 1 per cent of the value of all tanks produced, plus £455 6s 2d for Crompton's later costs in designing his Emplacement Destroyer. At a subsequent hearing the two shared an award of £1,550 for a steering system applied through the twin engines of the Emplacement Destroyer.

Joint claim of Sir William Tritton and Maj Wilson

It is to these two claimants that we attribute the credit of designing and producing . . . the 'Tank' and it is to them that in our judgement by far the largest award should be made, though allowance has to be made for the special opportunities afforded to Major Wilson by his official position.

It was objected on behalf of the Crown that Sir William Tritton at any rate had been sufficiently remunerated by the contracts placed with his company. But it is to be observed . . . that the principal contracts were placed with another Company who were supplied with the working drawings of Sir William Tritton and Major Wilson without any separate payment, and who fixed a price which was subsequently accepted without any addition by Sir William Tritton's Company. It was also objected on behalf of the Crown that some considerable defects in the design were discovered when the tanks were originally used. . . . But it would seem that the conditions of actual user of the machines were much more stringent and protracted than those stipulated for by the Government when ordering them. And further, the defects in question appear to us to have been no greater than those ordinarily discovered in . . . any novel mechanical contrivances. Indeed, the fact that within a few weeks of the first use of the Tanks on the Somme the Government ordered a very large additional number of the machines is the best proof of their generally satisfactory character.

We recommend that there be awarded to these claimants jointly the sum of £15,000.

Tritton and Wilson had jointly claimed £100,000 to be equally divided between them. Counsel for the Crown chose to challenge the design head-on, putting it to Tritton that the Mk I was 'an entire failure' which left tanks derelict on the Somme from defective track rollers, bad final drive design, liability to ditching, and speeds reduced to less than 1mph as track systems choked with mud. Tritton told him he could put it any way he liked, but the Army had ordered 1,000 more of the same. Mr Justice Sargant agreed, but gave Tritton no comfort on another matter. Before the war Foster's had collaborated with Daimler's in the design of the 105hp engine, as a result of which Foster's received commission of £90 per unit on sales to third parties, half going to Tritton personally. When Tritton adopted the engines for tanks he had voluntarily surrendered his commission to the Treasury. It totalled £115,000 and he asked the Commission to take this into account. It was a praiseworthy act to ensure there could be no taint of self-interest in his decision, but it obviously failed to impress the Commissioners.

CLAIM OF CPL DE MOLE, AUSTRALIAN ARMY

The Commission also heard the claim of a man whose invention amounted to a 'near miss' through no fault of his. When Lancelot Edin de Mole was doing road survey work in 1911 in Western Australia he noted the superiority of chaintracks over wheels in rugged terrain; he also noted their limited steering and a tendency to shed tracks. He devised a steering system acting on the front ends of the two track frames which were vertically hinged so as to pivot left or right, causing flexible tracks to lay a curve. De Mole submitted a sketch to the War Office in London in July 1912. He claimed his design would steer caterpillar machines at any speed as easily as four-wheeled vehicles, without riding off the tracks. The letter was passed to the Director of Artillery, Gen Stanley von Donop of imperishable memory. His aide informed de Mole that the Army had 'no intention of making further purchases of chain rail tractors', but invited him to send further details. By then de Mole had built a model armoured crawler with upturned tracks at bows and stern to facilitate climbing in forward or reverse gear. Its hull and track layout was far in advance of any tank for years to come. He sent drawings of the model to the War Office and offered to submit it for local inspection in Australia. De Mole's material reached the one department with any knowledge of and interest in chain traction – Maj Donohue's Motor Transport Committee. Capt Davidson, its secretary, minuted in December '[de Mole's] further particulars do not throw much light on the subject. Failing willingness of the inventor to enlighten us further, we must wait till the model blossoms into a full sized vehicle.'[7] It was a truly lamentable reaction.

De Mole wrote again in April 1913 enclosing three diagrams:

which I believe show all the main features of a serviceable vehicle which, when in use as an armoured gun-carriage mounting several machine guns, will have sufficient bearing surface to enable it to carry heavy armour across country and over trenches etc. at a good speed, and therefore get right up among an advancing enemy and cut them up. . . .[8]

The MT Committee concluded that the design was no improvement on the Hornsby system and de Mole's drawings were returned to him. One of his colleagues, Col G.W. Breadon, wrote to Kitchener in September 1914 earnestly requesting that de Mole's designs be put to a committee of experts 'with a view to the adoption of Travelling Forts . . . which if armoured and manned with small quick-firing guns and Maxims will quickly turn the most stubborn of armies'.[9] Nothing happened. Years later Col Johnson said that the first tanks were 'for all practicable purposes to de Mole's design'. The Royal Commission was sympathetic but stymied. It recommended payment of his expenses. De Mole asked for £40 but was persuaded by Johnson that £1,000 was more realistic. He was awarded £987. He became a CBE in 1933 following an outcry in the Australian Press alleging mean treatment.

*   *   *

The Commission's almost forensic investigations had confirmed the tank's inventors. Tritton and Wilson were justly acclaimed in the newspapers which had been reporting the hearings daily. To visualise the value of the awards relative to British house prices then and now in the Home Counties, the sums should be multiplied by 300 or more.

There remain the prime originators, the half dozen or so visionaries whose efforts opened the way for the inventors and gave them direction. Swinton and Tulloch contributed indirectly but to considerable effect. Their success in winning over Donald Hankey started a chain reaction which ran through his Boxing Day memorandum highlighting their scheme, Churchill's explosive reaction, and Hetherington's wheeled juggernaut idea which led Churchill to form the Landships Committee and give the project all-out Admiralty support. Churchill can fairly be honoured as the true father of the tank despite his infatuation with big wheels. Without his courage in sponsoring what was at that stage a wildly improbable scheme, the weapon would undoubtedly have remained a discredited theory in military circles until French tanks appeared in April 1917.

It was Macfie who secured the inclusion of chain traction in the landships experimental programme. He 'sold' the system to the committee at its first meeting. Crompton had arrived that day with plans for a wheeled machine in his briefcase. He left determined to redesign for tracks. Whatever Hetherington maintained later, he was also a 'wheels' man. D'Eyncourt and Dumble held no views favouring tracklayers. Later, the committee in turn imposed chaintracks on a still sceptical Tritton, but the credit must go to Macfie for setting them on the right course at the outset.

After Hatfield, Swinton and Stern had shared the heavy responsibility for producing tanks, tactics and trained crews. Their achievements were stunningly successful yet both men were rewarded with dismissal. Stern towers over the scene, ruthlessly autocratic, contemptuous of dissenters and indecision, and with the diplomatic finesse of a blunt shovel when obstructed. It progressively dug him and his department into a bunker mentality. Yet for all that, Col Stern managed the near impossible and delivered a great fleet of fighting tanks in eighteen months from a standing start. The achievement was underpinned by d'Eyncourt's powerful support and unshakeable confidence in Stern who had drifted into the RNAS by chance, having badly broken an ankle in 1913 which resulted in his rejection for military service. It was a lucky break in all senses. Stern's friendship with the Duke of Westminster brought an invitation to join the division.

Of the 2,470 fighting tanks built by the Armistice, Walter Wilson was responsible for the design of 2,120 and the co-design with Sir William Tritton of a further 150 Mk I types. The other 200 were Tritton's Medium A Whippets. Wilson also designed the Mk V Two Star, the Medium B, the Mk IX supply/troop carrier jointly with George Rackham, and the Mk I gun carrier with John Greg of Metro. His epicyclic transmission transformed the heavy tank's manoeuvrability and economy of manpower. Wilson was twice mentioned in despatches, and was appointed CMG in 1917, but he never received the full measure of recognition and honour which he so richly deserved. The indifference of the military and the wider establishment to such outstanding achievement on the part of a junior officer ensured that he remained a major and never received a knighthood. History at this distance can at least record that virtually every tank crew and unnumbered thousands of infantrymen had good reason to salute Wilson – and Tritton – for their engineering genius.

POSTSCRIPT

Gen 'Boney' Fuller's stint at the War Office ended in mid-1922. He had fought harder than anyone else to secure the future of the Tank Corps, but was less successful in his efforts to persuade the General Staff to adapt to the new machine warfare. On Fuller's departure Gen Ironside, the Commandant of the Staff College, called for him and made him a chief instructor, enabling Fuller to illuminate the thinking of a future generation of commanders. When he was refused permission to publish his lectures in book form he appealed to Lord Cavan, the CIGS, who told him that as a matter of principle no officer should be permitted to publish any book on a military subject as it may disagree with the manuals and disturb the minds of young officers.[10] Fuller's critical essays and books left him with few friends at court, though in 1925 he could count Gen Milne, the new CIGS, among them. Following promotion to Major-General in 1930 Fuller was put on half-pay before being offered, and refusing, a third-rate posting to Bombay. The Army Council wanted his resignation. When that failed he was ignored until it imposed retirement on him in 1933. The Army acknowledged much later that it had discarded a military genius.

Gen Hugh Elles unaccountably kept his head down during the years of controversy following the Armistice, leaving the fight to Fuller. Elles had taken command of the Bovington Centre on his return from France. He was appointed to the new post of Inspector of the Tank Corps in May 1923, but was transferred away from tanks to command of an infantry brigade that October, just four weeks after the permanent formation of the Corps. So ended his connection with the force which he had so magnificently led. Gen Capper was appointed the first Colonel-Commandant of what became on 18 October the Royal Tank Corps.

Sir Eustace Tennyson d'Eyncourt left the Admiralty in 1924, returning to Armstrong, Whitworth, his old firm. He moved on to join the board of Parsons Marine Steam Turbine Company before his retirement in 1948, having designed numerous merchant ships between the wars.

Albert Stern received a knighthood in 1918 and returned to the banking world. He was recalled in 1939 to assist in the revival of tank design. He chaired a Special Vehicle Development Committee at the Ministry of Supply which was required to design and build a heavy tank for evaluation. Stern assembled a team of old hands including d'Eyncourt, William Tritton, Gen Swinton, Walter Wilson, Kenneth Symes and Harry Ricardo. They produced several designs for a machine that would approach 100 tons in fighting trim. The series was prefixed 'TOG' – 'The Old Gang'. Almost inevitably, Wilson resigned on a policy issue. Stern ruefully observing, 'Major Wilson has always been on the verge of resigning since I have known him.' When Germany's Panzer *blitzkrieg* of 1940 pointed away from super-heavy machines to lighter, faster types of more advanced design, the TOG team disbanded. Bertie Stern once again threw his great energies into tank production and development, harrying ministers and not excluding Churchill from his advice and criticism. He eventually became ignored, a thorn in the Ministry's side, and departed in 1942. He was High Sheriff of Kent (1945–6) and a deputy lieutenant of the county from 1952.

Sir William Tritton took over Gwynne's of Hammersmith and formed Gwynne's Pumps of Lincoln in 1927. He was appointed a Justice of the Peace, and became Chairman of Foster's in 1939. He built the TOG experimental tanks for Bertie Stern's Design Committee in the Second World War.

Col Crompton's electrical engineering firm merged in 1927 to become Crompton, Parkinson & Company, in which he retained a directorship. A dinner was held in his honour in 1931 which was attended by what was believed to have been the largest assembly of leading scientists and engineers ever recorded at such a function; he was made an honorary member of the principal bodies governing civil, mechanical and electrical engineering. Crompton was elected Fellow of the Royal Society in 1933. A much respected and much loved man, he died in 1940 aged ninety-five.

Walter Wilson returned to motor engineering after the war, designing and patenting a revolutionary four-speed preselective epicyclic gearbox in 1919 which remained the basis for advanced gears for the next fifty years. It was taken up by Armstrong-Siddeley in 1927 and a joint company, Improved Gears Ltd (later, Self-Changing Gears) was formed with Wilson and John Siddeley as controlling directors. Wilson's gearbox was fitted as standard in Armstrong-Siddeley cars and was soon adopted by other manufacturers. He continued to develop tank transmissions, including geared steering. Many British tanks before, during and after the Second World War directly stemmed from his work, including Cromwell, Crusader, Churchill, Centurion and Conqueror. Wilson pursued numerous pet wartime projects including anti-aircraft explosive charges suspended from barrage balloons (not adopted), and directionally controlled bombs using a form of jet propulsion. After the war his gearboxes were built into aircraft, diesel-electric rail cars, marine craft and road transport. Wilson was made an Honorary Member of the Institution of Mechanical Engineers in 1947 aged seventy-three. He died ten years later.

Maj Gen Sir Ernest Swinton retired from the Army in 1919. He remained a director of the Citroën Company for many years after joining the board in 1922. Three years later he was elected Chichele Professor of Military History at Oxford, and Fellow of All Souls College, holding the chair until 1939. His most cherished honour was to have been saluted as 'The Father of the Royal Tank Corps', becoming its Colonel-Commandant from 1934 to 1938.

Maj 'Tri-Nitro Tom' Tulloch supported Philip Johnson in promoting mechanised cross-country transport in place of the horse, but Tulloch favoured a multi-wheel type as having better commercial potential. He briefly rejoined Chilworth Gunpowder after the war, the company ceasing to trade in 1920. He had a deep affection for the Holy Land and spent much of the rest of his life assisting the development of its mineral resources, joined by his brother Col Stephen.

Rear Adm Sir Murray Sueter became Superintendent of Air Construction in September 1915 until his 'banishment' to Italy for holding unorthodox views in advocating a separate air service. He was recalled home in 1918, having incurred the further displeasure of the Admiralty Board in appealing over their heads to the King for an investigation into the role of the RNAS in the origination of the tank. Sueter was put on half-pay and given no further naval employment. He was appointed Rear Admiral and retired in 1920, becoming MP for Hertford from 1921 until 1945. Sueter was instrumental in developing Empire air mail services.

Air Cdre Charles R. Samson and his squadron took part in the Dardanelles campaign in 1915, strafing Turkish positions and replacing regulation 20lb bombs with his own more powerful version based on a 26-gallon petrol drum. He later commanded a steamer adapted as an aircraft carrier based in Port Said, and carried out reconnaissance and bombing operations until his ship was sunk by Turkish gunfire. In 1917 Samson commanded an aircraft group at Great Yarmouth which shot down five Zeppelin raiders. He was nearly killed when his aircraft fell under a lighter on take-off from a makeshift platform at sea. His last appointment was as Chief Staff Officer, Middle East Command. He chose to retire early in 1929.

Gp Capt Tommy Hetherington was commissioned into the RAF on its formation in 1918. He was appointed CBE at Churchill's instigation the following year for services to the landships. In April 1920 he was on the Technical Staff (Engines) as a Squadron Leader. In 1926 Hetherington, then a Wing Commander, was sent to Washington as Air Attaché. He moved to Rome in 1931 with the rank of Group Captain to take up a similar appointment before retiring in 1935. In a long career Tommy Hetherington had seen service with the cavalry, airships, heavier-than-air craft, armoured cars, the creation of the first tanks, and had latterly become an aero-engine specialist.

Col Wilfrid Dumble RE left the Landships Committee in March 1915 to join Armstrong's at their Openshaw gun factory. He improved productivity there before moving at Dudley Docker's invitation to become the first Secretary of the new Federation of British Industries in 1916. Dumble later returned to active service, in Italy. His early services to landships were recognised with his appointment as CBE, probably on Churchill's recommendation. He went home to Canada after the war, to command an artillery brigade. Dumble was subsequently Honorary Lieutenant-Colonel of the 4th Field Brigade, RCA, based at Cobourg, Ontario.

Brig Gen Henry Holden received a knighthood in 1916 and moved to the Ministry of Munitions as Director of Mechanical Transport Supply for British

Forces. He was appointed Deputy Controller MT Supply the following year. When Churchill took over the Ministry his restructuring left no place for Holden save in a much reduced role as Technical Adviser, to which he was appointed in November 1917. Holden rejoined the BSA board after the war, resigning when the company suffered a catastrophic loss in 1931.

Shortly after the Armistice Philip Johnson had persuaded the War Office to release the commercial (but not military) rights to new track and suspension systems to the officers who had originated them while working on the Medium D. He formed Roadless Traction Ltd in March 1919 to sell licencing agreements for patents held by himself as managing director, and colleagues including Maj Harry Buddicum, Capt George Rackham and Lt Frank Shaw. They soon resolved to produce a crawler for heavy haulage in the Empire's remote territories.

For years Roadless led track technology and innovation in agriculture and forestry. The Institution of Agricultural Engineers was founded in 1938 largely through Johnson's foresight and energy. By the 1950s the company was turning to all-wheel-drive machines. When the big manufacturers eventually responded with their own models the market for Roadless declined. The company went into liquidation in 1983. Johnson was managing director for forty years, remaining on the board until his death aged eighty-eight in 1965.

PRINCIPAL BRITISH TANKS, 1916–18

Mk I Heavy Tank

The design brief from the Army was for a tracked and armoured gunship proof against machine-gun fire, which could climb a 4ft 6in parapet and cross a 5ft trench. It had no troop transport role. The characteristic rhomboid hull differed little from the 'Mother' prototype, with all-round tracks and projecting gun sponsons set in the track frames on either side. There were four points of entry in the gun-carrying male tanks: a door in each sponson, a rear door in the hull, and an 18in circular manhole in the roof. The female type differed in having only a small oval manhole below the machine-gun sponsons which slowed escape and reduced the chances of crew survival, particularly in case of fire. Male types carried a naval 6-pdr Hotchkiss QF gun in each sponson, with the 40-calibre (89.76in long) barrel. Their arcs of fire converged at a point some 60yd ahead of the tank, running back approximately 121° on either side. The gun's recoil distance in the cramped sponson was only 4in, the gunner standing to the left of the breech. The male version also carried four Hotchkiss portable machine guns for which a mounting was provided between the driver and commander, with additional ports in the rear door and in each sponson. Female types mounted a Hotchkiss machine gun in front for the commander, another optionally in the rear door, and two Vickers water-cooled MG in each sponson, each with a 120° traverse.

The engine and transmission as far as the differential's half-shafts came straight out of Foster's howitzer tractor, its gearbox giving two forward and one reverse speeds. At the end of each half-shaft a two-speed secondary gearbox in the track frame transmitted drive to the respective tracks via a heavy roller chain and pinions meshing with the track driving sprockets. The original tractor gearbox could not have moved 28 tons on its own without disintegrating, hence the secondary gears, each operated by a gearsman on the driver's instruction, giving him four forward and two reverse speeds in all. A track brake on each of the secondary gears was operated by the commander seated next to the driver. It thus took four men – half the crew including their leader – to drive the weapon. A 1.5-ton steel-framed steering tail between the projecting rear track frames or horns added 6ft to overall length. It was set to pivot fore and aft and carried two 4ft 3in iron tractor wheels on stub axles at its rear end which were steered on the Ackerman principle, controlled by the driver via cables to a hand wheel in his cab. In steering mode, powerful coil springs from the tank 'lifted' the fore end of the pivoting frame and so exerted an opposite downward force on the flanged wheels at its rear to maintain grip over rough ground. The tail could be raised hydraulically to project rearwards as a balance counterweight when breasting a steep rise, and to avoid nose or tail dives when trench-crossing.

Construction was apportioned between Foster's and Metropolitan by mutual agreement. Foster's had limited production capacity, and when a further fifty tanks were ordered, it secured only five, with a further seven going to neighbouring Robey & Company. These were transferred to Foster's when Robey's made little progress. Mks I and II from Foster's were distinctively close-riveted to boilermakers' pitch, this being the pattern the company's boiler shop was used to. From Mk IV onwards Foster's tanks were riveted at the wider intervals of girder pitch in conformity with other British tanks.

ORIGINATION

Design began: 24.8.15
Designed by: Lt W.G. Wilson and W.A. Tritton

First builder: Wm Foster & Co., Lincoln
Prototype build started: 28.10.15
  'Mother'
Prototype completed: 13.1.16
First series production machine completed:
7.6.16

First trials, 'Mother' prototype
14.1.16 initial run on Poppleton's Field, Lincoln
20.1.16 live firing, Burton Park, Lincoln
29.1.16 official trials began, Hatfield Park

WD serial numbers
Male 701–775
Female 501–575
6in yellow letters on each side of hull
Metro's 555 (female) was experimental

OUTLINE SPECIFICATION

Crew: 8
Commander
1 driver
2 gearsmen
4 gunners

Armament
Male: 2 × 6-pdr 40 cal. Hotchkiss QF,
  4 Hotchkiss MG
Female: 2 Hotchkiss MG, 4 Vickers MG

Engine
Daimler-Knight 6-cyl. sleeve valve 105hp
hp per ton: 3.75hp
Est'd endurance: 6.2 hrs
Max speed: 3.7mph on level

Transmission
Primary box: 2 forward and 1 reverse
Secondary gears: 2-speed to each track

Dimensions
Length with tail: 32ft 6in
Length without tail: 26ft 5in
Width: 13ft 9in
Height: 8ft 0.5in
Track width: 20.5in

Fighting weight etc.
Male: 28 tons
Female: 27 tons
Max trench crossing: 10ft

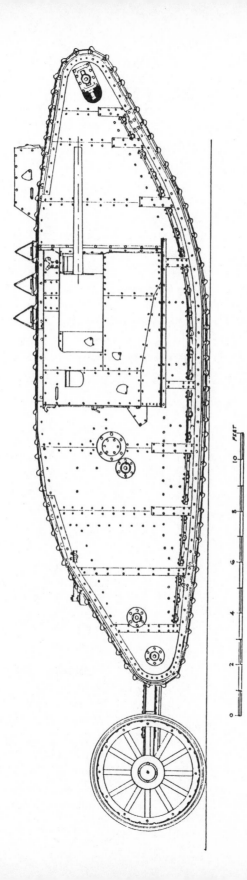

Mk I Heavy Tank

Mk II Heavy Tank

Shortly after the Mk I tanks first saw action at Flers on 15 September 1916, the Army declared the new weapon useless for further operations in its then state of development. Preparations for assembly of Mks I and III were too far advanced to cancel. They were assigned for training only, most if not all being plated in unhardened steel which was not bullet-proof. Some sets of a second 'skin' of armour had been made up for bolting to the sides of the Mk II machines as a shell-burster at Capt Tulloch's urging, but were not fitted. Steering tails were abandoned, having proved to be of little practical value and too vulnerable to battle damage. Most improvements were held over to Mk IV because to introduce them would have interrupted production. Modest changes incorporated in Mk II included the narrowing of the driver's turret to allow for tracks to be widened from 20.5in to 26.5in at a later date, an extra 2in of idler adjustment was provided to take up track stretch, and a wedge-shaped roof hatch with protected vision replaced the flush circular manhole. External angle-iron surrounds were fitted progressively to vision shutters and weapons ports to deflect bullet 'splash' and minimise its entry into the crew space.

ORIGINATION

Design began: February 1916
Designed by: Lt W.G. Wilson

First builder: Wm Foster & Co., Lincoln
Build started: *c*. Dec 1916
First tank completed: early January 1917

WD serial numbers

Male 776–800
Female 576–600

OUTLINE SPECIFICATION

Crew: 8
Commander
1 driver
2 gearsmen
4 gunners

Armament

Male: 2 × 6-pdr 40 cal. Hotchkiss QF,
    4 Hotchkiss MG
Female: 2 Hotchkiss MG, 4 Vickers MG

Engine

Daimler 6-cyl. sleeve valve 105hp
hp per ton: 3.75hp
Est'd endurance: 6.2 hrs
Max speed: 3.7mph on level

Transmission

Primary box: 2 forward and 1 reverse
Secondary gears: 2-speed to each track

Dimensions

Length: with tail 32ft 6in
Length: without tail 26ft 5in
Width: 13ft 9in
Height: 8ft 0.5in
Track width: 20.5in

Fighting weight etc.

Male: 28 tons
Female: 27 tons
Max trench crossing: 10ft

Mk III Heavy Tank

All Mk III were designated for training and all or nearly all were plated in unhardened steel, though side plates were increased from 8mm to 12mm thickness. A late decision to replace all MG with Lewis guns was partly implemented. Lewis guns replaced the two Vickers MG in each 'female' sponson, enabling the sponson to be reduced in size with much improved escape provision beneath. The sponsons still had to be removed for rail movement. Almost the only visible difference between Mks II and III was a rearrangement of the vision slits in the front of the driver's cab.

ORIGINATION
Design began: February 1916
Designed by: Lt W.G. Wilson

First builder: Metropolitan Carriage, Wagon & Finance Co. Ltd
First tank completed: January 1917

WD serial numbers
Male 801–825
Female 601–625

OUTLINE SPECIFICATION
Crew: 8
Commander
1 driver
2 gearsmen
4 gunners

Armament
Male: 2 × 6-pdr 40 cal. Hotchkiss QF,
    4 Hotchkiss MG
Female: 2 Hotchkiss MG,
    4 Lewis MG (sponsons)

Engine
Daimler 6-cyl. sleeve valve 105hp
hp per ton: 3.75hp
Est'd endurance: 6.2 hrs
Max speed: 3.7mph on level

Transmission
Primary box: 2 forward and 1 reverse
Secondary gears: 2-speed to each track

Dimensions
Length: 26ft 5in
Width: 13ft 9in
Height: 8ft 0.5in
Track width: 20.5in

Fighting weight etc.
Male: 28 tons
Female: 27 tons
Max trench crossing: 10ft

Mk IV Heavy Tank

Mk IV was a modest upgrade of previous types, more ambitious improvement still being impossible without halting tank production. Innovations included the shortening of the 6-pdr gun barrels from 40 to 23 calibres to reduce a tendency to dig into the ground if the tank heeled over; introduction of retractable sponsons for rail movement, relocation of fuel storage from inside the driver's cab to externally at rear for greater crew safety, and capacity increased from 46 to 70 gallons; and replacement of fuel gravity feed with a (troublesome) pressurised fuel feed. Petrol was now filtered at the fuel tank end rather than at the carburetter, resulting in scale in the fuel pipe entering the latter. As no immediate widening of the track was feasible, extension spuds were clamped to every 5th or 9th track shoe to project as a flat plate four or five inches beyond the 20.5in shoe for added grip and reduced ground pressure. The spuds collected barbed wire, however, which could completely seize the tracks and halt the tank; 26.5in shoes were fitted later on. The Lewis gun replaced Vickers and Hotchkiss machine guns, but its barrel jacket was vulnerable to battle damage and it was in turn replaced by an improved Hotchkiss towards the end of Mk IV production. A 125hp Daimler engine was installed later but the type remained underpowered.

There were several tank tender and supply tank derivatives, principally Mk IV machines fitted with large box-like stowage sponsons in 6mm armour plate in place of the fighting sponson. A single Hotchkiss MG was mounted ahead of the driver.

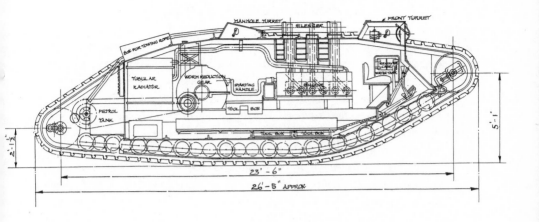

ORIGINATION
Design began: October 1916
Completed: December 1916
Designed by: Maj W.G. Wilson

First builder: Wm Foster & Co., Lincoln
First tank completed: March 1917

First trials
Developed from earlier marks so never tried
as a new type

WD serial numbers
Male: 2001–on
Female: 2501–on
The 2000 series was allocated to
Metropolitan
2066, 2792 (Female) were experimental
Later series: 4000, 6000, 8000
4616–4646 all Female; 4066 Male

OUTLINE SPECIFICATION
Crew: 8
Commander
1 driver
2 gearsmen
4 gunners

Armament
Male: 2 × 6-pdr 23 cal. Hotchkiss QF,
  4 Lewis MG
Female: 6 Lewis MG
Note: Lewis in M and F types were replaced
by Hotchkiss MG from *c*. July 1917

Engine
Daimler 6-cyl. 'vertical' 105hp
hp per ton: 3.75hp
Est'd endurance: 9.5 hrs
Max speed: 3.7mph on level
Later fitted Daimler 125hp

Transmission
Primary gears: 2 forward and 1 reverse
Secondary gears: 2-speed to each track

Dimensions
Length: 26ft 5in
Male width: 13ft 6in
Female width: 10ft 6in
Height: 8ft 2in
Track width: 20.5in (later 26.5in)

Fighting weight etc.
Male: 28 tons
Female: 27 tons
Max trench crossing: 10ft

Mk V Heavy Tank

Mk V was similar to its predecessors in general appearance, but Maj Wilson's hand-braked epicyclic gears on each end of the cross shaft revolutionised the final drive. Their constant mesh removed the need for clutched secondary gears and permitted one-man control for the first time, as well as bringing much improved manoeuvrability. The commander was no longer also the brakesman, and the two secondary gearsmen were released to become tank gunners. Engine power was increased with Harry Ricardo's purpose-built 150hp tank engine, the rear door was fitted with a much needed machine-gun mounting, the rear turret was enlarged, and there were lesser improvements covering mud clearance from tracks, the means of escape, observation and storage. The shortcomings of the Lewis gun resulted in the re-adoption of the Hotchkiss machine gun as standard. 26.5in track shoes were later tried before reverting to 20.5in shoes. Ventilation in the V series was notoriously poor. Whereas earlier tanks drew air for the radiator through the open crew space, in Mk V it was ducted all the way from a grill intake in the rear to the radiator and thence to a vent. The exhaust manifolds only inches from the men glowed red hot and temperatures of 120° Fahrenheit were recorded. Crews were considered unfit for duty for 36 hours after being closed up for action for 8 or 9 hours at a time. Some improvement followed the fitting of a cowling around the manifold through which air was fan-driven to vent through the roof. However, Mk V was an outstandingly successful fighting machine. Metropolitan's Birmingham factories at Oldbury and Saltley were cleared of work on other tanks, principally Mk VIII, in June 1918 and production of the Mk V series remained concentrated there.

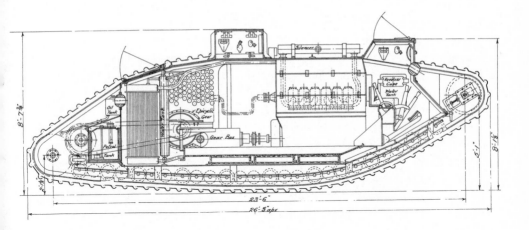

ORIGINATION

Design began: 24.9.16, but detailed design only got going in May 1917 when the Army's specification was finalised.
Designed by: Maj W.G. Wilson

Sole builder: Metropolitan Carriage, Wagon & Finance Co. Ltd
First series production tank completed: 11.1.18
An experimental machine was in existence in September 1917

First trials

Urgency precluded lengthy trials. The first machine began short trials mid-January 1918 at the Dollis Hill tank experimental ground

WD serial numbers

Male: 9001–9200
Female: 9251–9450

OUTLINE SPECIFICATION

Crew: 8
Commander
1 driver
6 gunners

Armament

Male: 2 × 6-pdr 23 cal. Hotchkiss QF,
    4 Hotchkiss MG
Female: 6 Hotchkiss MG

Engine

Ricardo 6-cyl. 'vertical' 150hp
hp per ton: 5.2hp
Est'd endurance: 10 hrs
Max speed: 4.6mph on level

Transmission

4-speed forward and 4-speed reverse
Epicyclic gear in final drive to each track, in permanent mesh

Dimensions

Length: 26ft 5in
Male width: 13ft 6in
Female width: 10ft 6in
Height: 8ft 8in
Track width: 20.5in

Fighting weight etc.

Male: 29 tons
Female: 28 tons
Max trench crossing: 10ft

Mk V Star Heavy Tank

The Allies were aware in late 1917 that the Germans were widening their trenches against tanks. Attempts were made to lengthen Mk IV and V tanks by the rearward extension of their track frames. 'Tadpole tails' were made up in mild steel to replace existing rear horns, but the 9ft tails lacked lateral rigidity and whipped when the tank turned in spite of extra cross bracing. Tank Corps Central Workshops in France were first to attempt the alternative of cutting a Mk IV in two and inserting extension frame members and armour. At home the Mechanical Warfare Department at the Ministry of Munitions then cut and shut a Mk V just behind the sponsons after inserting a 6ft extension. This boosted trench-crossing capability from 10ft to 13ft in width, and avoided recourse to giant drum-like fascines which had earlier been roof-mounted for release into the enemy trench as a bridging device. The enlarged fighting compartment was an added bonus. The rear turret's previously vertical end plates were sloped to allow greater elevation of its machine guns. In other respects the Star was generally the same as Mk V.

ORIGINATION
Design began: *c.* November 1917
Designed by: Maj W.G. Wilson

Sole builder: Metropolitan Carriage, Wagon & Finance Co. Ltd
First series production tank completed: female on 11 May and male on 1 July 1918

First trials
20.4.18. Brief tests by Metro on pre-production machine. No long-distance trials for this mark

WD serial numbers
Male: 9501–9700 and 10001–10300
Female: 9751–9950
Experimental: 9501, 9752, 9865

OUTLINE SPECIFICATION
Crew: 8
Commander
1 driver
6 gunners

Armament
Male: 2 × 6-pdr 23 cal. Hotchkiss QF,
    4 Hotchkiss MG
Female: 6 Hotchkiss MG

Engine
Ricardo 6-cyl. 'vertical' 150hp
hp per ton: 4.28hp
Est'd endurance: 9.5 hrs
Max speed: 4.6mph on level

Transmission
4-speed forward and 4-speed reverse
Epicyclic gear in final drive to each track, in permanent mesh

Dimensions
Length: 32ft 5in
Male width: 13ft 6in
Female width: 10ft 6in
Height: 8ft 8in
Track width: 20.5in

Fighting weight etc.
Male: 33 tons
Female: 32 tons
Max trench crossing: 13ft

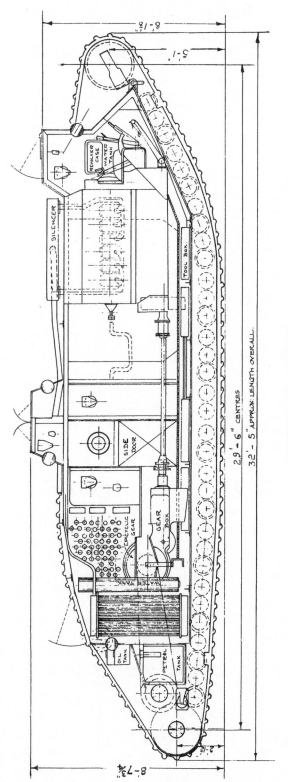

Mk V Star Heavy Tank

Mk V Two Star Heavy Tank

The Mk V Star was still on the drawing board on 11 January 1918 when the War Office considered ordering an initial 300 of the big Anglo-American Mk VIII tanks to follow it. News of a delay in securing release of the US-built Liberty engines for them led the Army to decide instead to order 300 of an uprated Mk V Star with a more powerful Ricardo engine. The resultant Mk V Two Star machines were to be 50/50 Male/Female, to complete delivery by 15 November 1918. They were the same length and width as the Star but track contour was altered with a greater camber on the lower run to improve manoeuvrability. Wider 26.5in track shoes were fitted. The engine in the earlier 'V' series was retained but its cylinders were bored out to develop 225hp. It was also located further back so that the fighting chamber lay largely ahead of it instead of around it. The commander's turret was enlarged and moved right up to the driver's to form one space. Metropolitan built all 1,125 tanks in the 'V' series, including 25 Two Star machines.

ORIGINATION
Design began: January/February 1918
Designed by: Maj W.G. Wilson

Sole builder: Metropolitan Carriage, Wagon & Finance Co. Ltd
First series production tank completed: December 1918

First trials
Late November 1918. Manoeuvred very well in first run

WD serial numbers
Male: 10501–10650 and 10901–11500
Female: 10701–10850
Experimental: 10704 (F) for bridging and mine clearance research

OUTLINE SPECIFICATION
Crew: 8
Commander
1 driver
6 gunners

Armament
Male: 2 × 6-pdr 23 cal. Hotchkiss QF,
   4 Hotchkiss MG
Female: 6 Hotchkiss MG

Engine
Ricardo 6-cyl. 'vertical' 225hp
hp per ton: 6.4hp
Est'd endurance: 12.9 hrs
Max speed: 5.2mph on level

Transmission
4-speed forward and 4-speed reverse
Epicyclic gear in final drive to each track, in permanent mesh

Dimensions
Length: 32ft 5in
Male width: 13ft 6in
Female width: 10ft 6in
Height: 9ft
Track width: 26.5in

Fighting weight etc.
Male: 35 tons
Female: 34 tons
Max trench crossing: 13ft

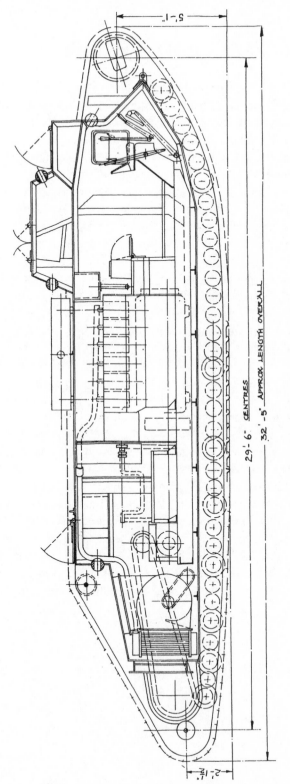

Mk V Two Star Heavy Tank

Mk VII Heavy Tank

This machine was intended to provide better one-man steering and speed control with less driver fatigue and improved trench-crossing capability. The hull was essentially a stretched Mk V, 3ft 6in longer, and fitted with clutchless variable hydraulic gears, one set for each track. A similar Williams Janney transmission had been installed in a Mk III and tested against other systems on 3 March 1917 at Oldbury. Although it was rejected in favour of Maj Wilson's epicyclic final drive, it was thought worth continuing to develop. That May twenty-four sets of hydraulic gears were ordered for a Mk VII to be built by Brown Brothers of Edinburgh, a Vickers subsidiary. The gears came from their sister company Variable Speed Gear Ltd. A Ricardo 150hp engine drove two VSG pumps coupled to a pair of hydraulic motors. Altering the pressure of the pumps produced infinitely variable speeds up to 4.25mph. As the two sets operated independently, power could be applied to either track through all forward and reverse speeds to give steering. There were separate radiators in the track frames for engine coolant and hydraulic oil. The two systems generated prodigious heat which was extracted from the engine compartment by twin 20in fans inducting and venting air through armoured roof grilles at 7,500cu ft per minute. Mk VII was one of the first tanks to be equipped with electric starting. A prototype was built and tested in October 1917 with promising results, followed in January by orders for a further seventy-four. Kitson's of Leeds were to share the work but their contract was later withdrawn to free capacity for locomotive construction. This was the only tank to be assembled by Brown's, whose suppliers included Greenwood & Batley of Leeds for the epicyclics, and rail wagon builders Hurst Nelson of Motherwell for hulls at a scheduled three per week. The first hull reached Brown's in May 1918 and only two more had arrived by the end of November, priority going instead to Medium C construction. Despite the Mk VII tank's fine manoeuvrability and ease of operation, its transmission was costly, came with a weight penalty, and was technically complex. Its power-to-weight ratio was poor and the engine remained in a cramped fighting compartment. The first Mk V Two Star machines with their superior internal layout and performance were ordered within days of Mk VII, followed soon afterwards by the even better Mk VIII. Thereafter the VII programme ran on 'near-empty'.

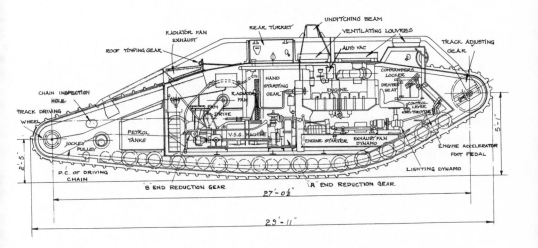

ORIGINATION

Design began: November 1916
Designed by: Maj H. Knothe
Contributors: Lt O. Thorneycroft, Mr John
Robson, Mr Hudd

Sole builder: Brown Brothers Ltd, Edinburgh
Prototype completed: October 1917
First series production tank completed: July
1918

First trials

November 1917. Promising results from
prototype
July 1918. 90-mile trial run of first
production machine; gearbox failed. In
August a 400-mile trial with redesigned box
was successfully completed

WD serial numbers

Brown: 5051–5088
(5051 was experimental)
Kitson: 5001–5036

OUTLINE SPECIFICATION

Crew: 8
Commander
1 driver
6 gunners

Armament

Male only: 2 × 6-pdr 23 cal. Hotchkiss QF,
 4 Hotchkiss MG

Engine

Ricardo 6-cyl. 'vertical' 150hp
hp per ton: 4.54hp
Est'd endurance: 11.5 hrs
Max speed: 4.25mph on level

Transmission

Clutchless. Williams Janney hydraulic
infinitely variable gear, 1 set to each track

Dimensions

Length: 29ft 10in
Width: 13ft 9in
Height: 8ft 7in
Track width: 26.5in

Fighting weight etc.

33 tons
Max trench crossing: 11ft 6in

Mk VIII Heavy Tank

The Mk VIII 'Liberty' or 'International' tank was co-designed by Britain and America primarily as a fighting vehicle but with troop carrier or supply tank capability. Variations in engines and details resulted in 'British' and 'Liberty' versions. Similar to the earlier tanks at a glance, it was in fact a completely new type taking the best of previous designs including Mk IX. 1,500 Liberty tanks were to be assembled in France. Britain would contribute hulls, guns, ammunition, track plates, rollers and instruments. The US would supply modified 300hp Liberty aero engines, transmissions and track parts. Larger-scale production in France and America was planned. At 37 tons and over 34ft long Mk VIII was the biggest and heaviest tank to date, its floor space allowing full bulkhead separation of the engine from the large fighting compartment in front. The 6-pdr guns were in doorless sponsons. Five machine guns had all-round fire from an 8ft long turret, as well as lateral arcs from mountings in the large side doors. Ground clearance at 1ft 9in was over 4in better than previous 'heavies', and track ground pressure was almost halved. To ensure the interchangeability of parts between Allied forces all jigs were made by one firm, the Leeds Forge Co.

The War Office considered ordering 300 British Mk VIII tanks in January 1918, but the supply of Liberty engines from the US was seriously delayed by the needs of their aircraft production, and there was fear of loss from U-boat activity. The order went to the Mk V Two Star instead. When 1,375 British Mk VIII machines were ordered in April, Harry Ricardo was asked to produce an engine for them comparable with the Liberty unit's 300hp output. His power plant delivered 330hp. Mk VIII production was cut to a handful that September in preference for the faster and more easily mass-produced Medium C. The war had become one of pursuit. The contract for Britain's contribution of 1,500 Liberty hulls had gone in March to a consortium led by Mr F.J. West, General Manager of West's Gas Improvement Co. Ltd of Manchester. The group was not given the labour and materials priorities to enable it to start work until November. A British-made Mk VIII Liberty hull and its guns were shipped to America in June for completion – it was one of two hulls in mild steel built by West's. America was in no position to start volume tank production in 1918, but the Ordnance Department purchased parts for 100 more Liberty machines after the war and assembled these at Rock Island Arsenal, completing in 1920.

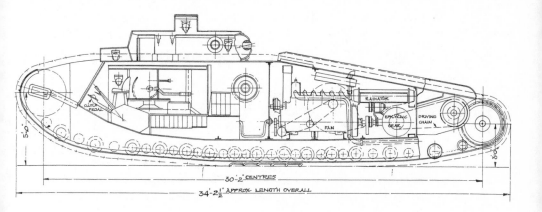

ORIGINATION
Preliminary design begun August/
September 1917 by: Lt G.J. Rackham
Formal design begun in December by:
US Army: Col Alden
Ministry of Munitions: Lt G.J. Rackham,
Maj W.G. Wilson, Sir E.T. d'Eyncourt
Tank Corps: Lt Col Green

First builder: North British Locomotive Co.
Ltd
Mock-up inspected: 11.1.18
2 mild steel prototypes were built by NB
Loco, August and September 1918
First British series production tank
completed by NB Loco, 18.10.18
2 mild steel Liberty hulls were ordered from
West's in April and delivered June 1918

First trials
August 1918: NB Loco prototype No. 1 was
fitted for short trial runs with a Rolls Royce
180hp engine pending delivery of the first
Ricardo unit
10.9.18: NB Loco No. 1 demonstrated to
Tank Board. Many defects. Transmission
unsatisfactory even under 180hp loads.
Epicyclic box covers broken twice in same
place. Track fouling.
18.10.18: NB Loco prototype No. 2 was
fitted with Ricardo 300hp V12 engine for
full endurance trials at Newbury Tank
Testing Station
23.10.18: Ricardo machine broke down
completely with engine bearing trouble 20
miles into its 1,000-mile trial
30.11.18: no major problems but 1,000-
mile trial still uncompleted

WD serial numbers
NB Loco: 12001–13040
Beardmore: 14001–14335

OUTLINE SPECIFICATION
Capacity
Commander
1 driver
6 gunners
20 infantrymen

Armament
2 × 6-pdr 23 cal. Hotchkiss QF
Main turret: 5 Hotchkiss MG
2 side doors: 1 Hotchkiss MG in each

Engine
Ricardo V12, 300hp – or Liberty V12, 300hp
Engines interchangeable.
hp per ton: 8hp
Est'd endurance: 9.7 hrs
Max speed: 7mph on level

Transmission
A 2-speed compound epicyclic gear to each
track giving two forward and reverse
speeds, 1.4 and 5.2mph. The British type
was designed to accept 4-speed gearing as a
later option

Dimensions
Length: 34ft 2.5in
Width: 12ft 4in
Height: 10ft 3.5in
Track width: 26.5in

Fighting weight etc.
37 tons
Max trench crossing: 14ft

Mk IX Infantry Supply Tank

Mk IX was arguably the world's first purpose-built tracked and armoured personnel carrier. Design by Lt George Rackham began in May 1917. A few months later he and Maj Wilson started to think about a fighting version (it eventually became Mk VIII) and much of Rackham's structural innovation was common to both types. Interior space was maximised by severely cutting back the internal track frames which had been over-designed. The box-like hull of the Mk IX had no sponsons, its smooth flanks being carried out flush to the limits of the rail loading gauge. A Ricardo 150hp engine was up front with only the driver and commander ahead of it. To maximise load space the gearbox and epicyclics were set in the far rear, their control rods running back to the driver along the underside of the roof. The resulting area of some 13ft 6in by 7ft 7in, with 5ft 5in of uniform height, was clear save for the unshielded drive shaft which ran from front to back down the centre of the space at shin height. Claimed capacity was thirty men or 10 tons of stores. Two machines could carry between them a day's supplies for an infantry brigade. But thirty troops laden with equipment in such a space would have suffered grievously. There were no seats or grab lines, and the swaying mass in the choking near-darkness was expected to stand clear of a rotating drive shaft. Two large oval doors on either side gave access.

Three machines reached France before the Armistice. When they got to Central Workshops it was found that the insides of the doors were painted white, no doubt to indicate their position in the interior gloom, but it brought a strong complaint from the workshops office because if opened for evacuation under fire the bright door would have been a gift to gunners. A cargo tray covered much of the roof. Fixed armament comprised a forward-firing Hotchkiss MG beside the driver and another in the machine's back plate covering its rear. Flank loopholes would enable passengers to use their small arms. In an attempt to improve ventilation, vanes were fitted to the enclosed flywheel to make it an extraction fan, drawing foul air from the interior and up through the sealed engine casing to discharge on the roof. Two or three prototypes in mild steel were built by Sir W.G. Armstrong, Whitworth & Co. One of them was sealed for flotation trials and fitted with pontoon cylinders strapped to the hull. A raised cab with extended exhausts was built in front, and hinged paddles were fitted to the tracks at intervals. A rear-mounted auxiliary motor gave propulsion. The 'Duck' was first launched on Armistice Day on London's Welsh Harp lake near the tank experimental ground at Dollis Hill.

The Mk IX machine proved to be underpowered and prone to sink under load, whether on land or water. The Army never got an effective all-terrain armoured carrier. It had been pressing the Mechanical Warfare Department for one since May 1917 and had called for 800 by mid-1918. Scarcity of materials and labour left auxiliary vehicle production well behind in the race to build more fighting types.

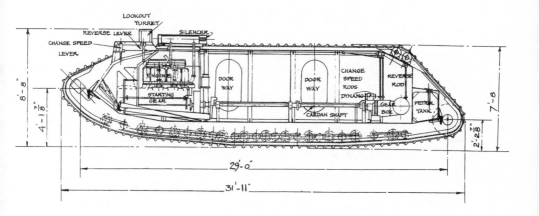

ORIGINATION

Design began: May 1917
Designed by: Lt G.J. Rackham supervised by
Maj W.G. Wilson
Design completed: September 1917

First builder, prototypes: Sir W.G.
Armstrong, Whitworth & Co.
Production machines: Wm Marshall Sons &
Co.
Mock-up: inspected late September 1917 at
Dollis Hill
First series production tank: delivered
8.6.18

First trials

January 1918. Prototype to Dollis Hill
where driving chains broke repeatedly. Slow
to steer due to greater track length in
ground contact

WD serial numbers

901–1100
903, 907, 909 went to France late October
1918, the only Mk IX to get there before
the Armistice

OUTLINE SPECIFICATION

Capacity

Commander
1 driver
2 machine-gunners
30 infantrymen or 10 tons of stores

Armament

Front plate: 1 Hotchkiss MG
Rear plate: 1 Hotchkiss MG

Engine

Ricardo 6-cyl. 150hp
hp per ton: 4.05hp
Est'd endurance: 9.75 hrs
Max speed: 4.3mph on level

Transmission

4-speed forward and 4-speed reverse
Epicyclic gear in final drive to each track, in
permanent mesh

Dimensions

Length: 34ft 2.5in
Width; 12ft 4in
Height: 10ft 3.5in
Track width: 20.5in

Fighting weight etc.

37 tons laden
27 tons unladen
Max trench crossing: 12ft 6in

Medium A 'Whippet' Tank

The Medium series of light tanks was introduced in 1918. It was a slow-motion but still deadly mechanical cavalry designed for pursuit and exploitation after a breakthrough. Speeds of 6–8mph in this class do not impress today, but the so-called 'chasers' were twice as fast as the heavy tanks and highly rated. The 'A' Type was an iron boot in shape. Its low-profile armoured chassis with almost continuous mud chutes along the track frames was topped by an angular fixed turret at the rear, providing a cramped fighting space for a commander, driver and one – or theoretically two – machine-gunners. A rear door gave entry. Ahead and below them between the independently driven tracks were twin commercial Tylor 4-cylinder 45hp engines, each with its own gearbox powering a track. The driver contended with a mass of controls. He had two sets of clutch pedals, gear change and hand-brake levers, plus a magneto control, a steering wheel of sorts, and a master throttle which uniformly governed both engines. Turning the steering wheel automatically closed the throttle of the engine on the inside of a turn and opened the other's – but naturally this risked an engine stall if the master throttle had been set either fully open or 'idle'. The method worked for slight turns; for bigger swings the driver could select differing ratios in the two gearboxes, even spinning the tank on its axis by reversing one and staying in forward on the other. Alternatively, he could drive round a turn on one track while declutched and hand-braked on the other.

A machine gun mounting was fitted in each of the four faces of the turret, which rotated only in pre-production designs. The Army had wanted a 2-pdr gun for destroying Maxim positions but it was impracticable in the small turret. An anti-aircraft MG mounting was fitted in April 1918. Some inevitable weaknesses emerged. Overall height exceeded the rail loading gauge, necessitating a part dismantling of the turret for transportation. Two engines doubled the chances of a failure, and stalling was a regular event. The crew could restart engines from inside the tank but anything else meant exposure to fire outside. If one engine failed, the clutch system could only deliver 24hp which might just move the machine in a straight line, but steering was unlikely with half that power going to each track through the locked differential. Ventilation was poor; 3 Battalion's War Diary recorded on 21 August 1918 that some of its Whippets were neutralised in two recent actions when one hour's running with the door closed in summer heat left them weaponless save for revolver fire. Ammunition swelled and jammed the guns. In several cases rounds exploded in the tanks. Guns and driver controls were too hot to grip. Nevertheless the Whippets gave most valuable service until the Armistice.

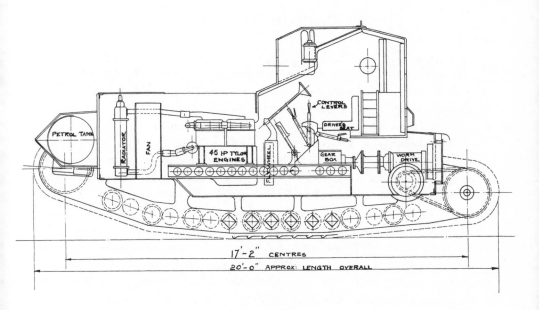

ORIGINATION

Design began: October 1916
Designed by: W.A. Tritton

First builder: Wm Foster & Co., Lincoln
Prototype first moved itself: 3.1.17
First series production tank completed:
October 1917 (first five machines in mild
steel)

First trials

4.1.17. Prototype's factory trials
3.3.17. Took part in the Oldbury
transmission trials. Coolant repeatedly
boiled. Fan belt problems
April 1917. Ran 120 miles on test with
overheating problems

WD serial numbers

A 200–399

OUTLINE SPECIFICATION

Crew: 3–4
Commander
1 driver
1–2 gunners

Armament

4 Hotchkiss MG
Anti-aircraft mounting added April 1918

Engine

2 Tylor JB4 4-cyl. each 45hp
hp per ton: 6.43hp
Est'd endurance: 10 hrs
Max speed 8.3mph on level

Transmission

A gearbox serving each engine provided
4 forward speeds and reverse

Dimensions

Length: 20ft
Width: 8ft 7in
Height: 9.0ft
Track width: 20.5in

Fighting weight etc.

14 tons
Max trench crossing: 7ft

Medium B Tank

The Medium A had proved its value as a chaser but was hard to handle, more liable to breakdown with twin engines, and lacked protected access to them. Maj Wilson's 'B' Type aimed to overcome these defects. It was effectively a scaled-down Mk V with separate crew and engine compartments. In place of sponsons a coffer-shaped door on either side formed a mini sponson projecting 9in, with a mounting for a single machine gun plus a revolver port. A large full-width turret on the forepart of the roof provided five further MG mountings to give all-round fire, and an anti-aircraft mounting. The turret's position almost on the nose ensured that the commander and the gunners got the earliest possible view ahead when the tank crested a rise. Track width was increased from the 'A' Type's 20.5in to 22.5in. Unfortunately, access to the engine and the transmission beyond it was so cramped that the 100hp Ricardo had to cool down for at least an hour before attempting even a plug change. Roof plates had to be removed in order to change inlet valves. A novel smokescreen generator injected sulphonic acid into the engine exhaust. As smoke could only be produced with a running engine, thirty smoke grenades were carried in case of engine failure under fire.

The introduction of the 'B' Type was delayed by repeated design changes and then a shortage of armour plate. The tank was 4 tons heavier than the Whippet, and with its 100hp engine its power-to-weight ratio was actually inferior. Gen Elles wanted production postponed until Ricardo's 150hp engine became available. The first 100hp Medium B was delivered in mid-October 1918, coinciding with a very adverse report from Col Fuller who had inspected the trials machine at Dollis Hill. The Tank Board decided to accept the type primarily as a training machine and to concentrate on the Medium C.

A male version of the 'B' Type with a 2-pdr gun was planned, but was abandoned in March 1918 because production of the gun would have seriously compromised Armstrong's output of 6-pdrs for the heavy tanks.

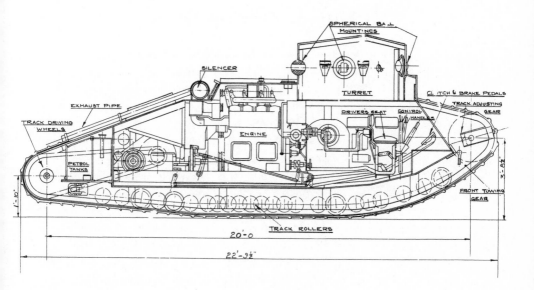

ORIGINATION

Design began: March 1917
Design by: Maj W.G. Wilson
Design still in early stages in October 1917
when priority switched to Mk V working
drawings
Design completed: January/February 1918

First builder: The Patent Shaft & Axletree
Co. Ltd
Build started: prototype completed July
1918
First series production tank completed:
9 September. Delivered *c*. 15 October to
tank experimental ground, Dollis Hill

First trials

September 1918: a short run with
No. 1201 at Oldbury. Minor alterations
only.
October 1918: 1,000-mile trial. Track
brakes failed and mud entered epicyclics.
Gearbox overheated. Trials recommenced
using 1202. Gearbox still overheating

WD serial numbers

Patent Shaft 1201–1450
Coventry Ordnance 1501–1600
North British Loco 1601–1700

OUTLINE SPECIFICATION

Crew: 4
Commander
1 driver
2 gunners

Armament

4 Hotchkiss MG

Engine

Ricardo 4-cyl. 100hp
hp per ton: 5.5hp
Est'd endurance: 12 hrs
Max speed: 6.1mph on level

Transmission

4-speed forward and 4-speed reverse
Epicyclic gear to each track, in permanent
mesh

Dimensions

Length: 22ft 9.5in
Width: 9ft 3in
Height: 8ft 4.75in
Track width: 22.5in

Fighting weight etc.

18 tons
Max trench crossing: 8ft

Medium C 'Hornet' Tank

When the working drawings for Maj Walter Wilson's much delayed 18-ton Medium B were nearing completion in February 1918, Gen Hugh Elles, the Tank Corps commander, complained that it was going to be too slow and should be shelved pending a more powerful engine from Harry Ricardo. Sir William Tritton was asked on the 5th to complete a rival design. He had been working on his 19.5-ton Hornet for several months. The tank resembled the 'B' Type externally and in its internal layout, but there was more superstructure above the tracks, it was 3ft longer (only 7in shorter than the Mk V heavy tank) and it was planned to take the forthcoming Ricardo 150hp engine with conventional Mk V-type transmission, giving a top speed of nearly 8mph against the 6.1 of the 'B'. The engine was highly accessible in a rear compartment, and the driver sat right up front. Immediately behind his lookout a full-width turret covered the crew compartment, fitted with two forward-firing machine-gun mountings and one each side and to the rear. The commander could perch on a small hinged platform and observe through a rotating mini turret set on the rear of the main turret's roof. The usual massive starting handle bisected the compartment at knee height but was demountable – a necessary innovation. A newly designed 2-pdr gun was planned for the female version to deal more effectively with Maxim positions but Gen Elles thought it inadequate and wanted a 6-pdr. Neither gun was installed.

A male version was designed but never built. It was to be a tank destroyer with a single Hotchkiss 6-pdr in the bows. The gun would have reverted to the longer 40-calibre barrel because muzzle blast from the current 23-calibre gun could have injured the driver directly beneath. The Medium C was unquestionably the best of the light tank series to date and promised to be one of the outstanding tanks of the war. When it was chosen to spearhead the breakout in the following year's offensive, its production orders leapt in September 1918 from 600 machines to 3,230. The Armistice halted almost all Hornet construction but the handful that were built remained in service for five or six years until the Vickers Medium Mk I with its sprung bogies and 30mph top speed replaced them.

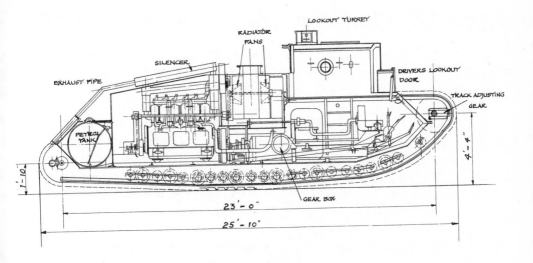

ORIGINATION

Design began: possibly August/September 1917 but contemporary records also state December

Designed by: Sir Wm Tritton

First builder: Wm Foster & Co. Ltd
Mock-up built: 4.4.18
Design approved: 19.4.18
First tank moved itself: 16.8.18, possibly a mild steel version
First series production tank completed: 3.9.18, female
Delivered: January 1919

First trials

16 August 1918. Tests began at Lincoln. Gearbox troubles, stripped pinions.
3 September. Generally satisfactory but coolant boiled and gearbox overheating threatened a possible box redesign.
6 October. Completed 1,000-mile test and ran the last 150 miles non-stop at 7.5mph. Gearbox redesign avoided

WD serial numbers

Female 1801–2000
No male tanks built

OUTLINE SPECIFICATION

Crew: 4
Commander
1 driver
2 gunners

Armament

Male (none built): 1 Hotchkiss 40-cal. 6-pdr; 3 Hotchkiss MG
Female: 4 Hotchkiss MG; A 2-pdr QF gun was planned but not installed

Engine

Ricardo 6-cyl. 150hp
hp per ton: 7.5hp
Est'd endurance: 16 hrs
Max speed: 7.9mph on level

Transmission

4-speed forward and 4-speed reverse
Epicyclic gear in final drive to each track, in permanent mesh

Dimensions

Length: 25ft 10in
Width: 8ft 10.5in
Height: 9ft 7in
Track width: 20.5in

Fighting weight etc.

19.5 tons
Max trench crossing: 10ft

Mks I & II Gun Carriers and Salvage variants

By spring 1916 it was clear to some at least that if newly gained ground was to be held by exhausted and lightly armed infantry, then heavy artillery must be brought forward into range at speed to continue to give fire support before the enemy counter-attacked. On 7 March, the day of his promotion to Major, Walter Wilson began design of a tracked and lightly armoured gun carrier with Maj John Greg of the Metropolitan Company, whose idea it was. GHQ in France formally requested the machine in May but the Ordnance Board raised objections and a hiatus ensued. Lloyd George the Minister of Munitions authorised construction of fifty machines without Army sanction. The first machine successfully completed firing trials from the vehicle in January 1917. The dual self-propelled gun/gun carrier was finally approved by the Army at the end of May, a year after its initial request.

The 30ft machine's low-profile track frames stood some 5ft high. Between and above them a tall armoured box body filled the rear half, straddling the tracks, the upper run of which passed through a tunnel at that point. The remaining space was an open well. Up front a narrow armoured cab perched above each track for the commander and driver. The machine was designed for a 6in howitzer or a 60-pdr Field Gun Mk II. The artillery piece was winched backwards up a ramp between the two cabs and into the open well in a firing position before securing against a recoil beam. Its wheels were removed and chained to either side of the box body, inside which was a compartment for a detachment of eight gunners, a Daimler 105hp engine and transmission similar to the Mk I tank's system, and two gearsmen. Mud and stones regularly built up in the tunnel trackways through the body, bursting the undersides of the left- and right-hand radiators above. The tunnels also prevented the use of track spuds. The first machine, No. 100, arrived in France complete with a steering tail in time for Third Ypres, which opened on 31 July 1917. Its intended role was overtaken by events and the tail soon disappeared. The carrier brought several hundred tons of ammunition forward, and a few 60-pdr guns. Once, at least, 'sniping' was accomplished by taking up a 6in howitzer and moving about during the night, firing it from the vehicle, which harassed and puzzled the enemy. Gun-carrying companies were formed, the first drawing its machines in France on 6 September. They were soon relegated to a supply role conveying gun ammunition and infantry stores for which they were invaluable. A carrier with its four-man crew could shift a 7-ton load which would otherwise require a carrying party of 290 men. The surviving vehicles were fitted at Central Workshops with cranes for salvage work in the spring of 1918.

The order for fifty carriers was altered in October 1916 to forty-eight plus two variants for salvage work. These recovery machines were not built until June/July 1917. The two forward cabs were omitted and the well was decked over for a hand-operated crane to lift 3 tons in jib form or 10 tons with sheerlegs. A winding drum for wire rope haulage was mounted on the box body, in front of which was a cab. A third machine was fitted that December with a large Priestman steam-powered grab.

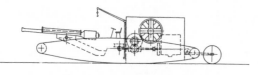

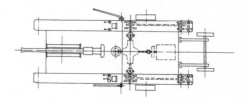

Gun Carrier Mk I

A GC Mk II was designed but only a mock-up was built. The general principles of the Mk I were retained but the hull occupied two-thirds of the machine's length and the open well lay at the rear. The front end was built on similar lines to Mks IV and V fighting tanks, with sufficiently angled track to enable the machine to climb. A Ricardo 150hp engine would drive through epicyclic gears. The guns were to board from the rear, retaining their wheels, but could not be fired from the machine.

ORIGINATION (MK I)

Design began: 7.3.16
Designed by: Majs J. Greg and W.G. Wilson
Outline design approval by GHQ only: 17.4.16
Construction order authorised unilaterally by Minister of Munitions: 16.6.16
Construction order formally confirmed by War Office: 29.5.17

First builder, prototype: Metropolitan Carriage, Wagon & Finance Co. Ltd
Prototype completed: 1.1.17
First builder, production machine: Kitson & Co. of Leeds
First series production tank completed: June 1917

First trials: *c.* 2.2.17. Prototype at Shoeburyness ranges fired 60-pdr (5in) gun from the carrier's well

WD serial numbers: began at GC 100

OUTLINE SPECIFICATION

Crew: 4 + 8
Commander
1 driver
2 gearsmen
Detachment of 8 gunners

Armament: 1 machine gun for defence. GC carried 1 6in howitzer Mk I + 60 rounds, or 1 60-pdr 5in Field Gun Mk II/L + 60 rounds

Engine

Daimler 105hp
hp per ton: 3.9hp
Est'd endurance: 11 hrs
Max speed: 3.7mph on level

Transmission

Primary box: 2 forward and 1 reverse
Secondary gears: 2-speed to each track

Dimensions

Length overall with tail and 60-pdr gun: 43ft
Length without tail and gun: 30ft
Width: 11ft
Height: 9ft 4in
Track width: 20.5in

Weight etc.

With 60-pdr and ammunition: 34 tons
With howitzer and ammunition: 31 tons
No gun: 27 tons
Max trench crossing: 11ft 6in

PRODUCTION HISTORIES OF PRINCIPAL BRITISH TANKS, 1916–19

Mk I Heavy Tank

builders (of first tank in bold type)	first orders February 1916	revisions April 1916	revisions June 1916	total built
Wm Foster & Co. Lincoln	25 M 12.2.16	30 M i.e. extra 5 M c. 21.4.16	37 M i.e. 7 M transferred from Robey's probably early June	37 M
Robey & Co. Canwick Rd. Lincoln	–	7 M c. 21.4.16	cancelled probably early June	nil
Metropolitan Carriage, Wagon & Finance Co. Ltd. Birmingham (built at Oldbury factory)	75 M 12.2.16	113 i.e. extra 38 c. 21.4.16 All Mk 1 to be 50/50 M/F so Metro now 38 M. 75 F	113 no change	38 M 75 F
TOTAL	100	150	150	150. Completed by 31.10.17

Mk II Heavy Tank

builders (of first tank in bold type)	first orders July 1916	total built
Wm Foster & Co. Lincoln	25 M 25.7.16	25 M
Metropolitan Carriage, Wagon & Finance Co. Ltd, Birmingham (built at Oldbury factory)	25 F 25.7.16	25 F
TOTAL	50	50. Completed by 31.1.17

Mk III Heavy Tank

builders	first order	total built
Metropolitan Carriage, Wagon & Finance Co. Ltd, Birmingham (built at Oldbury factory)	50 25 M. 25 F 3.8.16	50 25 M. 25 F
TOTAL	50	50. Completed by 28.2.17

Mk IV Heavy Tank and Tank Tender

builders (of first tank in bold)	first orders August–September 1916	revisions October 1916–January 1917	revisions February–April 1917	revisions September–December 1917	total built
Metropolitan Carriage, Wagon & Finance Co. Ltd, Birmingham	21.8.16 Metro was contracted to build 1,000 tanks as a continuation order on completion of Mk III. Initiated by Stern without WO sanction. 26.9.16 WO approved 1,000-tank order 'in continuation of existing orders'. 30.9.16 WO cancelled its letter of 26th and withdrew approval of 1,000-tank run-on. It authorised completion of 50 each of Mks II and III as previously ordered, and offered a continuation order as a stopgap pending switch to a new design when ready. Stern appealed to Lloyd George at the WO.	14.10.16 WO reinstated its letter of 26 September and confirmed the 1,000-tank order. 16.10.16 Stern reported contract for 1,000 tanks was placed with Metro 'today', the first 600 to be Mk IV (300 M, 300 F). Foster's had declined Stern's invitation to build up to 80 Mk IV on this order; lack of capacity. 25.11.16 Meeting Tank Supply Dept/Metro at Oldbury. Orders revised to: Metro – 440 tanks; Foster's – 100 tanks. Metro to supply Foster's with 6–8 hulls weekly.	21.3.17 WO authorised issue of a continuation order on completion of the first 1,000 Mk IV. No limit given. (Mk IV deliveries began 2 April). as at 7.4.17 Without informing WO Stern had increased Metro's Mk IV order from 440 to 1,000, bringing total production to 1,400.	29.9.17 WO ordered Mk IV production to cease. Stern confirmed 205 being converted to tank supply tenders: Metro – 180; Beardmore – 25. 15.10.17 WO advised it would take 950 Mk IV as fighting tanks plus 216 converted to tank tenders, the remaining 234 'definitely not required'. Late October 1917 Stern reduced Metro's Mk IV order from 1,000 to 820. i.e. 640 fighting tanks and 180 tank tenders.	640 (plus 180 tenders)
Wm Foster & Co., Lincoln	–	100 contracted 25.11.16. Metro to supply hulls from 1.2.17	100 no change	100 no change	100
Sir W. G. Armstrong Whitworth Co. Ltd, Close Wks, Gateshead	–	100 contracted c. Dec 1916	100 no change	100 no change Last to complete Mk IV, mid-Oct 1918. Armstrong's built 11 tanks in the 4 months from 8 June–5 Oct.	100
Coventry Ordnance Works Ltd, Glasgow	–	100 contracted c. Dec. 1916	100 no change	100 no change Completed 23.5.18	100
Mirrlees Watson Co., Glasgow	–	50 F contracted 25.1.17	50 F no change	50 F no change	50 F
Wm Beardmore Co., Glasgow	–	50 F contracted c. Jan. 1917	50 F no change	Reduction to 25 c. 3.10.17 plus 25 convert to tank tenders	25 (plus 25 tenders)
TOTAL	(1,000 as continuation of Mk III)	840 Mk IV by end of January 1917	1,400 Mk IV by 7 April	1,015 Mk IV by 31 October	M 420 F 595 Mk IV 1015 (Mk IV completion Oct 1918) Tenders 205

Mk V Heavy Tank

builder	first order	revisions	revisions	revisions	total built
Metropolitan Carriage, Wagon & Finance Co. Ltd, Birmingham (built at Saltley and Oldbury factories)	800 400 M. 400 F 22.9.17	400 i.e. 200 M and 200 F cancelled by 21.2.18	2,400 i.e. additional 2,000 c. Aug. 1918	Post-contract design changes were so many that the 2,000 tanks of the repeat order were redesignated Mk X on 31.10.18	400 M 200. F 200.
TOTAL	800	400	2,400	400	400. Completed by 8.6.18

Mk V Star Heavy Tank

builder	first order	revisions	built at 31 December 1918	total built
Metropolitan Carriage, Wagon & Finance Co. Ltd, Birmingham	300 M Nov/Dec 1917	700 i.e. additional 400 at February 1918 500 M & 200 F in all	632 i.e. 432 M and 200 F. Some later sources state 200 M/432 F but data is suspect	700
TOTAL	300	700	632 (579 at Armistice)	700. Completed by 14.3.19

Mk V Two Star Heavy Tank

builder	first order	revisions	revisions	built at 31 December 1918	total built
Metropolitan Carriage, Wagon & Finance Co., Birmingham	300 150 M. 150 F 17.1.18	900 i.e. additional 600 M March 1918	700 i.e. 200 cancelled after 20.8.1918	1 M only December 1918	20 M. 5 F all but first tank were built after 14.3.19
TOTAL	300	900	700	1 (nil by Armistice)	25

Mk VII Heavy Tank

builder (of first tank in bold type)	first orders	revisions	built at 31 December 1918	total built
Brown Bros Ltd, Edinburgh	38 12.1.18	31 i.e. 7 cancelled mid-August 1918	1 M	3 M
Kitson & Co. Ltd, Leeds	36 contracted by 27.2.18	cancelled mid-August 1918	–	–
TOTAL	74	31	1 (1 by Armistice)	3

Mk VIII Heavy Tank

builders (of first tank in bold type)	first orders March–April 1918	revisions at 5.6.18	revisions at 25.6.18	revisions at 14.8.18	revisions Sept–Nov 1918	built at 31.12.1918	total built
BRITISH TYPE							
North British Locomotive Co. Ltd Glasgow (Atlas Works)	1,040 April 1918	1,040 no change	1,040 no change	1,040 no change	prod'n halted mid-September 26 i.e. 1,014 cancelled late November	1 only	11 completed before 14.3.19
Metropolitan Carriage, Wagon & Finance Co., Birmingham	–	810 late May/early June	180 i.e. 630 cancelled	cancelled 4.7.18	–	nil	nil
National Projectile Factory Glasgow (a Ministry of Munitions shell factory managed by Wm Beardmore & Co.)	335 April 1918	335 no change	335 no change	335 no change	cancelled mid-September	nil	nil
TOTAL	1,375	2,185	1,555	1,195	26	1 only (by Armistice)	11
LIBERTY TYPE – hulls only							
West's Gas Improvement Co. (Manchester Tank Syndicate)	1,500 7.3.18	1,500 no change	1,500 no change	1,500 no change	cancelled November	30–40 hulls all in Nov.	30–40 hulls

Mk IX Infantry Supply Tank

builder	first order	revisions	revisions	built at 31 December 1918	total built
Wm Marshall Sons & Co. Ltd, Gainsborough	360 November 1917	200 i.e. 160 cancelled between December 1917 and February 1918	57 i.e. 143 cancelled late November 1918	35	46 completed by 14.3.19
TOTAL	360	200	57	35 (23 by Armistice)	46

Medium A 'Whippet' Tank

builders (of first tank in bold type)	first order	revisions	revisions	revisions	total built
Wm Foster & Co. Ltd, Lincoln	200 14.3.17	200 no change	400 i.e. 200 transferred from unidentified firm 4.9.17	200 i.e. 200 cancelled on 4.10.17	200 completion 5.10.18
unidentified contractor	–	200 June 1917	cancelled September 1917	–	–
TOTAL	200	400	400	200	200

Medium B Tank

builder (of first tank in bold type)	first orders Oct 1917	revisions Feb–April 1918	revisions etc Oct-Nov 1918	built by Armistice 1918	total built
Metropolitan CWF Co. passed to its subsidiary **Patent Shaft & Axletree Co., Wednesbury**	450 F 15.10.17	250 i.e. 200 cancelled c. 15 February 1918	250 no change	19	50
Coventry Ordnance, Glasgow	100 F 15.10.17	100 no change	200 i.e. 100 extra ordered in October	nil	11
North British Locomotive, Glasgow, (built at Atlas Works, Springburn)	–	100 contracted between 7 March–late April 1918 on transfer from Mirrlees Watson	100 no change	7	19
Mirrlees Watson, Glasgow	100 15.10.17	cancelled between 7 March–late April 1918. Work transferred to NB Locomotive	–	nil	nil
TOTAL	650	450	550	26 (39 by year end)	80

Medium C Tank

builder (of first tank in bold type)	first orders February 1918	revisions March 1918	revisions May–August 1918	revisions September 1918	built at 31 December 1918	total built
Wm Foster & Co. Ltd, Lincoln	130 F mid-Feb 1918	130 F no change	200 F i.e. 70 extra, from Coventry Ordnance Works, June 1918.	200 F no change	nil. authorised to build 50 only, 15.11.18.	36 completed by 14.3.19
Patent Shaft & Axletree Co. Ltd, Wednesbury	200 (M?) mid-Feb 1918	cancelled c. 8.3.18	–	–	–	–
Kitson & Co. Ltd, Leeds	–	–	200 F c. 23.8.18	200 F no change	cancelled 21.11.18	–
West's Gas Improvement Co. Ltd, (Manchester Tank Group)	–	–	200 M July/August 1918	200 M no change	cancelled	–
North British Locomotive Co. Ltd, Glasgow	–	–	–	1,440 F c. 20.9.18	cancelled	–
National Projectile Factory, 62 Robertson St, Glasgow (Wm Beardmore & Co.)	–	–	–	1,190 M c. 20.9.18	cancelled	–
Coventry Ordnance Works Ltd, Glasgow	70 (F?) mid-Feb 1918	70 (F?) no change	cancelled by 5.6.1918 Work transferred to Foster's	–	–	–
TOTAL	400	200	600	3,230	nil	36

Medium D Tank

builder	type	first orders	revisions	first completion	total built
John Fowler & Co. Ltd, Leeds	Medium D mild steel prototype	4 17.8.18	4 no change	March 1919	3
Vickers Ltd (built at Wolseley Motor Works, Birmingham)	Medium D mild steel prototype	4 10.9.18	2 i.e. 2 cancelled October 1919	before October 1919	2
Vickers Ltd (probably built by Variable Speed Gear Co., a Vickers subsidiary, at Crayford)	Medium D Star mild steel prototype	1 27.9.18	1 no change	c. December 1919	1
Vickers Ltd (built by Variable Speed Gear Co., a Vickers subsidiary, at Crayford)	Medium D Two Star mild steel prototype	1 27.9.18	1 no change	c. spring 1920	1
Royal Ordnance Factory Woolwich	Medium D (Modified)	62 c. summer 1919	20 i.e. 42 cancelled 28.11.19	uncertain	3

Mk I Gun Carrier and Salvage variant

builder (of first tank in bold type)	initial orders	revisions	Gun Carrier completions	GC Salvage completion
Metropolitan Carriage, Wagon & Finance Co. Ltd, Birmingham	1 only, pre-production machine June 1916	1 GC no change	1 only on 1.1.17	–
Kitson & Co. Ltd. Airedale Foundry, Leeds	49 date uncertain	47 GC and 2 Salvage. i.e. variation 16.10.16	first 6 between June–July 1917 / total 26 at 21.10.17 / last 5 in 1st quarter of 1918	2 June/July 1917
TOTAL	50	48 + 2 Salvage	48	2

BRITISH TANK CONSTRUCTORS, OUTPUT BY TYPE, 1916–19

Type	Contractor	Location	Built	Total built	Cost £000
Mk I	Metropolitan Carriage Wagon & Finance Co. Ltd	Birmingham	113		
	Wm Foster & Co. Ltd	Lincoln	37	150	750
Mk II	Metropolitan Carriage Wagon & Finance Co. Ltd	Birmingham	25		
	Wm Foster & Co. Ltd	Lincoln	25	50	250
Mk III	Metropolitan Carriage Wagon & Finance Co. Ltd	Birmingham	50	50	250
Mk IV	Metropolitan Carriage Wagon & Finance Co. Ltd	Birmingham	640		
	Wm Foster & Co. Ltd	Lincoln	100		
	Sir Wm Armstrong, Whitworth & Co. Ltd	Newcastle upon Tyne	100	1,015	5,075
	Coventry Ordnance Works	Glasgow	100		
	Mirrlees, Watson & Co. Ltd	Glasgow	50		
	Wm Beardmore & Co. Ltd	Glasgow	25		
Tenders Mk IV	Metropolitan Carriage Wagon & Finance Co. Ltd	Birmingham	180		
	Wm Beardmore & Co. Ltd	Glasgow	25	205	1,127.5
Mk V	Metropolitan Carriage Wagon & Finance Co. Ltd	Birmingham	400	400	2,400
Mk V Star	Metropolitan Carriage Wagon & Finance Co. Ltd	Birmingham	700	700	4,550
Mk V Two Star	Metropolitan Carriage Wagon & Finance Co. Ltd	Birmingham	25	25	170
Mk VII	Brown Bros. Ltd	Edinburgh	3	3	25.5
Mk VIII	North British Locomotive Co. Ltd	Glasgow	11	11	82
Mk IX	Wm Marshall Sons & Co. Ltd	Gainsborough, Lincolnshire	46	46	253
Medium A	Wm Foster & Co. Ltd	Lincoln	200	200	800
Medium B	Metropolitan Carriage Wagon & Finance Co. Ltd	Birmingham	50		
	Coventry Ordnance Works	Glasgow	11	80	360
	North British Locomotive Co. Ltd	Glasgow	19		
Medium C	Wm Foster & Co. Ltd	Lincoln	36	36	180
Medium D	John Fowler & Co. Ltd	Leeds	3		
	Vickers Ltd	Birmingham	2	5	60
Medium D Star	Vickers Ltd	London	1	1	12
Medium D Two Star	Vickers Ltd	London	1	1	12
Medium D (M)	Royal Arsenal	Woolwich	3	3	30
Gun Carriers	Kitson & Co. Ltd	Leeds	48	48	168
Salvage Tanks	Kitson & Co. Ltd	Leeds	2	2	10
TOTALS				3,031	16,565

Appendix 4

QUARTERLY OUTPUT OF BRITISH TANKS BY TYPE, 1916–18

Type	1916			1917				1918				total
	2nd qtr	3rd qtr	4th qtr	1st qtr	2nd qtr	3rd qtr	4th qtr	1st qtr	2nd qtr	3rd qtr	4th qtr	
Mk I	8	110	32	–	–	–	–	–	–	–	–	150
Mks II and III	–	–	–	100	–	–	–	–	–	–	–	100
Mk IV M	–	–	–	–	108	219	43	21	18	8	3	420
Mk IV F	–	–	–	–	214	258	68	38	17	–	–	595
Tender Mk IV	–	–	–	–	–	15	152	38	–	–	–	205
Mk V M	–	–	–	–	–	–	–	38	162	–	–	200
Mk V F	–	–	–	–	–	–	–	65	135	–	–	200
Mk V Star M	–	–	–	–	–	–	–	–	36	197	199	432
Mk V Star F	–	–	–	–	–	–	–	–	82	118	–	200
Mk V 2 Star M	–	–	–	–	–	–	–	–	–	–	1	1
Mk V 2 Star F	–	–	–	–	–	–	–	–	–	–	–	–
Mk VII	–	–	–	–	–	–	–	–	–	–	1	1
Mk VIII	–	–	–	–	–	–	–	–	–	–	1	1
Medium A	–	–	–	–	–	–	55	55	56	33	1	200
Medium B	–	–	–	–	–	–	–	–	–	1	38	39
Medium C	–	–	–	–	–	–	–	–	–	–	–	–
Gun Carrier and Salvage Mk I	–	–	–	–	2	14	29	5	–	–	–	50
Inf Supply Mk IX	–	–	–	–	–	–	–	–	1	12	12	25
TOTAL	8	110	32	100	324	506	347	260	507	369	256	2,819

REFERENCES

Principal sources are abbreviated as follows:

BL(N)	The British Library Newspaper Library, Colindale, London NW9
Bod	Department of Special Collections and Western Manuscripts, Bodleian Library, University of Oxford
CAC	Churchill Archives Centre, Churchill College, Cambridge
HLRO	House of Lords Record Office, London SW1
IME	Institution of Mechanical Engineers, London SW1
IWM	Imperial War Museum, Lambeth, London SE1
LHC	Liddell Hart Centre for Military Archives, King's College, London WC2. (The Stern papers have been recatalogued and references below may have been revised.)
LTM	London Transport Museum, Covent Garden, London WC2
NMM	National Maritime Museum, Greenwich, London SE10
PRO	Public Record Office, Kew, Richmond, Surrey
SML	Science Museum Library, South Kensington, London SW7. (Courtesy, Trustees)
TM	Tank Museum, Bovington, Dorset

Extracts from Maj Gen Sir Ernest Dunlop Swinton's *Eyewitness* (1932), and Sir Albert Stern's *Tanks 1914–1918, The Log-Book of a Pioneer* (1919), are reproduced by permission of Hodder & Stoughton Limited.

Extracts from Sir Murray Fraser Sueter's *The Evolution of the Tank* (Hutchinson, 1937) are reproduced by permission of The Random House Group Limited.

1. THE TRACKLESS WASTE

1. War Office Mechanical Transport Committee, Annual Report, 1911–12, PRO, WO107/63.
2. Lord Hankey, *The Supreme Command*, 1st edn (2 vols, London, George Allen & Unwin, 1961), vol. 1: *1914–1918*, p. 231.
3. E.D. Swinton, *Report on Experiments to Employ Hydraulic Jets for the Attack of Trenches*, 9.11.1915, PRO, CAB42/5/24/1/G34.
4. Sir E.W. Moir, note of interview on Ministry of Munitions (henceforth MoM) file, 10.11.1922. PRO, MUN 9/26.
5. Von Donop, statement to the Royal Commission on the Private Manufacture of Arms. Report, *Sunday Express*, 11.10.1935.
6. L. Lloyd, *Report on Hornsby's Endless Chain Wheel Tractor*, 31.3.1906. TM, Army Trials to 1915.
7. Ibid.
8. A.R. Bellamy to War Office, 27.3.1922. TM, Hornsby papers.
9. MT Committee Report, 1910–11. Ray Hooley archive, Lincoln.
10. MT Committee Report, 1911–12. PRO, WO107/63.
11. R.M. Wik, *Benjamin Holt and Caterpillar Tracks and Combines* (American Society of Agricultural Engineers, 1984), pp. 83–4.
12. 'Good-bye to the Gun Horse', *The Commercial Motor*, 27.3.1913.
13. Wik, *Benjamin Holt*, pp. 86–8.
14. PRO, WO32/6782.

2. EARLY TRIALS – AND VERDICTS

1. Scott-Moncrieff to Maj Gen F.R. Bingham, 4.11.18, PRO, MUN5/210/1940/13.
2. Swinton, interview, *Oxford Mail*, 19.11.1942.
3. Tulloch, interview at MoM, 18.12.1918, PRO, MUN5/210/1940/27. Also Tulloch's letter of same date to Lloyd, PRO, MUN5/210/1940/13.
4. Tulloch to MoM, 18.12.1918, PRO, MUN5/210/1940/13. Also Maj Hardcastle, reference in *Royal Artillery Journal*, vol. XXXIV, p. 377 et seq.
5. Tulloch, interview at MoM, 18.12.1918, and Tulloch to Lloyd of MoM, 2.12.1918, PRO,

MUN5/210/1940/27. Also Tulloch to Lloyd, 18.12.1918. PRO, MUN5/210/1940/13.

6. Marriott to M. Jules Schnerb, 11.12.1918, PRO, MUN5/210/1940/27.

7. Swinton to the Royal Commission on Awards to Inventors (henceforward Royal Commission), 7.10.1919, *Minutes of the Proceedings*, p. 15, PRO, MUN5/210/1940/13.

8. Swinton to Hankey, 11.11.1914, LHC, Swinton Papers.

9. Swinton to Liddell Hart, 14.4.1948, LHC, LH9/28/62.

10. Hankey, evidence before the High Court, *The Times*, 27.11.1925.

11. Hankey to Liddell Hart, 3.4.1948, LHC, LH9/28/60.

12. Hankey, memorandum, 28.12.1914, PRO, MUN5/210/1940/13.

13. Hankey to Swinton, 13.10.1919, LHC, LH9/28/62.

14. Hankey to Liddell Hart, 3.4.1948, LHC, LH9/28/60.

15. Churchill to Asquith, 2.1.1915, Bod, MS Asquith 14, fols 7–10.

16. Asquith to Churchill, 6.11.1918, PRO, MUN5/210/1940/13.

17. Jackson to Scott-Moncrieff, 20.1.15, PRO, MUN5/210/1940/13.

18. Tulloch to Jackson, 19.1.1915, PRO, MUN5/210/1940/13.

19. Jackson to D of A, DFW and MGO, 20.1.1915, PRO, T173/34B.

20. Holden to DFW, 25.1.1915, PRO, T173/34B.

21. Haynes, report, 19.2.1915, PRO, T173/34B.

22. Jackson to von Donop, 23.2.1915, PRO, T173/34B.

23. Scott-Moncrieff to Holden, 1.3.1915, PRO, T173/34B.

24. Holden to Scott-Moncrieff, 1.3.1915, PRO, T173/34B.

25. Tulloch to MoM, 2.12.1918, PRO, MUN5/210/1940/27.

26. Tulloch to Swinton, 20.8.1915, PRO, MUN5/210/1940/13.

27. Scott-Moncrieff to Tank Awards Committee, 10.10.1918, PRO, MUN5/394.

28. C. Callwell, *The Experiences of a Dugout, 1914–1918* (London, Constable, 1920), pp. 118–19.

29. Crompton to Counsel, 1919, TM, 069.02 (41) Crompton/29.

30. *The Scotsman*, 27.11.1925.

31. Law Report, *The Times*, 27 November 1925.

32. Bacon to members of the Tanks Awards Committee, 1918 (undated *Record of Proceedings*, p. 16), PRO, MUN5/394.

33. W.S. Churchill, *The World Crisis* (4 vols, London, Thornton Butterworth, 1923, repr. 1927), vol. 2, pp. 72–3.

34. W.A. Tritton, *The Tank, Its Birth and Development* (Wm Foster & Co. Ltd, *c.* 1919), pp. 15–17. Also his evidence to Royal Commission, 1919, p. 148, para 2486A, PRO, MUN5/210/1940/33.

3. WINSTON'S CIRCUS

1. Samson, reports from Dunkirk, 1 September–31 October 1914, PRO, ADM116/1339.

2. Inspecting Captain of Aircraft, Sheerness, Report, September 1914, PRO, AIR1/346/15/227/1.

3. Wedgwood to DAD, 3.10.1914, PRO, ADM116/1339.

4. It is clear from an undated progress report that the armour was to be delivered to the chassis builders for erection by them, see TM, RNAS papers. This is datable to mid-September by reference to a memo DAD to ICA of 17.9.1914 which also confirms that the first eight chassis went to Sheerness for plating – PRO, AIR1/185/15/226/2. See also ICA to DAD, 11.9.1914, PRO, AIR1/185/15/226/2.

5. Maj Risk reported in October that the consignment had comprised six armoured cars, but Scarlett's despatch report went out 'same day' and stated five: ICA to DAD, 25.9.1914, PRO, AIR1/346/15/227/1.

6. Wedgwood's delivery: ICA to DAD, 27, 28 and 30.9.1914. Hetherington's delivery: ICA to DAD, 2.10.1914, PRO, AIR1/346/15/227/1.

7. Report, 5.10.1914, PRO, AIR1/358/15/227/14.

8. Samson's service records, entry 21.12.16, PRO, ADM273/2.

9. Murray Sueter, *The Evolution of the Tank* (London, Hutchinson & Co., 1937), pp. 32–3.

10. Samson, report, 30.11.1914, PRO, AIR1/671/17/128/2.

11. DAD to ICA, 12.10.1914, PRO, AIR1/185/15/226/2. Also Churchill's instructions to Admiralty Commands, 10.10.1914, PRO, Kitchener Papers, PRO30/57/72.

12. Rawlinson to Churchill, 14.10.1914, PRO, ADM116/1339.

13. Admiralty Paper, 30.6.1915, Sueter, *Evolution of the Tank*, p. 245.

14. Asquith to Churchill, 18.12.1914, CAC, CHAR26/1.

15. Kitchener to Churchill, 23.12.1914, PRO, Kitchener Papers, PRO30/57/72.

16. Churchill to Kitchener, *c.* 24.12.1914, PRO, Kitchener Papers, PRO30/57/72.

17. MS draft, undated and unsigned, PRO, Kitchener Papers, PRO30/57/72.
18. Asquith to Churchill, 17.2.1915, CAC, CHAR13/47.
19. Asquith to Venetia Stanley, 18.2.1915, CAC, Montagu Papers.
20. Churchill to Kitchener, 19.2.1915, PRO, Kitchener Papers, PRO30/57/72.
21. Wedgwood to Churchill, 19.2.15, CAC, CHAR13/47/81.
22. PRO, MUN4/3460. BT31/18780/102286. ADM1/8403/428.

4. PRELIMINARIES TO A DINNER PARTY

1. Sueter, *Evolution of the Tank*, p. 53.
2. Admiralty press release, 28.7.1915, PRO, ADM1/8428/215.
3. Delacombe to Royal Commission, *Proceedings*, para. 1131. Hetherington said he made this remark at another time and disputed Delacombe's ability to recall it, paras 1242–5, PRO, MUN5/210/1940/13.
4. *Aeronautics Journal*, July 1911.
5. R.F. Macfie, report, 5.11.1914, TM, Macfie papers.
6. Air Station daily report, 16.11.1914, PRO, AIR1/188/15/226/5.
7. Air Station Vehicle Return, 16 November and 10 December 1914, PRO, AIR1/188/15/226/5.
8. Air Station Vehicle Return, 16.11.1914, records this as 'Seabrook lorry fitted with 3-pdr arrived yesterday evening from Huntingdon', PRO, AIR1/188/15/226/5.
9. Westminster to Churchill, letter, 18.4.1915, CAC, CHAR13/51/21–22.
10. Sueter, *Evolution of the Tank*, p. 53.
11. Churchill to Tudor, 18.1.15, PRO, T173/34B/ Part 2.
12. Sueter, *Evolution of the Tank*, pp. 55–6.
13. Ibid. p. 57.
14. 'Proposed [*sic*] to Build a New Type of Gun Carrying War Machine', unsigned undated T/S in Ministry of Munitions file, PRO, MUN5/210/1940/13 and 22. In his *The Evolution of the Tank*, p. 51, Sueter confirms his authorship saying he sent it to Churchill 'early in January'. This was contradicted by Hetherington and Briggs who indicated an end of January date to the Royal Commission in 1919; see esp. paras 629–30 and 1800 of the *Proceedings*. They said that Adm Scott dismissed the idea in the first week of February. As Churchill expected immediate action, Scott was

unlikely to have delayed some three weeks before responding. Sueter's memoirs are unreliable concerning the dates of events at this period.
15. Churchill, obituary for the Duke, *The Times*, 22.7.1953.
16. Churchill to Royal Commission, *Proceedings*, para. 33. Also his written statement to the Commission, 1.9.1919, PRO, MUN5/394.
17. Hetherington, statement, 28.11.1918, PRO, MUN5/210/1940/13.
18. Churchill to Royal Commission, *Proceedings*, para. 127.
19. Churchill to DCIGS, minutes, 29.9.1917, LHC, Stern papers 1/4/2.
20. Sueter to Royal Commission. *Proceedings*, paras 441–453.
21. Sueter, *Evolution of the Tank*, p. 66.
22. Churchill to Royal Commission, *Proceedings*, para. 35. Also his written statement to the Commission, 1.9.1919, PRO, MUN5/394.

5. THE SILENT SERVICE

1. Crompton, diary, 30.4.1915, SML, ARCH CRO/B130 (original diary). Incomplete copies at PRO, T173/181 and TM, Crompton papers, but some transcripts are unreliable.
2. Crompton to Holden, 7.9.1914, TM, Crompton papers.
3. Crompton, diary, 23.10.1914, SML, ARCH CRO/B130.
4. Crompton to Tanks Awards Committee, 'Proceedings', 18.12.1918, PRO, MUN5/394.
5. Crompton to Long, 19.2.1915, TM, 069.02/(41) Crompton 35.
6. Crompton, diary, 19.2.1915, SML, ARCH CRO/B130.
7. Ibid.
8. Mansell to von Donop, 20.5.1915, confirms Churchill's placing and later cancellation of order, PRO, MUN5/210/1940/13. Also W.S. Churchill, *The World Crisis*, 2nd edn (4 vols, London, Thornton Butterworth, 1923), vol. 2, *1915*, p. 73, in which Churchill confirms the date of placement of the order. Also *A History of the Ministry of Munitions*, internal pub. (14 vols, London, Ministry of Munitions, 1920), vol. XII: *The Supply of Munitions*, pt 3: *Tanks*, p. 7, which confirms Churchill's cancellation on 20 February.
9. Churchill, undated draft statement to Royal Commission on Awards to Inventors, 1919, CAC, CHAR2/109.
10. Crompton, 'A Self-Moving Armoured Fort for the Attack and Destruction of Enemy's Trenches', 22.2.1915, PRO, MUN5/210/1940/22.

11. Churchill, holograph annotation, 24.2.1915, PRO, ADM116/1339.
12. Crompton, paper, 'Admiralty Land-Ships', 11.6.1915, LHC, Stern papers.
13. Legros, draft proof of evidence to his solicitor H.C. Witt, 20.9.1919, TM, 069.02 (41) Crompton 1–39.
14. Tritton to Tanks Awards Committee, 1.11.1918, PRO, T173/776.
15. Sueter, *Evolution of the Tank*, p. 69.
16. Addendum to Minutes of meeting, 24.3.1915, PRO, ADM116/1339.
17. Brig Gen Holden in evidence at Capt Bentley's High Court action, Law Report, *The Times*, 27.11.1925.
18. Crompton's diary entry for 12 April records 'Hetherington . . . went to War Office about Armour', PRO, T173/181.
19. Crompton, reply to his solicitor Mr R. Witt, 9.9.1919, TM, 069/02 (41) Crompton 1–39.
20. Crompton to Palmer, 6.5.1915, TM, 089.02(41) Crompton 35.
21. Crompton to Smith-Dorrien, 30.4.1915, PRO, T173/34B.
22. Crompton, diary, 30.4.1915, SML, ARCH CRO/B130.
23. Sueter to Hetherington and Crompton, 30.3.1915, PRO, T173/34B.
24. Crompton to E.W. Moir, MoM, 30.7.1915, PRO, T173/34B.
25. Tritton to Crompton, 5.6.1915, LHC, Stern 1/6/1–82.
26. Tritton to Capt Moore Williams, Secretary, Tanks Awards Committee, 10.7.1918, TM, 623.438 (41) Tank Design/53.
27. Crompton to d'Eyncourt, 20 May 1915, PRO, T173/34B.
28. Crompton to Tanks Awards Committee, 18.12.1918, PRO, MUN5/394.

6. COMBINED OPERATIONS?

1. Tritton to Legros, at Lincoln, 2.3.1915. Legros' draft proof of evidence to his solicitor Mr H.C. Witt, 20.9.1919. TM, 069.02 (41) Crompton 1–39.
2. Sueter, *Evolution of the Tank*, p. 244.
3. Metropolitan CWF Co., letters of 10 May and 11 June 1915 to MoM, PRO, T173/34B.
4. Tudor to Scott-Moncrieff, 30.5.1915, PRO, T173/34B.
5. Scott-Moncrieff to von Donop, 10.6.1915, PRO, T173/34B.
6. The substance of Scott-Moncrieff's letter is quoted in the agenda for a DNC's Committee meeting held 22.6.1915. PRO, T173/34B.

7. Swinton to CGS at GHQ, 1.6.15, PRO, T173/34B.
8. Fowke to Sub-Chief Gen Staff, 3.6.1915, PRO, MUN5/210/1940/13.
9. Swinton to Sub-Chief Gen Staff, 4.6.1915, PRO, T173/463.
10. Cavan to Swinton, 12.6.1915, PRO, WO158/831.
11. Churchill, *World Crisis*, vol 2, pp. 404–5.
12. Scott-Moncrieff to d'Eyncourt, *c.* 30.6.1915, PRO, MUN5/210/1940/22.
13. Boothby to Crompton, undated letter *c.* June 1915, TM, 069.02 (41) Crompton 1–39.
14. Wilson, Proof of Evidence to Royal Commission, undated but *c.* September 1919, TM, Wilson papers.
15. Tritton to Stern, telegram 27.7.1915, TM, Tritton papers. See also Tritton to Royal Commission, 21.10.1919, *Proceedings*, p. 150, para. 2536.
16. Tritton to d'Eyncourt, criticising Crompton's chaintrack design, 8.9.16, NMM, DEY/50.
17. *The Tank. Its Birth and Development* (Wm Foster & Co. Ltd., *c.* 1919), p. 18.
18. Lt Col Sir Albert Stern, *Tanks 1914–1918. The Logbook of a Pioneer* (London, Hodder & Stoughton, 1919), pp. 41–2.

7. LANDSHIPS

1. *Tank. Birth and Development* (Foster), p. 22.
2. Crompton to Lord Moulton's Tanks Awards Committee, 18.12.1918, PRO, MUN5/394.
3. Crompton to d'Eyncourt, 6.8.1915, PRO, T173/34B.
4. Field, note written aboard *Lapland*, 13.8.1915, PRO, T173/218.
5. Churchill, in cross-examination before the Royal Commission on Awards to Inventors, 7.10.1919, *Minutes of the Proceedings*, paras 199–200, PRO, MUN5/210/1940/13.
6. Crompton, to the Tanks Awards Committee, 18.12.1918, PRO, MUN5/394.
7. D'Eyncourt to Swinton, 28.9.1915, NMM, DEY/45.
8. Macfie to Boothby, 13.4.1915, PRO, T173/34B.
9. Macfie's name is pencilled on the back of the drawing found among Stern's papers, LHC, Stern 1/19/5 and 1/19/1 (orig. 016/20).
10. Stern, to the Tanks Awards Committee, 10.10.1918, PRO, MUN5/394.
11. Macfie, letter to Stern, 8.12.1916, Bod, MS Addison dep. c56, fols 28–9.
12. Churchill, minute of 21.10.1915, PRO, ADM/116/1339.
13. Von Donop, minute to Lt Gen Sir J. Wolfe-Murray, CIGS, 19.10.1915, PRO, T173/34B.

14. Moir to Lloyd George, 16.10.1915, PRO, MUN5/43/263/8/7.
15. Swinton to War Office, 13.8.1915, PRO, T173/34B.
16. Glasfurd, 'A Suggestion for Neutralising the Power of the Trench and Obstacle', 23.9.1915 (Foreign Office pub.), HLRO, (LLG) D10/6/2.
17. Rose to Swinton, undated but *c.* September 1915, PRO, CAB17/120B.
18. Field, Statement of Claim to the Royal Commission, 1919, PRO, T173/218.
19. Tritton to d'Eyncourt, *Tank. Birth and Development*, (Foster), p. 22. Tritton confirmed the track was co-designed with Wilson; see Tritton to the Royal Commission, 21.10.1919, p. 153, para. 2638, PRO, T173/218.
20. Swinton, letter to Liddell Hart, 30.4.1948, LHC, L HART 9/28/62.
21. Tritton, marginalia in his personal copy of Col J.F.C. Fuller's *Tanks in the Great War* (London, John Murray, 1920), p. 29, TM library.
22. Sgt Chadwick to Capt Basil Liddell Hart, May 1967, LHC, Liddell Hart papers.
23. Churchill, 'Variants of the Offensive', memorandum to Sir John French, 4.12.1915. CID paper 7.1.1916, PRO, CAB42/7/4/6/2/229B.
24. D'Eyncourt, Admiralty minute, 4.11.1915, PRO, ADM116/1339.
25. E.D. Swinton, *Eyewitness* (London, Hodder & Stoughton, 1932), p. 187.

8. Preparations for Battle

1. Churchill, letter to Capt Sir Archibald Sinclair, Bt, 29.12.1917, Thurso papers. Reproduced with permission of Curtis Brown Ltd, London, on behalf of the Estate of Sir Winston S. Churchill. Copyright Winston S. Churchill.
2. Swinton, letter to *The Royal Tank Corps Journal*, 1937. Swinton added that Tritton had recently confirmed to him these details of his discussion with Kitchener, TM, archives.
3. Swinton, *Eyewitness*, p. 196.
4. David Lloyd George, *War Memoirs of David Lloyd George*, 1st edn (6 vols, London, Ivor Nicholson & Watson, 1933), vol. 2, pp. 643–4.
5. FM Sir William Robertson, *From Private to Field-Marshal* (London, Constable & Co., 1921), p. 268.
6. War Committee, meeting 3.2.1916, Secretary's Notes No. 26, p. 13, PRO, CAB42/8/22/3/2.
7. D'Eyncourt to Churchill, 14.2.1916, PRO, ADM116/1339.
8. Tritton, initialled holograph marginal note on his copy of Fuller's *Tanks in the Great War*, TM archive.
9. Haig to War Office, 9.2.1916, PRO, WO32/5754.
10. Swinton to War Office, 8.2.1916, PRO, MUN5/210/1940/13.
11. Lloyd George, unsigned undated fragment of a memoir, probably for the Ministry of Munitions historian, PRO, MUN9/37.
12. T. Pidgeon, *The Tanks at Flers* (2 vols, Cobham, Surrey, Fairmile Books, 1995), vol. 1, p. 30.
13. Swinton, *Eyewitness*, p. 234.
14. Hankey to Sir Wm Robertson, 20.4.1916, PRO, CAB17/167.
15. Stephen Roskill, *Hankey, Man of Secrets* (2 vols, London, Collins, 1970), vol. 1, *1877–1918*, p. 266.
16. Burnett Stuart to Bird, 7.6.1916, PRO, WO158/843.
17. The Tank Supply Committee initially decided (15 May) to number male tanks 500–74 and females 800–74. This was changed on 22 May to 701–75 and 501–75 respectively. LHC, Stern 1/3/2.
18. Kiggell to War Office, 1.5.1916, PRO, WO32/5754.
19. Robertson to Haig, 25.7.1916, PRO, WO158/843.
20. Burnett Stuart to Bird, 10.7.1916, PRO, MUN4/4979.
21. Swinton placed the order with Stern on 24 July. War Office confirmed by letter to MoM, 25 July. PRO, MUN4/2790.
22. Stern, questioned by Mr G. Cunningham, Ministry of Supply, 23.5.1942, PRO, AVIA22/3336.
23. Stern to Wilson, 1.9.1916, TM, box 069.02(41) Wilson.
24. Wilson, 4.9.1916, TM, box 069.02(41) Wilson.
25. Stern to Montagu, 3.8.1916, PRO, MUN4/4979 (folder 15).
26. Whigham to Kiggell, 25.8.1916, PRO, WO158/843.
27. Butler to Whigham, 26.8.1916, PRO, WO32/5754.
28. Burnett Stuart to Butler, 10.8.1916, PRO, WO158/843.

9. First Blood

1. Elles to GHQ, 31.12.1916, PRO, WO158/844.
2. Letter, 17.4.1917, Anne Williamson, *A Patriot's Progress* (Stroud, Sutton, 1998), p. 97.
3. For much information on individual tank actions on 15/16 September the author is indebted to Trevor Pidgeon's *Tanks at Flers*.
4. GHQ War Diary, 10.30 hrs 15.9.1916, PRO, WO95/7. For detailed account of Hastie's movements see *Tanks at Flers*, vol. 1, pp. 166–9.

5. *The Times*, report, 25.10.1916.
6. Stern, *Tanks 1914–1918*, p. 96.
7. Bacon, letter to *Daily Telegraph*, 30.6.1933.
8. Official record of meeting, 19/20.9.1916, PRO, WO158/836.
9. Butler to Elles, 22.9.1916, PRO, WO158/836.
10. Butler to Whigham, 25.9.1916, PRO, WO158/836.
11. War Office to MoM, 26.9.1916, PRO, MUN4/2790.
12. Record of 188th meeting of the Army Council, 27.9.1916, para. 121/8797, PRO, WO163/21.
13. War Office to MoM, 30.9.1916, PRO, MUN4/2790.
14. MoM Contracts Dept, review of negotiations with MCWF, *c*. August 1917, PRO, MUN4/4175.
15. F. Stevenson, private diary, 23.5.1919, HLRO, F. Stevenson papers.
16. *History of the Ministry of Munitions*, vol. XII, pt 3: p. 37.
17. Haig to War Office, 2.10.1916, PRO, WO158/836.
18. Parliamentary report, *The Times*, 13.10.1916.
19. Tritton to d'Eyncourt, 13.10.1916, NMM, d'Eyncourt papers.
20. D'Eyncourt to Balfour, 18.9.1916, PRO, ADM116/1339.
21. Butler to Whigham, 25.9.1916, PRO, WO158/836.
22. Steedman, memoir, PRO, WO95/116.
23. Whigham to Butler, 28.9.1916, PRO, WO158/836.
24. D'Eyncourt, draft memorandum intended for Lloyd George and Gen Robertson, 6.10.1916, PRO, MUN5/210/1940/22.
25. *History of the MoM*, vol. XII, pt 3, p. 43.
26. Kiggell, 5.10.1916, NMM, DEY/42. See also 'Memorandum on the Output of Tanks', MoM, 10.3.1917, PRO, MUN4/2790.
27. War Office to MoM, 30.11.1916, PRO, MUN4/2796.
28. From record of Army/Ministry of Munitions meeting, 1.5.1917, LHC, Stern 1/4/2.
29. Patent 17801/1916.
30. Fowler's light machine: record of MWSD meeting, 6.11.1916, LHC, Stern papers. Also Wilson to Stern, 2.12.1916, TM: 069.02(41) Wilson A1–A15. For the call for a supply tank: minutes of a meeting at the War Office, 1.5.1917, PRO, MUN4/2790 and LHC, Stern 1/4/2. For 'Fowlers Supply Tank': minutes of MWSD Experiments Committee, 22.5.1917; record of MWSD meeting with AEC and Fowler's, 7.9.1917; and Stern's reference to 'Medium A', report, 7.9.1917, see LHC, Stern 1/M/9.
31. 'Major Greg suggested the design of the Gun Carrier' – inscription on a MWD Design Dept commemorative card dated 16.12.1918, TM, 438.(41) Design & Dev't 84-on, Piece 63.
32. War Office to Controller of Munitions Inventions, MoM, 2 May 1916, PRO, MUN7/280.
33. Metropolitan is recorded specifically as builder of the first gun carrier in an undated unattributable printed sheet 'Table of Main Dimensions and Particulars of Tanks' found among d'Eyncourt's official papers. It names Kitson's as principal makers, and the chart has the appearance of a MoM publication, NMM, DEY/60.
34. Elles to GHQ, 31.12.1916, PRO, WO158/8449.

10. Divisions

1. Searle to Elles, 24.3.1917, PRO, WO158/838.
2. Crompton to Goold-Adams, 17.6.1916, PRO, MUN7/280.
3. Stern confirms this and implies that all 100 of Mks II and III were so plated. Stern, *Tanks 1914–1918*, p. 148.
4. Anley to Director of Artillery, 24.2.1916, PRO, WO158/845.
5. Stern to Addison, 12.3.1917, LHC, Stern papers.
6. T.M. Taylor, MoM Labour Dept, to Kellaway, 27.2.1917, PRO, MUN4/2791.
7. WO to MoM, 21.3.1917, PRO, MUN4/2791.
8. Tritton to Capt Moore Williams, 10.7.1918, TM, Tritton papers.
9. MWSD report to Stern, 21.12.1916, PRO, MUN4/5219.
10. Stern to Addison, 7.3.1917, Bod, MS Addison dep. C56.
11. Stern to Layton, 1.9.1916, PRO, MUN4/2790.
12. Stern to Layton, MoM, 24.2.1917, PRO, MUN4/2791.
13. Ibid. Also Stern to Furse, 7.5.1917, LHC, Stern 1/4/2. Also Stern, *Tanks 1914–1918*, p. 150.
14. Searle to Elles, 24.3.1917, PRO, WO158/838.
15. Elles to Anley, 30.3.1917, PRO, WO158/845.
16. Haig to Robertson, 25.4.1917, PRO, WO158/845.
17. WO to MoM, 9.5.1917 and MoM internal memoranda of 12 May, PRO, MUN4/2790.
18. Stern to Lloyd George, 2.7.1917, LHC, Stern papers. Also Stern, *Tanks 1914–1918*, pp. 160–2.
19. Legros, presidential address to the IAE, 11.10.1916, IME, Legros papers.
20. Capper's account to War Office, 25.8.1917, PRO, MUN4/2790.
21. Record of MWSD meeting with Metropolitan, 22.8.1917, LHC, Stern 1/M/9.
22. Letter, 22.1.1917, PRO, WO/158/845.

23. Tritton, conference at Lincoln, 30.4.1917, PRO, MUN4/2790.
24. Stern to Churchill, 4.9.1917, PRO, MUN5/211/1940/37.
25. Minutes of conference on tank policy, 28.9.1917, PRO, WO158/818.
26. H. Ricardo, *Memories and Machines* (Shoreham, Sussex, Ricardo Consulting Engineers Ltd, 1990), p. 177.
27. TM, Wilson papers.
28. Duckham to Churchill, 'Memorandum on the Position of Tank Supply', 4.10.1917, LHC, Stern papers.
29. Stern to Leslie Burgin, Minister of Supply, 10.4.1940, Bod, Cherwell G364/9.
30. Stern to Hanson, 16.8.1917, PRO, MUN4/4175.
31. MoM Warfare Group, minutes, 8.7.1918, PRO, MUN4/4979.
32. Stern to Hanson, 23.8.1917, LHC, Stern 1/13/1–111.
33. Hamond, letter to Capt Bill Arnold, October 1917, LHC, L Hart 9/28/63–65.

11. CRISIS

1. Ricardo to Lord Hankey, 13.2.1942, PRO, CAB63/166.
2. Elles to War Office, holograph footnote to his 'Note on the proceedings of Conference', 7.10.1917, PRO, WO158/859.
3. D'Eyncourt to Addison, 4.4.1917, Bod, MS Addison dep. c.56, fols 157–8.
4. Addison to Lloyd George, 27.4.1917, Bod, MS Addison dep. c.56, fols 159–60.
5. Note on MoM file, PRO, MUN4/1235.
6. Churchill to Layton at MoM, 3.8.1917, PRO, MUN5/211/1940/37.
7. Stern, memorandum, 4.9.17, PRO, MUN5/211/1940/37.
8. Meeting of the Munitions Council Committee on Tanks, 5.9.1917 (transcript), CAC, CHAR15/86A.
9. Churchill to Lloyd George, 9.9.1917, HLRO, LG/F/8/1/11.
10. Elles to War Office, 7.10.1917, PRO, WO158/859.
11. Stern to Lloyd George, 15.10.1917, TM, 069.02(41) Stern/5. Also Stern, *Tanks 1914–1918*, pp. 175–6.
12. Ibid. See also Stern's note of interview with Duckham, 15.10.1917, LHC, Stern 1/1/1–8.
13. Stern, note of interview with Churchill, 16.10.1917, LHC, Stern 1/1/1–8.
14. Stern to Mr Graham-Cunningham, Ministry of Supply, 28.5.1942, PRO, AVIA22/3336.
15. John and David Stern, interviewed by the author 22.2.1999.
16. Ricardo to Lord Hankey, 13.2.1942, PRO, CAB63/166.
17. Lord Weir to Mr Graham-Cunningham, Ministry of Supply, 4.6.1942, PRO, AVIA22/3336.
18. Elles to Stern, 26.11.1917. Stern, *Tanks 1914–1918*, p. 195.

12. THE PRODUCTION BATTLEFIELD . . .

1. Churchill, 'Munitions Programme 1919,' 5.3.1918, Trinity College Library, Cambridge, Layton papers, box 29/16.
2. Stern to Churchill, 29.10.1917, CAC, CHAR15/86A/32.
3. D'Eyncourt, draft memorandum, 24.11.1917, NMM, DEY/43 (Part 2). Also his comments on response of General Staff, 15.1.1918, NMM, DEY/53.
4. War Office General Staff to Prime Minister, 28.12.1917, NMM, DEY/53. Also PRO, WO32/5933 Copy 1.
5. J.F.C. Fuller, *Memoirs of an Unconventional Soldier* (London, Ivor Nicholson & Watson, 1936), p. 201.
6. Capper, 'Lessons from the Cambrai Battle', 19.12.1917, PRO, WO32/5933.
7. Capper, letter to Elles, 18.5.1918, PRO, WO158/859.
8. D. Fletcher, *The British Tanks 1915–19* (Marlborough, Wilts, The Crowood Press, 2001), p. 140.
9. Moore to d'Eyncourt, 18.12.1917, NMM, DEY/43 (Part 2).
10. Unsigned undated typescript in Capper's own file responding to a memorandum of 27.5.1918 from Stern and d'Eyncourt, PRO, WO158/826.
11. Elles to Capper, 24.2.1918, PRO, WO158/859.
12. Moore to Duckham, 21.2.1918, PRO, MUN5/211/1940/37.
13. War Office to MoM, undated and unsent draft, late February 1918, PRO, WO32/9288.
14. Lord Derby, minute 13, 8.3.1918, PRO, WO32/9288.
15. Minutes on War Office file, PRO, WO32/9288.
16. Stern, memorandum, 14.2.1918, CAC, CHAR 15/86A/25.

17. Churchill, 'Munitions Programme 1919',
    5.3.1918, Trinity College Library, Cambridge,
    Layton papers, box 29/16.
18. Fuller to Churchill, undated memorandum
    relating to forthcoming meeting of War
    Cabinet on 8.3.1918, CAC, CHAR
    15/86B/111–112.
19. Minutes of conference at GHQ, 10.6.1918, PRO,
    MUN5/210/1940/21.

13. . . . AND A BODY COUNT

1. Harington to Sackville-West, 21.5.1918, PRO,
   CAB25/12.
2. Ibid.
3. Sackville-West to Gen Dawnay, GHQ, 16.5.1918,
   PRO, CAB25/12.
4. Dawnay to Sackville-West, 26.5.1918, PRO,
   CAB25/12.
5. Haig to War Office, draft dated June 1918, PRO,
   WO158/830.
6. Capper to Harington, minutes 24 and 26A, 11 and
   14.5.1918, PRO, WO32/9288.
7. Stern to Duckham, 6.5.1918, LHC Stern papers.
8. D'Eyncourt to Lloyd George, 30.7.1918, NMM,
   DEY/44.
9. Fuller, *Unconventional Soldier*, p. 240.
10. Churchill to Lloyd George, 22.7.1918, House of
    Lords (D. Ll. G.) F/8/2/29.
11. Report from O&A Supply Section to Stern,
    12.11.1918, PRO, MUN4/5194.
12. Perry, cable to MoM, 1.10.1918, PRO,
    MUN4/6400.
13. Elles to Gen Edmonds, Official Historian, 4.9.1934,
    PRO, CAB45/200.

14. POWER DOWN

1. G. MacLeod Ross, 'The Utility of the Tank', *RUSI
   Journal*, 1931.
2. Quoted by Sir Basil Liddell Hart, *The Tanks – The
   History of the Royal Tank Regiment and its
   Predecessors 1914–1945* (2 vols, London,
   Cassell, 1959), vol. 1. p. 201.
3. Vickers Ltd, letter to Maclean, 21.10.1918, PRO,
   MUN4/5201. Also MWEE vehicle index, entry
   31.8.1921, PRO, WO194/1.

15. BUT WHO INVENTED THE TANK?

1. Swinton, letter to Sir Basil Liddell Hart,
   24.2.1948, LHC, L Hart papers.
2. H.G. Wells, letter to *The Listener*, 14.5.1941. See
   also his letter of retraction, 31.7.1941.
3. Churchill, memorandum of 25.9.1917, PRO,
   MUN5/210/1940/2.
4. Findings of the Royal Commission, presented
   17 November, published 28 November 1919,
   PRO, T173/16.
5. Churchill, written statement to the Royal
   Commission, 1.9.1919, PRO, MUN5/394.
6. Production data and valuations from Mr Justice
   Sargant's briefing papers, October 1919, PRO,
   T173/34B.
7. Davidson, 9.12.1912, PRO, T173/195.
8. Royal Commission, *Proceedings*,
   20.10.1919, paras 2264, 2271, PRO,
   MUN5/210/1940/33.
9. G.W.D. Breadon to Minister for War, 19.9.1914,
   CAC, CHAR2/143–5.
10. Liddell Hart, *The Tanks*, vol. 1, p. 224.

SELECTED BIBLIOGRAPHY

PRIMARY SOURCES

PUBLIC RECORD OFFICE, KEW
Private papers, official correspondence, minutes, reports
Admiralty 1914–16: ADM series
Cabinet papers 1914–19: CAB series
HM Treasury 1919: T series
Kitchener papers: 30/57/72
Ministry of Munitions 1915–20: MUN series
Ministry of Supply, 1939–43: AVIA series
Royal Naval Air Service 1914–15: AIR and ADM series
War Office 1900–23: WO series

Other contemporary material
'A History of the Ministry of Munitions', 14 vols,
    Ministry of Munitions, 1920, MUN5/321A (reprinted
    by Harvester Microform Press, Sussex, in 12 vols,
    1976)
'History of Heavy Section Machine Gun Corps',
    WO158/804
'History of Inspection & Progress, Mechanical Warfare
    Supplies Dept', MUN5/42/263/71/3
'History of Supply Branch, Mechanical Warfare
    Department', MUN5/391/1940/6
'History of Tank Corps Workshops', WO158/799
'History of 20 Squadron Royal Naval Armoured Cars',
    MUN5/391/1940/5
'History, Tank Corps Depot, Bovington/Wareham',
    WO158/810
'History, Training and Reinforcement Depot, France',
    WO158/810
'Origin of the Tank Committee', WO158/812
'Proceedings', Royal Commission on Awards to
    Inventors, 7–21 October 1919, MUN5/210/1940/33
'Tanks and Ancillary Vehicles 1915–1918', WO194/54

THE TANK MUSEUM, BOVINGTON, DORSET
Private papers, official correspondence, minutes, reports
Col R.E.B. Crompton; Col N.M. Dillon; Maj T.G.
    Hetherington; Col P. Johnson; Maj E.R. Parsons; Maj
    W.G.Wilson

Other contemporary material
Clark, Col C.W., 'A Record of memories of Col Charles
    Willoughby Clark', 069.02(41) W. Clark/1
Diplock's Pedrail, 623.437.425(41)
Hornsby tractors, 623.437.425(41)
Lanning, T.E., memoir, tank workshops,
    RH86.TC/3398
Motor Transport Committee, reports, 1902–14,
    623.438(42)
Tank Design and Development, papers, 1915–23,
    623.438(41)
Tank types, 1915–23, 623.438.3(41)
'War History of Central Workshops', RH86/TC 104.06
'Weekly Tank Notes' 1918–19, RH86/TC/3581

LIDDELL HART CENTRE FOR MILITARY ARCHIVES, KING'S COLLEGE, LONDON
Private papers, official correspondence, minutes, reports
Maj Gen Sir John E. Capper; Maj Gen John F.C. Fuller;
    Capt Sir Basil H. Liddell Hart; Lt Col Sir Albert G.
    Stern; Maj Gen Sir E.D. Swinton; Maj W.G. Wilson

Other contemporary material
Cambrai, precis for a battlefield tour by Royal Tank
    Corps officers, 1935, LH 15/12/20
Johnson, Lt Col P.H., 'Mechanical Development of Tanks
    in France, and the medium D', LH9/28/110
Stern, Lt Col Sir Albert, 'Mechanical Warfare – A
    Summary of British Tank Development 1914–1918',
    Stern 1/24
Windle, Col C.E., 'Notes on the Machine Gun Corps
    (Heavy Branch) and Tank Corps in 1917 and 1918',
    Windle papers

CHURCHILL ARCHIVES CENTRE, CHURCHILL COLLEGE, CAMBRIDGE
Sir Winston Churchill papers
Edwin Montagu papers

THE BODLEIAN LIBRARY, OXFORD
Lord Addison papers
Lord Asquith papers

NUFFIELD COLLEGE, OXFORD
Lord Cherwell papers
Lord Mottistone papers

UNIVERSITY OF GLASGOW
Wm Beardmore & Co. Ltd records
R.F. Macfie papers
Mirrlees, Watson & Co. Ltd, workshop records
North British Locomotive Co. Ltd, records

HOUSE OF LORDS LIBRARY
D. Lloyd George papers
Frances Stevenson diaries

IMPERIAL WAR MUSEUM
Beall, R.E., 'The Green Fields Beyond', 82/22/1
Churchill, Maj E.F., memoir, 83/23/1
Denison, D.G., 'Reminiscences, P/191
Hetherington, Gp Capt T.G., papers, 94/40/1
Hickey, Lt B.G.L., papers, 96/48/1
Hotblack, Maj Gen F.E., papers, 76/136/1
Powell-Chandler, Capt W.R., memoir, 90/28/1
Thompson, Capt G.E.V., memoir, 75/36/1
Viner, G.L.M., letter, 18.9.1916, 85/11/1

ROYAL AIR FORCE MUSEUM, HENDON
Wg Cdr F.L.M. Boothby papers
Rear Adm Sir Murray Sueter papers

INSTITUTION OF MECHANICAL ENGINEERS, LONDON
Papers relating to membership
Proceedings of the Institution
Minutes of the Council, Institution of Automobile
   Engineers

LINCOLNSHIRE ARCHIVES, LINCOLN
Wm Foster & Co. Ltd, records
Wm Rigby papers

OTHER PRIMARY SOURCES
Armstrong, Whitworth & Co. Ltd, company
   records, Tyne & Wear Archives, Newcastle
   upon Tyne

Maj E.E. Baguley, Baguley–Drewry Co. Ltd, company
   records, Staffordshire County Record Office, Stafford
Col R.E.B. Crompton papers, Science Museum Library,
   London
Sir E.T. d'Eyncourt papers, National Maritime Museum,
   Greenwich
Col W.C. Dumble service records, National Archives of
   Canada, Ottawa
Lord Layton papers, Trinity College Library, Cambridge
London General Omnibus Co., board minutes, London
   Metropolitan Archives, EC1
Roadless Traction Co. Ltd, company magazines, Ven
   Dodge, Guildford
Wm Foster & Co. Ltd, company and associated papers,
   Ray Hooley, Lincoln Tank Group
Ricardo tank engines, reports, Ricardo Consulting
   Engineers Ltd, Shoreham, Sussex

SECONDARY SOURCES

BOOKS
Please note that where the place of publication is unstated,
   it is London.

Personal accounts of the pioneers and fighting men
Anon., (Charteris, Capt The Hon E.E), *H.Q. Tanks*
   1917–1918, privately printed, 1920
Bacon, Adm Sir R., *From 1900 Onwards*, Hutchinson,
   1940
Baker–Carr, Brig Gen C.D., *From Chauffeur to Brigadier*,
   Ernest Benn, 1930
Browne, Capt D.G., *The Tank in Action*, Wm Blackwood,
   1920
Churchill, Winston S., *The World Crisis*, 4 vols,
   Thornton Butterworth, 1923–7
Crompton, Col R.E., *Reminiscences*, Constable, 1928
Foot, S., *Three Lives*, Wm Heinemann, 1934
—, with E. Wood, *Tank Tales*, Cassell, 1919
Fuller, Maj Gen J.F.C., *Tanks in the Great War*
   1914–1918, John Murray, 1920
—, *Memoirs of an Unconventional Soldier*, Ivor Nicholson
   & Watson, 1936
Haigh, Capt R., *Life in a Tank*, Boston, Mass, USA,
   Houghton Mifflin, 1918
Hankey, Lord, *The Supreme Command, 1914–1918*,
   2 vols, Geo. Allen & Unwin, 1961
Henriques, B.L.Q., *The Indiscretions of a Warden*,
   Methuen, 1937
Hickey, Capt D.E., *Rolling into Action; Memoirs of a Tank
   Corps Section Commander*, Hutchinson, 1936
Jenkin, A., *A Tank Driver's Experiences*, Elliot Stock, 1922
Lloyd George, David, *War Memoirs*, 6 vols, Ivor
   Nicholson & Watson, 1933–6

Mitchell, F., *Tank Warfare. The Story of the Tanks in the Great War*, Nelson, 1933

Ricardo, Sir Harry, *Memories and Machines*, Constable, 1968

Stern, Lt Col Sir Albert, *Tanks 1914–1918, the Log–book of a Pioneer*, Hodder & Stoughton, 1919

Sueter, Rear Adm Sir Murray, *Airmen or Noahs*, Pitman, 1928

—, *The Evolution of the Tank; a Record of Royal Naval Air Service Caterpillar Experiments*, Hutchinson, 1937

Swinton, Maj Gen Sir Ernest, *Eyewitness*, Hodder & Stoughton, 1932

— *Over my Shoulder*, Oxford, George Ronald, 1951

Watson, Maj W.H.L., *A Company of Tanks*, Wm Blackwood, 1920

Wilson, C.M. (compiler), *Fighting Tanks*, Seeley, Service, 1929

Company histories

Anon., *An Account of the Manufactures of the North British Locomotive Co. Ltd during the Period of the War 1914–1919*, pub. by the company, c. 1920

Anon., *Birth of the Crawler*, USA, The Caterpillar Tractor Company, 1954

Frost, Geo. H., *Munitions of War. A Record of the Work of the BSA and Daimler Companies during the World War 1914–1918*, pub. by the companies c. 1920

Gibbard, S., *Roadless, the Story of Roadless Traction from Tracks to Tractors*, Ipswich, Farming Press, 1996

Lane, M., *The Story of the Wellington Foundry, Lincoln*, Unicorn Press, 1997

Newman, B., *One Hundred Years of Good Company*, pub. by Ruston Hornsby Co. Ltd, 1957

Payne, W.A., *Benjamin Holt, the Story of the Caterpillar Tractor*, Stockton, California, USA, The University of the Pacific, Stockton, 1982

Scott, J.D., *Vickers. A History*, Weidenfeld & Nicholson, 1962

Tritton, Sir Wm, *The Tank, its Birth and Development*, Lincoln, Wm Foster & Co. Ltd, c. 1919

Weaver, R., *Baguley locomotives 1914–31*, Greenford, Industrial Railway Society Publications, 1975

Wik, R.M., *Benjamin Holt and Caterpillar Tracks and Combines*, USA, American Society of Agricultural Engineers, 1984

Other books

Adams, R.J.Q., *Arms and the Wizard: Lloyd George and the Ministry of Munitions, 1915–1916*, Cassell, 1978

Addison, Christopher, *Politics from Within, 1911–1918*, 2 vols, Herbert Jenkins, 1924

—, *Four and a Half Years*, 2 vols, Hutchinson, 1934

Addison, P., *Churchill on the Home Front, 1900–1955*, Pimlico, 1993

Anon., *A Short History of the Royal Tank Corps*, 2nd edn, Aldershot, Gale & Polden, 1931

Banks, A., *A Military Atlas of the First World War*, Heinemann, 1975

Blake, R., *The Private Papers of Douglas Haig 1914–1919*, Eyre & Spottiswoode, 1952

Blumenson, M., *The Patton Papers 1885–1940*, New York USA, Da Capo Press, 1998

Bruce, R., *Machine Guns of World War 1*, Windrow & Greene, 1997

Burg, D.F. with L.E. Purcell, *Almanac of World War 1*, Lexington, Kentucky, USA, University Press of Kentucky, 1998

Burk, Kathleen, *Britain, America and the Sinews of War, 1914–1918*, Boston, Mass. USA, Geo. Allen & Unwin, 1985

Callwell, Gen C., *The Experiences of a Dugout, 1914–1918*, Constable, 1920

Chamberlain, P. with C. Ellis, *Pictorial History of Tanks of the World 1915–45*, Arms & Armour Press, 1986

—, *Tanks of World War 1*, Arms and Armour Press, 1969

Crow, D., *AFVs of World War One*, Windsor, Profile Publications, 1970

Davenport–Hines, R.P.T., *Dudley Docker. The Life and Times of a Trade Warrior*, Cambridge, Cambridge University Press, 1984

Dewar, G.A.B., *The Great Munition Feat 1914–1918*, Constable, 1921

Diplock, B.J., *A New System of Heavy Goods Transport on Common Roads*, Longmans Green, 1902

Edmonds, Brig Gen Sir James E., *Official History of the War: Military Operations in France and Belgium, 1918*, vols IV and V, HMSO, 1937

—, *Official History of the War: Military Operations in France and Belgium, 1917*, compiled by Capt Cyril Falls. Imperial War Museum, 1992

Ellis, C., *Military Transport of World War I*, Blandford Press, 1970

Fletcher, D., *British Tanks 1915–19*, Marlborough, Crowood Press, 2001

—, *Landships. British Tanks in the First World War*, HMSO, 1984

—, *War Cars. British Armoured Cars in the First World War*, HMSO, 1987

Foley, J., *The Boilerplate War*, Frederick Muller, 1963

Gibot, J–L. with P. Gorczynski, *Following the Tanks, Cambrai*, privately pub. 1999

Gilbert, M., *Winston S. Churchill*, vols III (1971) and IV (1975), Heinemann

Grieves, K., *The Politics of Manpower, 1914–18*, Manchester, Manchester University Press, 1988

Halle, A., *Tanks, an Illustrated History of Fighting Vehicles*, Patrick Stephens, 1971

Hamilton, Peggy, *Three Years or the Duration*, Peter Owen, 1978

Hankey, Lord, *Government Control in War*, Cambridge, University Press, 1945

Harris, J.P., *Men, Ideas and Tanks*, Manchester, Manchester University Press, 1995

Haythornthwaite, P.J., *The World War One Source Book*, Arms & Armour Press, 1992

Henniker, Col A.M., *Official History of the War: Transportation on the Western Front 1914–18*, HMSO, 1937

Hogg, Ian V., *Armour in Conflict*, Janes Publishing, 1980

Humble, R., *Tanks*, Weidenfeld & Nicholson, 1977

Hundleby, M. with R. Strasheim, *The German A7V Tank*, Sparkford, Haynes Publishing Group, 1990

Hutchison, Lt Col G.S., *Machine Guns, their History and Tactical Employment*, Macmillan, 1938

Icks, Lt Col R.J., *Tanks and Armored Vehicles*, New York, Duell, Sloan & Pearce, 1945

Jenkins, R., *Asquith*, Collins, 1964

Jones, Maj R.E. with Capt G.H. Rarey and 1st Lt R.J. Icks, *The Fighting Tanks since 1916*, Washington DC, USA, National Service Publishing Co., 1933

Legros, L.A., *Les Chars D'Assault*, Paris, Société des Ingénieurs Civils de France, 1921

Liddell Hart, Capt Sir Basil, *History of the First World War*, Cassell, 1970

—, *The Real War 1914–1918*, Faber, 1930

—, *The Tanks, the History of the Royal Tank Regiment and its Predecessors, vol. 1: 1914–1939*, Cassell, 1959

Macintosh, J.C., *Men and Tanks*, John Lane, 1921

Macksey, K. with J.H. Batchelor, *Tank. A History of the Armoured Fighting Vehicle*, Military Book Society, 1970

Maurice, Maj R.F.G., compiler, *The Tank Corps Book of Honour*, Spottiswoode, Ballantyne, 1919

Miles, Capt W., *Official History of the War: Military Operations in France and Belgium, 1916*, Macmillan, 1938

Ogorkiewicz, R.M., *Armour*, Stevens & Sons, 1960

Perrett, B. with A. Lord, *The Czar's British Squadron*, Wm Kimber, 1981

Pidgeon, T., *The Tanks at Flers*, 2 vols. Cobham, Surrey, Fairmile Books, 1995

Reid, B.H., *J.F.C. Fuller: Military Thinker*, Macmillan with Kings College, London, 1987

Reynolds, J., *Engines and Enterprise. The Life and Work of Sir Harry Ricardo*, Stroud, Sutton Publishing, 1999

Robertson, FM Sir William, *From Private to Field–Marshal*, Constable, 1921

Roskill, Stephen, *Hankey, Man of Secrets*, vol. l, Collins, 1970

Rubin, G.R., *War, Law and Labour. The Munitions Acts 1915–21*, Oxford, Clarendon Press, 1987

Samson, Air Cdre Charles R., *Fights and Flights*,

Nashville, Tenn, USA, Battery Press, 1990

Schneider, W. with R. Strasheim, *German Tanks in World War I*, West Chester, Penn., USA, Schiffer Publishing, 1990

Smithers, A.J., *A New Excalibur*, Leo Cooper, 1986

Stevenson, Frances, *Lloyd George. A Diary by Frances Stevenson*, ed. by A.J.P. Taylor, Hutchinson, 1971

Thompson, R.W., *The Yankee Marlborough*, Geo. Allen & Unwin, 1963

Trythall, A.J., *'Boney' Fuller, the Intellectual General 1878–1966*, Cassell, 1977

Ventham, P. with D. Fletcher, *Moving the Guns, the Mechanisation of the Royal Artillery 1854–1939*, HMSO, 1990

White, B.T., *Tanks and Other Armoured Fighting Vehicles 1900 to 1918*, Blandford Press, 1974

Williams–Ellis, Maj C. with A. Williams–Ellis, 'The Tank Corps', *Country Life* with Geo. Newnes, 1919

Wilson, A.G., *Walter Wilson, Portrait of an Inventor*, Duckworth, 1986

Wrigley, C., 'The Ministry of Munitions: an Innovatory Department', in *War and the State*, ed. Kathleen Burk, Geo. Allen & Unwin, 1982

Zaloga, S.J., *The Renault FT Light Tank*, Osprey, 1988

RESEARCH PAPERS, THESES

Hooley, R., 'Hornsby Chain Track Tractors', Lincoln Tank Group

Verrall, M.J., 'Landships', Tank Museum, Bovington, 623.438(41) Design/8

—, 'No. 1 & No. 2 Lincoln Machines – Little Willie and Mother', Tank Museum, Bovington, 623.438(41) Design/8

JOURNALS AND PERIODICALS

Anon, 'Good–bye to the Gun Horse', *The Commercial Motor* (27 March 1913), 69

Anon, 'The Evolution of the Chain Track Tractor', *The Engineer* (10 August–21 September 1917)

Butler, Capt R.P., 'Reminiscences of Salvage Work', *The Royal Tank Corps Journal* (June/July 1932)

d'Eyncourt, Sir Eustace H., 'British Tanks', *Engineering* (12 and 19 September 1919)

de Wend–Fenton, W.F., 'Who Really invented 'Tanks'?', *The World* (26 September 1916), 656; and related correspondence etc. editions of 24, 31 October; 28 November; 5, 19 December 1916

Fletcher, D., 'The Innovators: Bramah J. Diplock', *The Tank* (May 1993), 6–8

—, 'The Medium Mark B Tank', *Wheels & Tracks* (42/1993), 31–7

—, 'The Medium C Tank', *Wheels & Tracks* (43/1993), 28–34

—, 'Philip Johnson and Roadless Traction', *Army and Navy Modelworld* (August 1984), 136–9; (March 1985), 372–3; (July/August 1985), 568–70

—, 'Vintage Tracks', *Wheels & Tracks* (12/1985), 28–33

Freybe, Capt P., 'A German Narrative of the Battle of Cambrai', *RUSI Journal* (1921)

Fuller, Col J.F.C., 'The Influence of Tanks on Cavalry Tactics', *The Cavalry Journal* (April 1920), 109–31

Germains, V., 'The Limitations of the Tank', *RUSI Journal* (February 1930)

Haig, Col N., 'Substance or Shadow', *RUSI Journal* (February–November 1921), 117–19

Hetherington, H.A., 'The Ricardo 150hp Tank Engine', *The Automobile Engineer* (April/May 1919)

Johnson, Lt Col P., 'The Use of Tanks in Undeveloped Country', *RUSI Journal* (May 1921), 191–204

Legros, L.A., 'Traction on Bad Roads or Land', *Proceedings of the Institution of Mechanical Engineers* (spring, 1918)

Macfie, Lt R.F., Editorial, *Aeronautics Journal* (July 1911)

MacLeod, Ross, 'The Utility of the Tank', *RUSI Journal* (February–November 1931), 786–94

Ogorkiewicz, R.M., 'Armoured Fighting Vehicles', *The Chartered Mechanical Engineer* (February 1962), 75–82

Pemberton, M., 'The Battle of the Tanks', *The War Illustrated* (7 October 1916), 179, 182

—, 'The Triumph of the Tanks', *The War Illustrated* (8 December 1917), 322

Wells, H.G., 'The Land Ironclads', *Strand Magazine* (December 1903); reprinted November 1916 edn, omitting illustration of Pedrail wheels!

—, Letters to *The Listener* (14 May and 31 July 1941)

INDEX

Numbers in bold relate to significant references.